They Died Waiting

They Died Waiting

The Crisis in Mental Health - Stories of Loss and Stories of Hope

Edited by Caroline Aldridge and Emma Corlett

First published in Great Britain in 2023
by Learning Social Worker Publications

DISCLAIMER: This book has been written by the editors and authors in their personal capacities, the views and opinions expressed are those of them alone. The author has made every effort to ensure the accuracy of information contained in this book, but assume no responsibility for any errors, inaccuracies, inconsistencies and omissions.
Likewise, every reasonable effort has been made to trace copyright holders of material in this book, but if any have been inadvertently overlooked the publishers would gladly receive information enabling them to rectify any error or omission in subsequent editions.

A CIP record for this book is available from the British Library

ISBN: 978-1-8382420-3-9

Cover image source: Caroline Aldridge
Cover design: Clare Brayshaw

Printed and bound in York by YPS Printing Services

Learning Social Worker Publications, Norwich
Contact details:
Website: www.learningsocialworker.com
Email: caroline.aldridgesw@yahoo.com

Dedication

In memory of all the people who have died waiting for support with their mental health.
Their whispered lives echo loudly in the hearts of those who loved them.
Always loved. Always remembered.

This book is dedicated to those who mourn, those who speak out, and the people who are trying to keep themselves, or someone they care about, alive. We stand with them.

The stories in *They Died Waiting* and the chapters written by Caroline and Emma, are based on the contributors' opinions and recollections of real-life events. Everyone writing in this book does so in a personal capacity and their views are not representative of any current or previous employers. We acknowledge that others might see things differently. There are gaps in these accounts. Some pain is unspeakable. The stories presented intertwine and they are a tiny part of a bigger tapestry.

To protect people's identities, with the exception of public figures, some names and other distinguishing details have been altered or omitted. Documents already in the public domain are reported in their original form. We have not indicated where pseudonyms have been used for editorial reasons.

Our aim is to illuminate not alienate. It is no secret who some of the organisations are in this narrative. However, the experiences shared in this book are not unique and there are similar stories coming from across the nation. We hope *They Died Waiting* will encourage readers to open their minds and consider what might be happening in their area.

They Died Waiting – Review
By Jessica Presland

In this sequel to *He Died Waiting*, Caroline Aldridge and Emma Corlett have woven together the stories of people who died waiting, as exquisitely as one of Caroline's incredible quilts. Each account is accompanied by a piece of quilt, undertaken with help and guidance from Caroline. The finished quilt brings the stories together and demonstrates beautifully the unique life of the person who died. Personalities shine through the pages of this book; the individuality of each person who died is evident and yet they are intrinsically joined by a common fatal thread.

Like its precursor, this book is not easy reading. It is, however, a book which needs to be read, and read widely. Healthcare practitioners, social workers, teachers, students of the aforementioned professions, government ministers, politicians, policy-makers - the list goes on. When mental health is treated with the same regard as physical health, then we will have no need of books like this one, that highlight the ways in which our societies are failing and our communities are being let down.

People with mental health conditions continue to be stigmatised. Addictions, which often go hand in hand with psychological distress, tend to be seen as the fault of the person with the addiction. The smoker who develops lung cancer can reasonably expect treatment and a measure of compassion. All those written about so poignantly in *They Died Waiting,* had the right to expect the same care and treatment. However, we appear to have allowed an under-class to develop; those who hang onto the edges of society, ostracised by their mental health conditions and/or their addictive behaviours. This is indeed Marcuse's 'déclassé'. A world-class psychiatrist who has worked with people who have addictions, Gabor Mate, insists we do not ask "why the addiction?" but rather, "why the pain?" When we see the pain, we cannot fail to see the humanity. When we see the humanity, we must acknowledge our connection and know that we too could be where they are.

In this book, Caroline and Emma present a strong case that from the 'cradle to grave' we not only should but must, tend to the mental health of those around us. We need to listen and we need to hear. People cannot be defined by a series of tick boxes on an intake or discharge form. There is no 'one size fits all' approach that can be adopted. There has to be the flexibility to respond to the uniqueness of the human in pain and distress. Mental health professionals are on the whole very good people, struggling to survive in an antagonistic culture with regards to mental health and with chronic underfunding from successive governments. Are our governments guilty of tacit eugenics in not adequately resourcing mental health services? An outrageous suggestion possibly, but if you join the dots in *They Died Waiting*, this is the emerging picture.

Along with her co-editor Emma, Caroline has done it again. She has knit together the tales from the hearts of those left behind with sound academic knowledge of theory and practice, as well as an ethical framework that has kept her contributors safe and which shows the same concern for you, the reader. I suspect that she will keep on 'doing it' until her message is heard that, 'no-one should die waiting'. Prepare to laugh, weep, to feel anger, to feel the unbearable pain of those left behind, and to allow yourself to be educated. Caroline and Emma have given a voice to those who have felt not listened to by services. Those voices are the voices of the true experts because they knew and loved those who have been lost, in a way that professionals never could. This book is a call to arms and maybe if we all shout from the roof-tops, the message might be heard.

Foreword

Deathmaking: Holding on to what kind of hope?
By Siobhan Maclean

In the 36 years since I started my social work journey, there are a couple of books that have had a profound impact on me. *He Died Waiting*, which *They Died Waiting* follows on from, is one of those books. I remember clearly my emotional responses to reading the book. To the point that I can recall where I was and how I was sitting when I read some of Caroline's writing. Students often tell me about lightbulb moments in their learning and I had the sense of a whole set of lightbulbs going off as I read. Maybe, in fact, it was more like a huge searchlight encouraging me to look back at my career to examine my own practice, the journey I had taken, and the way that I might have contributed to some of what is happening in mental health services. I therefore, felt hugely privileged when Caroline invited me to write a foreword to this book.

Caroline and Emma offer advice on reading *They Died Waiting* 'through a trauma lens' which I think is incredibly helpful. Being mindful of the possible impact on me emotionally, I have read this book in parts, and I have kept a few notes about my experiences reading it in my reflective journal. Looking at these notes has helped me to think about what I would like to share in this foreword. The notes have also helped me to process my learning, reflect on my career, and explore what actions I need to take in the future. I would encourage you to keep some notes on your thoughts and responses as you read, noting your physical as well as emotional responses.

I began my reflective notes on the reading process by exploring the importance of hope to me, and the way that this has impacted in both my personal and my professional life. The subtitle of this book tells us that we will read 'stories of hope'. Hope is an essential aspect of social work practice and research indicates that professionals who recognise the intrinsic power of hope and hopefulness are more effective in their work[1]. Clark (2017)[2] argues there is always something to hope for and everyone has the right to hope, asserting that there is no such thing as false hope, there can be false reassurances but never false hope, because

---

1 Clark, E.J. and Hoffler, E.F. (Eds) (2014) *Hope Matters: The Power of Social Work*. New York. NASW Press.

2 Clark, E. (2017) 10 essentials social workers must know about hope. Available online at http:// www.socialworker.com/feature-articles/practice/10-essentials-social-workers-must-know-abouthope/

hope does not require certainty. Whilst I did read many stories of hope in the book, I also read that some people had lost hope which made me feel very sad, particularly because Farron, Herth, and Popovich (1995)[3] told us that it is easier to prevent a person from becoming hopeless than to help a person who has lost hope find it again. In the chapter *Holding On To Hope,* I found Caroline's exploration of the theory of hope really helpful, and this chapter helps us to consider how we might be able to hold on to hope in hopeless situations. As hope is so important to me, I knew that I wanted to hold on to hope as I was reading this book, but I also knew that this might be a challenge. I wondered whether there was a particular type of hope that I could hold on to and even build on as I read and so this question formed part of my note-taking.

Deathmaking

When I was training to be a social worker, I wrote an essay about the concept of 'deathmaking' introduced by Wolf Wolfensberger in the 1970s[4]. He describes the way that the deaths of devalued people are brought about prematurely, categorising this into direct and indirect deathmaking. His writing can be difficult to penetrate as it is couched in very academic terms, but the key points are clear. Wolfensberger states that deathmaking is often "concealed, disguised and detoxified" by authorities. One connection that has interested me is that Wolfensberger self-published his work on deathmaking as no publisher would carry the ideas. Caroline has self-published both *He Died Waiting* and now *They Died Waiting.*

I recall being really angry about deathmaking and, when I began my first professional role, as a resettlement social worker moving people out of the old Victorian 'asylums', I was determined that my work would be radical in challenging deathmaking. I had confidence that my profession could, and would, disrupt the powerful systems which created the environments where people were devalued to such an extent that they were 'made dead'. I have reflected back on this period of my life many times, especially since reading *He Died Waiting.* In thinking that we could, as a profession, disrupt deathmaking was I hopeful or naïve? It is very clear from practice, personal experience, reading *He Died Waiting* (and now *They Died Waiting)* that, as a profession, social work

3 Farran, C. J., Herth, K. A., and Popovich, J. M. (1995). *Hope and hopelessness: critical clinical constructs.* (California) Sage Publications.

4 You can read about Wolfensberger and the concept of deathmaking at https://wolfwolfensberger.com/life-s-work/deathmaking

has failed to disrupt deathmaking and, indeed, may be contributing to the factors which bring it about.

In the 1980s Wolfensberger wrote:

> *"The most subtle, and therefore least explicit, form of deathmaking of devalued people today is large-scale, systematic marginalization of devalued groups, which then results in many secondary and tertiary causes of death, though the death rates and the real underlying dynamics are deeply hidden."*

This could have been written yesterday.

In reading the contributions to *They Died Waiting* I have asked myself whether anything has changed in over 40 years, and unfortunately, I have concluded that things have maybe become even worse. Duncan[5] tells us that "although the traditional asylums have closed, bureaucratic practices still exist in modern community mental health services". Although I have read everything that I can get my hands on which refers to deathmaking, I have never read anything which describes it as clearly as Melanie[6] who tells us "My sweet boy had become a corpse". When I read that phrase, I caught my breath and I noticed that I moved my hands towards my body as if to either comfort or protect myself. It is hard to imagine the pain of the authors and it is hard to read their stories, it causes us to look inside ourselves and think about our own responsibilities. Wolfensberger says one of the things that has to be in place for deathmaking to happen is a process which "nullifies people's sense of responsibility", we all have responsibilities as well as rights. Unfortunately, this is often twisted and used 'against people' Lynne [7]tells us that "John was regularly told, by clinicians, that he needed to take responsibility for his behaviour". The question I am left with is - when will services acknowledge and live out their responsibilities?

The subtitle of this book refers to the 'crisis' in mental health services. Caplan's crisis theory[8] has been around for many years and is still widely used in human services. Caplan asserted that there are three stages to a crisis – impact, recoil, and adjustment/adaptation. Since Caplan's initial writing the third stage has been more recently referred to as 'recovery, reorganisation or reimagining'. I would suggest that the

---

5 *In Solidarity With Those Who Have Died and Those Left Behind* by Duncan

6 *The Case For a Statutory Public Inquiry* by Melanie

7 When *Time Runs Out* by Lynne

8 Caplan (1964) says a crisis occurs when people face irresolvable problems which leads to an inability to function.

impact of the mental health crisis can be clearly seen in the narratives included in this book. I wonder whether mental health service providers have become stuck in the second stage of recoiling, stepping back from their responsibility to reimagine services. As you read this book, think about where you are in relation to the crisis in mental health services. What is your responsibility to support mental health services in moving into 'recovery'?

One of the phrases that really jumped out at me in *He Died Waiting* that appears again in this book, was "emotionally barren organisations". I had never heard that phrase before and yet as soon as I read it, I knew what it meant. I have been employed in emotionally barren organisations and I have sat in countless emotionally barren meetings. Mental health professionals should take a 'person in environment perspective'[9]. Seeing the wider context for professionals who are employed in emotionally barren environments may help us to see why so many professionals are leaving mental health services. Emma[10] tells us:

"*Since I left my mental health nursing career, I consider that I have done more grassroots 'proper' community mental health nursing than I was ever able to working inside the system that is meant to provide it.*"

When committed passionate professionals cannot provide good care and support as part of the 'system' then we have to acknowledge that the system is broken.

Different kinds of hope

Why do people need to leave the system in order to try and bring about change? Many professionals do acknowledge the state of the system and yet so many others (as Melanie tells us) 'deny and defend'. Reading that Rebecca[11] said "this system is shit", and to have a professional respond "I don't have to take this abuse from you" (putting the phone down) was saddening, but not at all surprising. In what way was criticising the system abusing the professional? Perhaps that professional was honestly recognising that in fact, we are all a part of 'the system' in different ways. Although we are all part of it, some of us are certainly more

9 Mary Kondrat (2013) describes the 'person in environment perspective' as a guiding principle of social work practice that understands individual behaviours within the context of their environment.

10 *Abandoned by Mental Health Services* by Emma

11 *'Angry of Bury'* by Rebecca

powerful within the system than others. Sheila[12] tells us that "the power structure needs disrupting" so maybe *disruptive hope* is what I am looking for?

In the introduction to this anthology, Caroline and Emma refer to 'whispered lives, whispered deaths, and whispered organisational behaviours'. When I was part way through reading this book, the death of Dame Deborah James was all over the news. Her death was very sad, but was it more of a loss than any other person? It left me questioning why was her death 'shouted' while the deaths explored in this collection were 'whispered'? Dame Deborah used the phrase 'rebellious hope' many times during her cancer treatment and in part of her final message to the public she said, "find a life worth enjoying; take risks; love deeply; have no regrets; and always, always have rebellious hope". It is a beautiful message which was read on the news so many times. It made me stop and think about the stories in this book. In reading the narratives brought together here, I was struck and saddened by the number of people who talked about a loss of hope. I felt that all the authors had regrets relating to services but all of the people who died waiting had a life worth living and they loved (and were loved) very deeply. Maybe *rebellious hope* is a phrase which I could use to describe what I want to keep hold of?

Although I have never physically met Caroline, I do feel a strong connection to her. There are a number of reasons for this – one of which is that we both have an acquired brain injury. Mine is the result of an arterial dissection which caused a stroke that has led to an increase in my use of visual thinking. I have been incredibly struck by the visual images in *They Died Waiting*. In this book, the visual image created by each author is included with the adage 'a picture can speak a thousand words' truly demonstrated. However, it is perhaps the photo of the poem Shirley[13] wrote on a page torn from a notebook that affected me the most. The poem has a line "only those who love you knew" the image seems to show that initially the line said 'loved' not 'love' but the crossing out of the 'd' shows that love doesn't die with the person. Lucy[14] says "I cannot see you with my eyes or touch you with my hands but I will feel you for eternity in my heart". I have been thinking more recently about theories of grief and loss demonstrating the importance of recognising relationships that continue beyond death.

---

12 *84 Symptoms and Loving Notes* by Sheila

13 *She Wasn't Fine* by Laura and Caroline

14 *The Beast of Grief* by Lucy

Tolle[15], a spiritual teacher, writes - "*Death is not the opposite of life. Life has no opposite. The opposite of death is birth. Life is eternal*". Perhaps I am looking for *eternal hope*?

A great deal of my professional life is about supporting students to learn about theory and critical reflection. This book has so much to offer all of us, but for students, in particular, it will help you to explore theory that comes from real life. Using a narrative approach with the addition of some connecting chapters, Caroline and Emma help us to reflect more on theories of grief and loss; theories of hope; models of risk assessment and risk management; relationship-based approaches; trauma-informed practice; leadership and organisational management; the wide use of skills and methods; along with new ideas like the 'pit of inaction' and 'heart work'. The theory contained in this book is raw, it's emotionally challenging and it should be practice changing. Perhaps I need to find *raw, real hope*?

Holding on to hope and challenging deathmaking

Wolfensberger noted that "Whenever one lays the truths about deathmaking before people, one will almost always be asked – or even challenged – what the 'evidence' is". This book is full of evidence of deathmaking. There is a significant focus on evidence-based practice in social work and nursing. What evidence is the practice described in these pages based on? The 'evidence' here should be quoted in every student essay or talked about at every opportunity. These stories, these deaths, must be shouted about.

One of the things that I made a note of in my reflective journal is what I saw as repeated words as I was reading. On reflection, I saw those that I made a particular note of related to feelings. I listed angry, abandoned, and shame. I looked these up later and found that they were repeated a number of times – anger/angry (55 times), abandoned (12 times), shame (22 times). As I thought a little more about what I had written, I realised that I hadn't made a note of some key repeated words, so I looked for how many times the following words were repeated – love (237), hope (167), and kind (142). Why hadn't I initially made a note of the more positive words, even though these were repeated many more times? Perhaps because the feelings that I had when reading were largely anger and shame. As I hadn't written the word hope, I asked myself - do I really feel a sense of hope or am I clutching at it?

15 A New Earth: Awakening to Your Life's Purpose by Eckhart Tolle

I think that everyone who reads this book will be angry. Many of the narratives included are based around anger, for example, Kate's *Staying Angry* and Rebecca's *Angry of Bury*. How can we not be angry that deathmaking is alive and well and thriving in mental health services in the UK? How can we not be angry about the way that the authors and their loved ones have been treated? How can we not be angry about the misuse and abuse of power that threads through every story?

Whatever you do, when you read this book. Reflect, imagine, and hold on to hope. Angry, noisy, shouting, rebellious, disruptive, raw, radical, loving, kind, evidence-based, eternal hope!

Chapters

Part Four - Agitating for Change

Part Five – What Does This Mean?

Part One - Introduction

Caroline uses sewing, in particular quilting, as a way of processing emotions, expressing herself, and protesting. The cover of this book is based on a quilt made from squares created by *They Died Waiting's* contributors. Each section and contributor chapter opens with a photo of their 'square' which is a hand-crafted memorial heart. These visual vignettes are an evocative and a salutary reminder that *They Died Waiting* is about the premature loss of people due to mental illness. Most of these squares arrived through the post, it was both a sadness and joy to receive them. Some were made alongside Caroline and she treasures the confidences shared during their making. Putting the quilt together was a privilege and something Caroline did with respect and care. What is striking is how vibrant and diverse the quilt is – this reflects the vitality of people who have died and the hope that is threaded through this book.

Introduction
By Caroline and Emma

Rising demand, coupled with shrinking resources, has led to a crisis in mental health services. Across the UK, reports of people unable to get the support they need, staffing and bed shortages, and mental health trusts unable to cope, abound. Covid-19 added pressure to an already creaking system. Services are threadbare, stretched so thin that they are worn through in places. Partner agencies are similarly strained which means those unable to get support from mental health services present elsewhere. In a recent report, The Royal College of Emergency Medicine found that an additional 13,000 staffed beds would be needed across the NHS and that more people presented at A and E in a mental health crisis than at mental health services[16]. Whether it's concerns about the rising prevalence of children requiring support, people with serious mental illness falling through the gaps, or members of our aging population with dementia, unmet need is flagged up for every age group. Sadly, some people have paid the ultimate price.

There is very little published about the experiences of those who are bereaved due to mental illness. In her book, *He Died Waiting*,[17] Caroline exposed how some lives and some deaths are 'whispered' because they are largely invisible to society. We think that *They Died Waiting* also speaks into a void. It makes a valuable contribution to health and social care knowledge because it contains material that would not usually be available to students and practitioners. It shines a light on some whispered lives, whispered deaths, and whispered organisational behaviours. We also believe that this book will be helpful to anyone with an interest in mental health or bereavement.

It has been a privilege for us to curate the stories of loss and hope in this book. We began by asking some people if they would like to contribute. Then our contributors made suggestions about people who had important stories to tell. The diverse contributions cover a range of issues relating to the crisis in mental health services. The narratives come from different regions in England, Wales, and Northern Ireland. We suggest that wherever you are in the UK (and beyond) you will find people dealing courageously with similar adversities. And what courage some of our contributors

---

16 https://res.cloudinary.com/studio-republic/images/v1653920684/RCEM-Acute-Insight-Series-Beds-1/RCEM-Acute-Insight-Series-Beds-1.pdf?_i=AA

17 *He Died Waiting: Learning the Lessons - a Bereaved Mother's View of Mental Health Services* by Caroline Aldridge (2020).

demonstrate. For some, it is the bravery it takes to keep going each day or the courage to whistle-blow. For others, it is delivering compassionate care or walking alongside those who have been bereaved. For every one of them, contributing to this book meant taking a brave step. The flip side of courage is fear and several of the contributors articulate the risks they take in speaking out.

We are honoured that our chapter writers decided to share their stories with us. Initially, we planned to have a section written by bereaved relatives and another from 'commentators', people who in some capacity support bereaved people or champion good mental health practice. There is, of course, no clear delineation between the two. A sizeable proportion of those working in the field of mental health and bereavement, or campaigning for safer services, have lived experience of mental illness or bereavement.

Caroline has worked with the contributors to help them tell their stories in whatever way worked best for them. Although they were not gathered for research purposes, the narratives have all the features of emotive autoethnography as described by Bochner and Ellis[18]. We adopted robust ethical principles at every stage of this project. We wanted every contributor to make fully informed decisions about what to share and how to share it. This included thinking about the impact on their wider networks. For this reason, some details have been changed to protect people.

We also wanted the process of contributing to be positive and empowering and to equalise the power differential between those who deliver services and those who experience them. At the same time, several of our contributors wanted to use pseudonyms to protect themselves or others. So, a decision was made for each chapter to be attributed to the contributor's first name. Where a chapter writer is already known in the public domain there will be a link to their biography in the footnotes[19].

In some chapters it might be obvious which organisation is being referred to. Where this is the case, the authors are expressing their opinion on the situation. We accept that not everyone will share the same truth. We know we might 'ruffle some feathers' and prompt some defensiveness. Our aim is not to insult or malign. We are hoping to prompt your curiosity. We want our readers to question, could this be happening where I live?

---

18 *Evocative Autoethnography: Writing Lives and Telling Stories* by Arthur P. Bochner and Carolyn Ellis (2016).

19 If you need to reference for academic writing we suggest you use chapter author's first and last names where known. Where not known, use the author's first name and Caroline and Emma as editors: For example, ('Bridget' cited in Aldridge, C. and Corlett, E. (2023), etc.).

This book is structured in a way that enables readers to dip in and out as they need to. We want the individual stories to speak for themselves. Therefore, our analysis is restricted to the introductory and concluding chapters. The material in the sections overlaps and several of the chapters could easily have fitted in elsewhere. Nevertheless, we have grouped them into sections:

Introductory section: This includes chapters about our rationale for the book. Some of the chapters relate to suicide or other traumatic events and all are potentially triggering. Therefore, there is a chapter by Caroline and Lisa[20], a trainer with lived experience, on trauma and how to approach the book in a trauma-informed way.

A 'special death' in the family: This section, begins by explaining the theoretical construct of 'special deaths' and what this means for relatives bereaved due to their loved one's mental illness. Each chapter tells an emotive personal story that is rich in detail about the person who died, their value, and what happened to them. Some discuss the brutal processes the contributor encountered after their loved ones died. Some of the contributors discuss various initiatives, aimed at making a difference, that they are involved in.

Holding on to hope: As in the previous section, most of the stories are deeply personal and they are based on lived experiences of traumatic bereavement. Some of these chapters are written by people with experience of working in mental health services. You will read about various ways people are trying to support others. The term 'postvention' is used in this book to refer to the support and interventions (such as counselling or support groups) conducted after someone dies by suicide or traumatic death because it has a dual aspect (healing and reducing risk of suicide for the bereaved person).

Agitating for change: In this section we explore different ways that people are agitating for positive change. All the contributors are courageously standing up for what they believe. What shines in this section is the authenticity of the contributors.

---

20 Lisa Morrison is a trainer with lived experience of mental illness. For more information see her website: www.lisamorrison.co.uk

What does this mean?: We conclude by drawing together the themes from the book.

We have made every effort to be fair and balanced. We are aiming to highlight poor practice and challenge professionals and organisations to consider what needs to improve. As editors, we acknowledge our personal and professional experiences make us biased. We are leaning into our personal perspectives and celebrating our lived experiences. We believe that integrating the personal and professional aspects of ourselves enables us to be authentic. We are offering a view of mental health services that is subjective and reflects our values. This book is unashamedly emotive because we feel that best practice is underpinned by a reflexive approach that connects hearts, minds, and actions.

We also recognise the pressures mental health services are under. Therefore, through our amazing contributors, we are offering hope in the form of ideas. Whether you are a citizen, carer, service-user, student, practitioner, leader, or interested other party, please involve yourself in being part of positive change. However small, we can each contribute. Whether it is supporting a friend or family member who is struggling with their mental health or a bereavement, through to leading a campaign or organisation, we can, together, make a difference.

We hope you will embrace the narratives presented in this book and adopt a curious approach that asks: Why? Why have the events happened? Also, how? How could things be better? And, what? What could I do?

Threads of Love
By Caroline

Sewing is my self-soothing activity. I particularly like to make quilts – some for function or gifts and others as a way of expressing my feelings or opinions. When my eldest son, Tim, died, I literally sewed my way through the grief. I used his clothes to make memory quilts. For some reason, I couldn't quite bring myself to use the distinctive logo from his favourite and well-worn Star Wars t-shirt. Finally, the time feels right.

About Caroline

Caroline[21] introduces herself in workshops as a social worker, educator, author, activist, bereaved mother, and so much more. The more refers to her relationships with family and friends, her lived experiences, and her creative activities. Caroline believes that people working in health and social care should use their values as a base for their practice. Caroline is an experienced children and families social worker, who has undertaken a variety of roles, including safeguarding, fostering and adoption, and Child and Adolescent Mental Health Services (CAMHS). Caroline is a practice educator and has taught on health, mental health, and social work programmes.

In this chapter, Caroline gives an overview of the journey that led to curating the stories in this book.

21 You can read more about Caroline on her website: www.learningsocialworker.com

Threads of Love

In February 2021, *He Died Waiting: Learning the Lessons – A Bereaved Mother's View of Mental Health Services*, a book about my experiences, was launched. Since then, I have been on a personal and professional journey. The different threads of my life are coming together in a purposeful way. *They Died Waiting* is one of those threads.

One of my favourite, and most used, quotes from *He Died Waiting* relates to love:

> "*Anyone who has experienced loss will find elements in my narrative to relate to. But this is not a grief story. It is a love story. The intensity of my love for Tim correlates to the pain of my grief. My love of, and for, my family has kept me strong. They are my reason to continue. And I am theirs. I feel a sense of love for my fellow humans. I empathise with them and react emotionally to their pain and loss. It is this love that underpins my passion for practice and social justice. In the end, what matters most is love.*" (Aldridge, 2020 p319)

Curating the individual stories for *They Died Waiting* has been a labour of love. Each chapter is bursting with strong emotions and love is the common theme. It's the strength that is threaded through the stories. I have immersed myself in the narratives and I hope readers will too. I have vicariously felt the intense love of families, alongside their correlating feelings of fear, anger, loss, or grief. Love-in-action is demonstrated by those writing about how they reach out to people in pain or fight for others' rights. Although, many of the chapters are acutely sad, there is a sense of hope within them. They portray a love of life and a desire to bring others peace, healing, inspiration, or joy. To offer hope. Essentially, *They Died Waiting* is a collection of love stories.

I am so honoured to be in the position of gathering and editing these heartfelt and inspirational stories. Getting to this point has been a process. My lived experiences have shaped me and form the foundation on which I stand. Ever since I became a mother, I have been picking up threads in my life that connect me to who I am now personally, professionally, and academically.

What started as the tentative strand of first-time motherhood, gained strength because it was wrapped around a core of love. Through the twists and turns of life, other threads have joined and spun together to form a cord. Each of my children added threads that are cleaved with my own.

Sometimes the thread has become entangled with pieces such as, jobs, people, or experiences. These may have become ongoing or more short-lived filaments. Positive or negative, gossamer-thin or slubby, light or dark: they all add texture. Cords of my career and education entwine with my persona colourful and multi-stranded life-cord.

When Tim died in 2014, his thread remained securely attached to mine. An integral part, that initially was hidden in the depth of stigma, shame, and grief, gradually spun out onto the surface. Concurrently, other threads of my life changed. I changed. I was drawn into a peer group of similarly bereaved people. They extended their threads of love and I was strengthened by my connection to them.

My life cord became a heavy rope. I was carrying too much. I needed to practice some self-love and let go of what was weighing me down. This became critical after I sustained a head injury in 2018 and I needed to adjust to having a disability. Trimming what overloaded me was not a straightforward, or particularly conscious, process. Not everyone appreciated, or understood, that I could no longer incorporate their messy cords with mine. I was reluctant to discard elements that were exhausting me. My inability to perform all the functions that I once had meant that some people ripped their cords away from mine. Overall, it was a painful and untidy unpicking of snarls and knots.

Writing *He Died Waiting* was important part of my processing the loss of Tim and adapting to my physical limitations. I started writing as part of my neuro-rehabilitation. On an emotional level, the book was a way of coming to terms with my grief, though that was not my intention. The journey from conception, through publishing, to working on a sequel, was supported by encouragement and help from others. People generously offered their advice, wisdom, and their kindness. I was lifted by their love.

When *He Died Waiting* was published, I was surprised to receive hundreds of messages and emails from people who had had similar experiences to me. Some were heartbreaking, some were encouraging, and most showed how hidden many bereaved people are. And how silenced and abused they feel. Ignoring these messages was not an option because I try to be led by love. I felt compelled to respond. I discovered that I can manage engaging with people who are heartbroken and lost in grief. More than that, I have gained strength from these interactions. I have been inspired by, and learnt from, those who have been generous in sharing their experiences with me.

One of my motivations for publishing Tim's story, was that I wanted to make a difference. I did not want others to experience the agony of losing a child because their mental health needs had not been met. I was humbled by how well-received the book was. Its key themes of love, kindness, decency, and valuing people, are my guide. I took a brave leap and followed where *He Died Waiting* was leading me and, in 2021, I resigned from my social work lecturing post to become a freelance trainer and speaker. This was not an easy decision, and neither was it the plan I had in mind when I published the book. It can feel a bit precarious, but it is the right thing to do. I feel that Tim is by my side.

I did have a vague plan to write a sequel to *He Died Waiting.* I knew I would need a co-editor to help me manage the emotions, and practicalities, of working with authors who have experienced traumatic bereavements. Emma is someone whose love overflows and she has an abundance of wisdom and compassion. She consistently brought love into her practice as a mental health nurse. Her love for fellow humans is evident in the way she supports bereaved families, champions people in mental distress, campaigns, and in her political activities. Emma wraps her thread of love around others. In my darkest times, she has extended her love and enfolded me and my loved ones. With Emma as co-editor, I knew we were in safe hands.

Many of the chapter writers in *They Died Waiting* have expressed how they have found writing, or telling, their story emotional but also cathartic and restorative. It has been such a privilege to support contributors to formulate their ideas into polished chapters. I approached the editing with kindness and love. I have tried to be mindful of the impact of the published chapters on the contributors and the people they are connected to. I know from my own writing that trauma can make it hard to recall events coherently. Some of the contributors found this difficult too. For some of them, the collaborative editing process became almost therapeutic. Making sense, putting in to order, and cutting the 'white noise' (excess words) has enabled poignant and important stories to emerge. And to shine. Any sadness or anger that I absorbed through empathising with contributors, was outweighed by the joy of enabling them to feel heard and validated.

Another thread that runs alongside my work is research. At the time of writing, I am part-way through a doctorate in health and social care. I wanted to research how professionals and organisations could 'learn the lessons' from bereaved relatives after an unexpected death. When I started the doctorate, I was unaware of how my work-life would change. Having spent two years literature-searching, consulting with bereaved parents, and planning my creative research, and another year in the ethical approval process, I find myself no longer sure that I want to go where the academic road is taking me. Whatever I decide, my decision will be based on doing what I feel might make the biggest difference.

The 'golden thread' in my cord of life is love. I have received the unconditional love of family which provided me with core strength. The love of friends has kept me going. When threads break it is love that helps repair or release them. There are some threads that time, distance, or even death cannot sever. Their colour and form changes but they remain part of me because they are bound to me. The love and encouragement of others enabled me to write and publish *He Died Waiting* and *They Died Waiting*. Threads of love connect the stories and provide hope by reminding us how intrinsically good, kind, and resilient most people are. You are invited to pick up the threads and use the stories to extend the love into your life and work. It is the love I receive, and my love for others, that fuels me. Love gives me courage and sustains me. In the end, what matters most is love.

Abandoned by Mental Health Services
By Emma

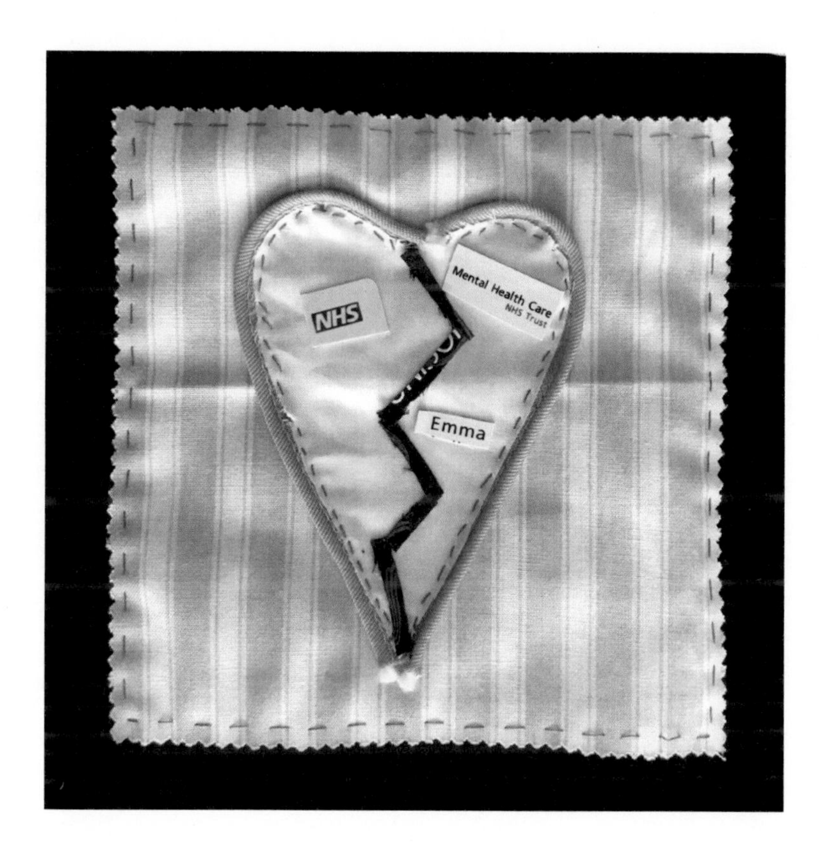

Emma's heart represents how heartbroken she feels about having to leave mental health nursing. It also reflects how she feels about the people who have lost their lives and those who are left behind. The fabrics and piping are a reminder of the different uniforms she has worn during her career. She made this from her ID card and lanyard which she cut up as a form of protest.

About Emma

Emma has a wealth of experience in mental health. She has worked in a variety of posts within the NHS as a mental health nurse. Emma's clinical practice in Early Intervention (EI) for Psychosis has been recognised as an exemplar[22]. Passionate about genuine coproduction, Emma set up an innovative youth participation project with the young people using EI services. With her encouragement and belief in them, this group of marginalised (and sometimes very unwell) young people developed the skills and confidence to challenge service leaders, lobby MPs, and deliver workshops for professionals. Emma supported the young people in creating some videos about mental health from their perspective[23]. Emma is involved in her community in a range of voluntary roles as a County Councillor. She is incredibly resourceful and she provides support and advocacy to people who find it difficult to access services and comfort to bereaved people. Emma is an active campaigner for mental health service improvements.

In this chapter, Emma gives an overview of her experience and her motivations.

---

22 There is a case study about Early Intervention in Psychosis by Emma on the SCIE website: https://www.scie.org.uk/files/children/transition/Casestudy_Norfolk.pdf

23 *Mind. Your Language* was produced for use in schools: https://www.youtube.com/watch?v=fqbm1eU2ODg *As This is Only Now* was produced by the youth participation group for their presentation at an international conference.

Abandoned by Mental Health Services

It's 7 am and I am in shock. For the first time in almost three years, I haven't woken at 3 am with palpitations and crushing anxiety. I actually 'slept right through'. I handed my notice in yesterday and 'voluntarily' put an early end to my 17-year career as an NHS mental health nurse.

I had been desperate to leave for several months, to preserve my own mental health, but I was supporting young people that I worked with on a couple of big projects and I was committed to seeing that through. I carefully worked out how much time I was owed and how much leave I had left to take. I handed in my notice the day of the launch of a public health campaign designed and created by those brilliant young people. I never again had to set foot back inside the broken NHS Trust that employed me.

I knew I was doing the right thing. The most validating thing that was said to me was by one of the young people I had worked alongside in the youth participation group for a few years. I had told the group while they were together that I was leaving: they waited for everyone to leave, then popped back in and said, "To be honest I'm surprised you stuck working for those c***s for so long. Thank you."

My route to becoming a mental health nurse began following exposure to bereavement through suicide when I was 18. The parent of a family that I regularly babysat for ended their own life. Their partner and three primary school-aged children had to cope with the fall-out that comes with traumatic bereavement. I grew up in a small village and I was shocked at how much stigma there was around suicide; how awkward most of the local community was in their response to this death; about the treatment of the family by local and national media; by the lack of support for children and families bereaved through suicide; and the brutality of the inquest process. At the time, I had little idea these were things that I would witness repeatedly over the decades.

Having dropped out of university after a term, I started work as a care assistant in a residential home for people living with dementia. The brilliant women that I worked with instilled in me two things that had a huge impact on my future career, "look after anyone in your care as you would a member of your own family" and "join a trade union". The care they provided was delivered with kindness, compassion, and love. They told me proudly that no one in their care had ever had a pressure sore. They showed me how to care for someone at the end of their life, and how to respectfully deal with a body following death. They honoured the lives previously lived and gave genuinely humane and person-centred care. In my naivety, I presumed that this is what care was like everywhere.

With the support and encouragement of the women from the care home, I applied for nursing training and got a place to study Mental Health Nursing in 1996. My nursing training was, at best, mediocre. I cringe when I reflect on how ill-equipped I was as a newly-qualified nurse to hold open, frank, and compassionate conversations with those in mental distress.

I got a job working as a staff nurse in a secure unit and learned more from the patients that I was looking after than I had during my training. The importance of understanding trauma and distress was blatantly obvious. Distress could be alleviated, and risk reduced, through the establishment of a respectful and trusting relationship. Good care is not that complex - listen, be respectful, don't judge, and do what you say you are going to do. Pull out all the stops to make sure that you don't become another person in the long list of people who have let the person down.

Nowhere does early intervention make more sense than in a secure unit. They are full of people who got the absolute opposite of early intervention. Often, they had been asking for help in their teenage years (either explicitly or implicitly through alarming behaviour that should have been understood as trauma-driven) but they were turned away or criminalised. Their case-notes chronicled repeated failures and missed opportunities to protect them from harm and abuse. I worked with some amazing, caring people but also with some who seemed to exhibit higher levels of psychopathy than some of the patients. You really don't need to lord it over people in a locked environment when you have a key and they don't. The power imbalance is already clear. Small things that set the culture of care, such as knocking on someone's bedroom door with a key rather than your hand and being wilfully rude or obstructive to patients, began to increasingly bother me. I left in 2003 to join a newly created Early Intervention in Psychosis Team.

Early Intervention was a joy to work in. It showed what could be achieved with a strong evidence base, sufficient resources (ring-fenced so they couldn't be raided by other parts of the service), and good quality leadership with the right values[24]. Our caseloads were capped, we had no waiting list, so we could work with people for at least three years.

---

24 Emma co-authored a paper on the effectiveness of early intervention: Lower, R., Wilson, J., Medin, E., Corlett, E., Turner, R., Wheeler, K. and Fowler, D. (2015) Evaluating an early intervention in psychosis service for 'high-risk' adolescents: symptomatic and social recovery outcomes'. *Early Intervention in Psychiatry* Vol 9 (3).

We were resourced to ensure that young people had support to remain in or regain education, work, and enjoy a social life. We also provided support to families and siblings which built and strengthened people's natural networks. We did not have a death by suicide in seven years. With small caseloads, we could be flexible to respond to crises and increase the frequency of face-to-face contact to several times a week, thus reducing the need to involve the crisis team or hospital admission. On the rare occasion that someone was admitted to hospital, we had capacity to go and visit and actively plan discharge (including to those aged under 18 who were admitted sometimes hundreds of miles away). It was a privilege to work alongside numerous young people who made good recoveries and built lives worth living. Occasionally, I hear from former patients letting me know how life is going for them. Some are working in health, social care, or education, managing their own homes and family and social relationships, and some have become parents.

I became increasingly aware that there is only a limited impact that a mental health service can have. Mental health is an issue of social justice and inequality. Mental health practitioners have limited impact on issues like domestic abuse and violence; sexual violence and abuse; bullying at school and in the workplace; narrowing of the school curriculum; quality of housing; and whether people have enough income to live with dignity.

I did my training as a trade union representative to be able to support colleagues (especially those working in teams with a worse culture than I was lucky enough to work in). I started to get more involved in standing up for staff and trying to tackle the pockets of bullying and poor practice across the organisation. This led to me becoming more involved in campaigning for change.

I was elected as a County Councillor in 2013. I was increasingly finding people in my community living with severe mental ill-health who had been abandoned by services. I tried to use the knowledge of my dual roles of knowing how the mental health system should work to advocate loudly on their behalf. The first piece of policy that I was able to implement at the County Council was to get unanimous cross-party support to sign-up to the Local Authority Mental Health Challenge[25] and I was appointed as the Mental Health Champion. The mental health champion role is a non-party political role, and the job is basically to keep banging on about mental health at every opportunity and to provide challenge within and outside of the Council. Every decision taken by government, public, or community

25 Mental Health Challenge Template is available online: https://www.centreformentalhealth.org.uk/mental-health-challenge-template-motion

body has the capacity to help or hinder the mental health of citizens. I saw my role as calling out suggestions that clearly risked worsening the mental health of the population and advocate for policies that would have a positive impact on mental health.

In this role, I also started picking up mental health casework from around my county. Increasingly, individuals or families at breaking point would find my name and contact details via an internet search and ask for help. I was able to do some effective advocacy from my Councillor role – often emailing the relevant director at the NHS trust that employed me to say, "this isn't good enough, sort it out". This was usually effective for those individual cases but it is no way to run a service. It was reliant on the randomness of someone finding their way to my inbox and my happening to know who is the most senior decision-maker to ask to sort it out. I became increasingly worried by all the people out there who didn't know where to go for help, or who didn't have families or friends with the ability to take up the fight for them.

I was able to give examples of the systemic failings in care and neglect that I was witnessing in my community to chief executives, directors of nursing and operations, and Trust chairs. Concern and horror were expressed. The right noises were made. Then absolutely nothing was done to address it.

I've lost count of the people who don't even know whether they are still under the 'care' of a service or whether they have been discharged. Here are some examples I stumbled across in my work as a councillor:

-The person who had been well supported by the assertive outreach team and then 'lost' to the system after the team was axed. When he was eventually detained under the Mental Health Act, the only food in the house was a tub of mouldy margarine.
- Someone with untreated acute psychotic symptoms who had been 'cuckooed'. Criminals had taken control of his money and turned his flat into a drug factory. When the police intervened, he was found to be sleeping in the bath and eating from a tin of cat food. One of our local police officers choked up with emotion when he described what they saw.
- The older resident, with a long-term psychotic illness, who used to be regularly visited by a community nurse at home. Their care was reduced to attending a depot clinic at a community centre once a month. He was relieved of tens of thousands of pounds of his life savings by scammers. It was obvious the minute I set foot in his house because I could see mountains of post offering 'too good to be true' offers. He was subjected to relentless phone calls offering insurance, and other products that he had

no need for, because his details had been sold on by unscrupulous tele-sales companies. He would pay immediately by debit card over the telephone. He paid for thousands of pounds worth of unnecessary roofing work that was never completed. Several years later this remains with Action Fraud, with no progress on the investigation. There seems no prospect that this gentle and decent man will ever get any of his money back.

-The numerous people who had their power capped, and therefore no access to heating (and in one case no water), because their mental health had been left to unravel to the extent that they were no longer opening their post and they were too terrified to let anyone into their flat.

- The person who was left with no bereavement support after the sudden death of their partner, and descended into squalor following the subsequent traumatic death of a friend in their flat. The emergency services had left behind the mess that goes with a death scene. I noticed the smell of rotting body fluids some weeks later and demanded that some assistance and support was provided.

I could fill a whole book with the consequences of the systemic failings of abandonment of those with chronic and enduring mental illness.

Things got to the stage that the very act of walking through the door at work made me feel complicit with the harm that was happening. I realised that despite my best efforts (and thanks to the behaviours of those who bullied, undermined, and tried to discredit me) that I was not going to be able to change anything from within. Since I left my mental health nursing career, I consider that I have done more grassroots 'proper' community mental health nursing than I was ever able to working inside the system that is meant to provide it. A lot of it is about addressing the absolute basics of shelter, warmth, food, and human contact.

Within a week of the first Covid lockdown, working with local volunteers and my fellow ward councillors, we had set up a foodbank. The levels of unmet mental health need that we discovered through people's access for food support was staggering. In addition to people already struggling with their mental health and the inaccessibility of services, new mental health needs were emerging as a result of sudden isolation and sudden loss of income or status.

Covid also brought my return to nursing. I took up the request from the Nursing and Midwifery Council to join the temporary Covid register for nurses who had left practice within the previous three years. I haven't returned to mental health nursing, but have been able to put my skills to good use working in the vaccination team for NHS staff. I've also worked in the outreach community bus, vaccinating in communities where take up is low or where people face particular barriers to accessing health care. For example, at homelessness drop-in services or out on farms for migrant workers.

When Caroline wrote *He Died Waiting*, she included a chapter about my work in early youth participation, which included going with a party of young people to a conference in Canada. Having felt bullied out of the career I loved, it was emotional to read about myself from the perspective of someone I respect valuing me. When Caroline asked me to co-edit this book, I felt excited but also daunted because writing is something out of my comfort zone. I wasn't sure if I had the skills to do justice to the people who have bravely shared their stories with us. I hope that it will be of some comfort to people, who have been failed by services in the most traumatic of ways, to know that there are many staff who speak up about the unsafe system they practice in. The accounts that people have provided make very difficult reading. I feel uplifted by their humility and bravery but also at times experience a raging anger because so much harm was so very avoidable.

There is no way back to mental health nursing for me. That career option has been damaged beyond repair. I'm proud of the work that I did during that phase of my life. The community work that I do now is just as important and, psychologically, not having an employer has been very helpful. I am committed to doing what I can for those who have been abandoned by mental health services. The electorate is my employer, and if they don't think I'm up to the job they can vote me out. I can continue to strongly advocate for people being failed by the system because I have nothing more to lose.

Stories of Loss and Stories of Hope
By Caroline

Bereavement and grief are part of life - none of us can escape experiencing it at some point. Yet, as a society, we find it difficult to talk about death and dying. This discomfort is shared by professionals. Denise Turner, who researched experiences of parents whose child had died at home[26], found that the 'most sensitive and least defensive' professionals were funeral directors. In this book, there are numerous examples of a dissonance between what bereaved people want and need and professional perceptions of the same. This is most apparent in the accounts of anticipated grief (where someone is fearful their loved one could die) and in the stories that describe the processes that bereaved families went through after a sudden or unexpected death.

In my experience, many professionals, including mental health practitioners and social workers, are uncomfortable talking about bereavements and they can find it emotionally triggering. I think this is due to a variety of reasons, which include: a general lack of understanding of thanatology[27]; their own unresolved losses; a fear of making things worse; or simply not knowing what to say. Avoiding the topic of death enables us to put aside the possibility of our own or a loved one's demise. As Giddens, 1991[28] says:

> "Death, revealing the ultimate frailty of each individual's life project and of the body on which it depends, therefore becomes existentially threatening. If everyday life is to continue unruffled, death must be sequestrated, sidelined from the mainstream of social life."

I have not always been as relaxed about talking about death and dying as I am now. Developing my confidence and skills is down to exposure. The loss of Tim, and going public about my bereavement, has meant that I've had a lot of practise at being with bereaved people. The stories of loss in this book will provide exposure by inviting you to *be with* the writers for short periods. However, as the reader, you are in control of your exposure and can dip in and out to suit your needs. We offer some advice about how to do this in the chapter, *Through a Trauma Lens*.

---

26 Turner, D. (2014). *Telling the story: What can be learned from parents' experience of the professional response following the sudden, unexpected death of a child.* A doctoral thesis, University of Sussex.

27 Thanatology is the study of death and dying.

28 Giddens cited in Walter, T. (2020). *Death in the modern world.* London. Sage.

I acknowledge how hard it can be for professionals to engage with people's grief. However, loss is integral to health and social care work. Catherine Seigal says, "familiarity with death allows a calm competence that brings welcome relief [to others]"[29]. In *He Died Waiting* I describe how my friend, Lynne, was way more skilful at being with me empathically, than any of the professionals I encountered. Practitioners need to be able to have sensitive and difficult conversations. I have increasingly wondered about the robustness of the training people have in terms of loss, grief, and bereavement. I know from my lecturing roles, that educators are mindful of the emotional impact on students of triggering painful emotions, and they want to act responsibly. We give students and practitioners trigger warnings and offer options to disengage from potentially distressing discussions (for example saying, "You can leave the room at any time"). For some, an unintended consequence is that we send the message, "death and bereavement might be too difficult to talk, or even think, about". Whilst I agree that we should avoid traumatising or re-traumatising students and practitioners, we should be facilitating them to find ways of overcoming emotional barriers to engaging in taboo topics. Because, the people we serve, who are living through distress and bereavement, cannot disengage from their loss and trauma. The contributors to this book cannot leave the room they found themselves in.

There is not space in this book to cover theories of grief and loss. I recommend reading Caroline Lloyd's book, *Grief Demystified* (2018) for a readable overview. I would urge practitioners to familiarise themselves with some theories of grief but to exercise caution. Theories are contested, some are based on outdated ideas, or are unhelpful because they might not fit people's situations. There are a few general points, gleaned from my reading and experience, that are worth bearing in mind as you read *They Died Waiting*:

- There is no right way of grieving. We need to stop judging people for the way they express (or maybe appear not to express) their feelings.
- Most theories of grief are based on White-Eurocentric models. Every culture, religion, society, community have ways of expressing or processing grief. We need to respect and honour that.
- In the chaos and pain of grief, people can find comfort in rituals, memory gathering, meaning-making, inactivity or activity. This can change, sometimes from moment-to-moment.

29 Seigal C. (2017). *Bereaved parents and their continuing bonds: love after death.* London Jessica Kingsley Press.

- Too often, grief is pathologicalised. We expect people to conform and 'get over it'. Many of the contributors to this book endured long waits (months and years) for funerals, inquests, and investigations to conclude. Some are still waiting.
- Continuing bonds with lost loved ones is okay[30]. This can be expressed in many public and private ways (such as talking to the deceased, remembering them on birthdays, and talking about them).
- We all need to be aware of how our experiences of loss might be impacting on our ability to respond to other people's feelings of loss. Pay attention to your feelings.
- Grief has a nasty habit of taking us by surprise. We can think we are managing it, and without warning, we can drop into a sinkhole.
- Cumulative grief means that one bereavement can bring back feelings from a previous one. This can present as compassion fatigue.

Grieving can make us feel hopeless. In some of the stories presented, you might sense a lack of hope that things can ever be better for the writer and hope seems in short supply. Therefore, without offering false positivity, which only serves to make people feel worse, we sometimes need to hold on to hope for others[31].

Most bereaved people will not need any support from professionals. We can all be that caring family member, colleague, or friend that is prepared to talk about death and dying. Or to simply be with someone who is hurting. When I was struggling with grief, other people, who had walked a similar path, reached out and lit the path ahead. They showed me that it was possible to survive traumatic loss and in time to enjoy life again. In turn, I want to reach out to people who have lost all hope, to stand with them. To light their paths.

So many of the narratives in this book are stories of hope. Of ordinary people who are doing extraordinary things. People who have known the depths of despair and who are standing with those who need comfort and solidarity. Lighting safe paths and offering reassurance and encouragement. If you have lost hope, please reach out for help[32]. If you know someone who is experiencing loss, please be their beacon.

---

30 In 1966, Klass, Silverman and Nickman introduced the idea that we might continue in relationship with a deceased person, albeit in a different way.

31 We explore this further in *Holding On To Hope* by Caroline and Emma.

32 The Samaritans offer 24/7 support for anyone who needs it their number is: 116 123

Through a Trauma Lens
By Caroline and Lisa

A key theme that runs throughout *They Died Waiting* is trauma. Many of the chapters offer descriptions of harrowing experiences. The most traumatic elements, such as means of suicide or graphic descriptions, are not included in the lived experience accounts. Nevertheless, the stories include: the trauma associated with mental distress or of caring for someone with mental illness who is at risk of dying; working in trauma-loaded settings; traumatic deaths (sudden and/or premature); and the trauma of bereavement and post-bereavement experiences. The authors lay their trauma bare and invite you to experience it vicariously in their emotive narratives. The motivation for this is to illuminate how traumatic many people's experiences of professionals and mental health services are and to encourage trauma-sensitivity.

Before reading the individual accounts, we advise pausing and considering what you might read and how you can do that in an emotionally safe way. To support readers, we have written this chapter to explain more about trauma, how it might affect us, and strategies for managing it. We want to model trauma-sensitive practice which begins by educating about trauma. Some knowledge of trauma theories can help us understand trauma and distress.

There is a growing move towards making services 'trauma-informed' or some version of this term. It is written into policy documents and training requirements. There can be confusion about the word 'trauma' which, understandably, results in people believing it does not apply to them or the system where they work. Some of the confusion arises because trauma might refer to specific incidents or events, from long-term exposure to adversity, or from developmental (relational) distress. Louise Harm's (2015) book, *Understanding Trauma and Resilience*, brings different theoretical perspectives and explanations together.

Dr Karen Treisman refers to 'trauma, adversity and culturally informed' systems. This helps broaden our perspective on trauma. It is the nature of being human to experience distress and adversity and including the term 'culture' ensures we don't overlook this often-neglected area. Treisman suggests a move from trauma-sensitive, to aware, to trauma-informed, and then trauma-responsive[33]. She also highlights the difference between trauma-specific and trauma-informed.

---

33 From Karen Treisman's book, *A Treasure Box for Creating Trauma-Informed Organisations Volume 1* (2021).

Trauma-specific would be 'interventions' designed to help people address the trauma itself. Staff in mental health or emergency services don't need to be trained in trauma-specific interventions to be trauma-informed. And something trauma-specific might not be trauma-informed if the values and principles of trauma-informed practice are not evident in action.

Reading this book will not make anyone 'trauma-informed'. Neither will a few 'trauma- informed' training sessions create a trauma-informed practitioner, team, or organisation. Trauma-informed is not a 'tool' to be implemented with a checklist to be ticked off. It is a way of doing and being, that is inherently organic and dynamic. It is built upon foundational values and principles. Trauma-informed practice is not simply being kind and decent, though that is a good starting point given some people's experiences. It requires a system-wide, multi-level, and layered response. It is how things are done. And *the way we are with people* when doing what needs to be done. It's walking the talk.

Trauma is underpinned by hierarchies and power differentials. Issues such as defensive practice and fragmented multi-agency working mean that people fall through the gaps. The disparity between physical and mental health funding reinforces the stigma, shame, and lack of value placed on people with mental illness. This discrimination goes against our basic Human Rights. Discrimination can be disguised as care: inpatient units that keep people contained but offer few truly meaningful activities or opportunities to learn regulating techniques and little, if any, access to evidence-based therapies. Some environments and practitioners are unable to tolerate or be with people in distress (which is not simple at all). Likewise, people who are placed on practitioners' 'caseloads' or waiting lists but don't get seen.

Trauma and oppression go hand in hand. Discrimination is embedded in the language and labels used in services that dehumanise and depersonalise people. For example, labelling people as 'hard to reach' when the services are inaccessible. When the word 'recovery' came along, the nuances and complexities were often missed. It became another way for services to blame people for 'not getting better' and another exclusive term for those who 'fit' a box determined by services. So often the problems lie with services that cannot provide the person-centred, trauma-informed treatment or options that people need.

Everybody, whatever their diagnosis, symptoms, or presentation, has the right to lead a good quality, meaningful life as defined by themselves. People aren't too 'complex', 'not motivated', 'unwilling to engage', or 'hopeless'. Our ability to respond and co-create environments and conditions in which people can live well, takes us back to social justice issues.

Social determinants of health, as identified by the World Health Organisation, directly impact mental health. Naturally, there is a complex interplay of factors that affect people's mental health. But, if we continue addressing 'symptoms', without addressing fundamental issues at a societal, community, organisational, and personal level, people will continue being failed and die. If it was anything but mental health, there would be collective outrage at the fact that those living with serious mental illness die 15 – 20 years earlier than the general population (the mortality gap). People might not be the 'right kind of ill', such as those with complex trauma or delusional beliefs, who do not fit the services on offer. There is no outcry and, in our opinion, anti-stigma campaigns tend to ensure that those most stigmatised and judged remain unheard, unseen, misunderstood, and marginalised. These things compound trauma.

The idea that people who have experienced trauma, especially repeated or childhood trauma, have nervous systems that are 'wired differently' underpins many therapies. Trauma can be passed down through generations if not healed[34]. Explanations of behaviours, based on neuroscience, are contested and can be oversimplified[35]. One example is the debate about Adverse Childhood Experiences (ACE) that gained widespread appeal in children's services. When used in a process-driven and judgemental way, to assess whether a child might be permanently damaged by adversity, it perpetuates hopelessness and became a weapon used by some to further traumatise parents[36].

The good news is that neuroplasticity means our brains can reorganise given the right stimuli. We believe it is possible to process trauma, change, and heal, given the right circumstances and healthy, trustworthy relationships. Whether or not you agree with neuroscience theories, we are advocating adopting a trauma-informed approach. Because, if implemented with a kind heart, it is calming, empathic, emotionally-containing and regulating, and gentle.

Uncontained trauma can impact on people who provide care for others. In their chapters, Billy and Heidi[37] show how, without the support they deserved, their loved one's trauma spilled over and was absorbed by them. Professionals too can experience vicarious or secondary trauma[38].

---

34 Mark Wolynn, *It Didn't Start With You* (reprint 2017).

35 David Wastell and Sue White's (2017) book, *Blinded by Science*, offers a critique of neuroscience in social policy.

36 A critique of ACEs is available online: https://www.researchgate.net/publication/332181235_A_Critique_of_the_Adverse_Childhood_Experiences_Framework_in_Epidemiology_and_Public_Health_Uses_and_Misuses

37 *If Only We Knew…* by Billy and *Love Will Find a Way* by Heidi.

38 A straightforward explanation of vicarious trauma can be found here: https://www.goodtherapy.org/blog/psychpedia/vicarious-trauma

This can express itself in many ways, from impacting on practitioners' mental health or, more worryingly in compassionless, defensive, and emotionally barren responses from professionals or organisations. This is where we see trauma-saturated services, the very services set up to support distressed people, heap trauma on top of trauma. Many of the chapters portray this. For example, in their chapter, *Peggy: Not 'Acting Up' But Dying*, Nick and Maxine, describe how traumatised they were not just by Peggy's traumatic death but by the behaviours of organisations and individuals afterwards. Likewise, in their chapters, Rose and Lynne[39] discuss the way inquests and investigations have added to their trauma.

A lot of people know about the adrenalin-driven fight, flight freeze response and it's often referred to when trying to help people manage anxiety. Polyvagal Theory[40], is one way to help make sense of why we behave and react as we do, and the impact of trauma, adversity, and stress on our autonomic nervous systems. Through working with clinicians, most notably Deb Dana[41], the theory has become accessible and applicable to understanding and working with trauma. According to Polyvagal Theory, co-regulation is a biological imperative (think babies) and remains so for the rest of our lives, even when we have well-developed self-regulating tools. This is hugely important in the context of being with people in distress and/or in crisis as well as the people potentially supporting them. Telling highly distressed people to 'use positive affirmations', their 'coping strategies', or to take a bath, or sip some chamomile tea, is generally not helpful. What people need is another person to help calm their nervous systems enough that we can try some of the things we know help. Lisa explores how important co-regulation has been for her recovery in the chapter *Blinded.*

However, co-regulation can only work if the person helping is regulated themselves. It is not simply contact with another person. It is the nature and quality of the interaction: body language, tone of voice, vocabulary, and speed of speech; active listening; giving the person time to talk; being heard; and feeling that someone is interested and cares. Jumping in to provide solutions or tell a person to 'use their tools' is not real listening. This response could potentially escalate any distress as the person feels dismissed, invalidated, worthless, and unsafe. Without some degree of trust, important information about the person's current safety and wellbeing might not be shared.

---

39 *A Place of No Return* by Rose and *When Time Runs Out* by Lynne

40 Stephen Porges, *Polyvagal safety: Attachment, Communication, Self-Regulation* (2021).

41 Deb Dana, *The Polyvagal Theory in therapy: Engaging the Rhythm of Regulation* (2018).

We see some of the best examples of trauma-informed practice when we read the accounts of those offering bereavement support. For example, Frances[42] approaches her work in an attuned, authentic, empathetic, and gentle way. She validates people's traumatic experiences and distress and creates spaces where people can feel seen and truly heard.

Working with trauma is not easy. People who are having trauma-responses have dropped into emotional time-holes, where cognitive processing and reasoning have been shut down in favour of survival behaviours. A person whose nervous system has been affected by trauma will find it far more difficult to emotionally regulate as their nervous system is wired for protection not connection. They might interpret a neutral facial expression as angry. Kindness and care can feel scary and unsafe because it might trigger feelings associated with times when this was used to groom and then exploit and abuse them.

So many clinical environments are dysregulating and retraumatising. Devoid of any visual or sensory regulating cues and no thought in how the seating is arranged. Often bleak posters on the walls, little privacy, and a sense of confinement. Feeling trapped and exposed does little to engender a sense of welcome and calm. Several of the chapter authors describe the bleak or sensory triggering environments that they, or their loved ones, have experienced. Staff work day in and out in these same environments. Space is often at a premium and desk hopping has become the norm. There is little consistency for people.

If services want to be trauma-informed these are some things they need to ask:

- What conditions are the staff working under?
- Is the organisation a place where honesty, transparency, compassion, curiosity, and humility are practiced?
- Do staff and those using services have a sense of autonomy? Do they have voice and choice?
- Is sufficient time allocated for reflective practice, supervision, and training?
- Are people supported when mistakes happen? And if challenges arise, does the learning and action reflect the values of dignity, respect, and compassion - even when the consequences are not nice but necessary?
- What is, or is not, tolerated in the use of appropriate language in record writing and discussions about people they work with?
- What is communication like?

---

42 *We Need to Talk About Death and Dying* by Frances

There are no easy answers. Being present with and alongside people on their journeys, and exercising values like respect, kindness, and dignity, can have a lifetime's impact on their lives. We believe that the key to containing, ameliorating, and even healing trauma, lies in healthy relationships. In *The Boy Who Was Raised as a Dog*, Bruce Perry writes, "people, not programs, change people" (p85). The chapters in *They Died Waiting* are full of the hope that comes from encounters with people who understood and responded to their trauma. Despite, or perhaps because of, their traumatic experiences, some people shine with hope and courage.

Given what we know about trauma, and the possibility that any of the chapters could trigger a trauma-response or be dysregulating, what might you want to consider when reading this book?

Babette Rothschild, author of *The Body Remembers* (2000), uses the analogy of 'brakes and accelerators' to manage trauma responses. We would advocate a similar approach. Before diving in to the rich narratives, that are bursting with evocative lived experience, take a moment to identify your emotional brakes. What is it that helps when you become emotionally overwhelmed or distressed? What works to calm you down? If something begins to trigger you, then remove your foot from the accelerator and if necessary, *apply the brakes*. Go and do whatever it is that will help you emotionally calm and regulate. Similarly, don't rush through the chapters like a sports car in the fast lane of the motorway. You could crash. Pace yourself. Apply moderate pressure to the accelerator and slow down if you need to. You might even take a diversion around chapters that look potentially too triggering.

If you are a student or practitioner in health and social care, you will encounter people who are traumatised, or traumatising to be around, and potentially triggering situations, on a daily basis. Somehow, you need to find ways of engaging with people's stories, however distressing they might be. When you read the accounts of professionals who were cold, unsympathetic, even compassionless, consider how trauma might be playing a part. Simply avoiding potential triggers is not a good idea. That way leads to trauma-insensitive practice. The authors in this book have lived/are living the trauma. When someone dies waiting, it can feel impossible for their loved ones to escape from further trauma. We invite you to engage with the narratives in this book and to be willing to explore some difficult topics. If it triggers a trauma-response, we urge you to apply the brakes, seek support, and use your own tools (via supervision, counselling, and wellbeing services) to address that.

Part Two - A 'Special Death' in the Family

Caroline made this heart to represent how her son, Tim, was portrayed in the distressing paperwork she received after his death. The background reflects Tim's love of 'techno' music and the heart the way he could be like fireworks or, as his younger brother would say, "he was beautifully crazy". The vibrant aspects of Tim were overlaid by inquest statements written by professionals. These present a partial picture in which Tim was unrecognisable because they are indistinct, almost monotone, and lacking in context. They contained derogatory and emotionally-distanced language.

A 'Special Death' in the Family
By Caroline

In this section, the chapters all relate to the 'unexpected death' of a family member. The impact on families is exposed in these emotive accounts. They contain repeating, and distressing, themes: of frustrated and fearful relatives desperately trying to get help for their loved one; families who are ignored or excluded; the raw grief of those left behind; and the devastation that a traumatic and sudden death causes.

Nearly all the deaths in this book would be categorised as 'special deaths' according to Margaret Holloway's (2004) criteria[43]. These are deaths that involve psychological trauma, stigma, disenfranchised grief[44], and might threaten our existential security. Deaths by suicide, due to drug or alcohol use, misadventure, and/or deaths of people stigmatised in their lifetime (perhaps due to their mental health or lifestyle) come under this umbrella. Research shows that these deaths are often harder to grieve which can lead to complicated or prolonged grief reactions[45]. Different theorists and researchers have presented arguments that one sort of death is more difficult than another.[46] I do not think it is helpful to rank bereavements in this way. All the stories in *They Died Waiting* relates to people who have died prematurely and whose deaths were avoidable.

What is striking within the accounts is the low value placed by society, professionals, and organisations, on some of those who have died. In *He Died Waiting*, I refer to people who have whispered lives:

"*There is a lack of societal curiosity and outrage which mirrors the low value placed on marginalised people. Preventable and predictable deaths occur too often: deaths in my community; in your community; in care homes; in hospitals; deaths on the streets; or behind closed doors. Some people are deemed to be of so little worth that their lives (and their deaths) are mere whispers*" (Aldridge, 2020, pages 18,19).

---

43 From *Negotiating Death in Contemporary Health and Social Care* by Margaret Holloway (2004).

44 Kenneth Doka introduced the concept of 'disenfranchised grief', sometimes referred to as 'hidden sorrow' because it is grief that is not acknowledged or validated by social norms.

45 There is lots of information available online about complicated or prolonged grief/bereavement. However, much of it pathalogicalises individuals.

46 Two journal articles that discuss different kinds of special death are; Guy and Holloway's (2007) https://www.researchgate.net/publication/240729360_Drug-related_Deaths_and_the_%27Special_Deaths%27_of_Late_Modernity which looks at drug-related deaths and Chapple et al's (2015) Taboo and the different death? Perceptions of those bereaved by suicide or other traumatic deaths - https://onlinelibrary.wiley.com/doi/10.1111/1467-9566.12224

You will read examples of people who were no longer 'seen' or valued because their issues with drugs and alcohol, learning disability, or age, have diagnostically overshadowed their mental illness or vice-versa. Discrimination adds another layer of awfulness to the terrible services some people receive. There is a plethora of research to show that Black people are more likely to be diagnosed with a mental illness, detained under the Mental Health Act, imprisoned, or restrained. Racism is explicit or implicit within some of the accounts. People with whispered lives become invisible. 'Care' slips into indifference, or even abuse, as people are dehumanised and seen as having no worth. To their families, those who have died are prized and valued. When there is a special death in the family the wider network is affected.

One of the things that I found hardest to hear in these stories is how clearly some people expressed that they were at risk of dying, by their words or their actions, yet they were ignored. The risk was dismissed. The notion that it is okay to deem people who are suicidal or managing their distress through risky behaviours, self-medicating, or self-neglect as having 'capacity', and saying that it's their 'right to die', has to stop. We know from the accounts in this book that the people who died would have preferred to live. They did not want to die, they wanted to live bearable lives. However, without the support they deserved, life was unbearable and they either gave up hope or died trying to obliterate the pain. We should not accept people dying as inevitable and somehow normalise it. We should be holding on to hope for people and keeping them safe until they can feel that hope again.

Mental health practice abounds with theories and policies built on evidence that involving families and carers works. Sadly, this is far from the reality of many people's experiences. Coroner reports often cite how families have tried desperately to keep their loved one safe and well. Too often families are ignored, excluded, or even vilified. This is graphically highlighted in several of the chapters. Parental bereavement is also recognised as particularly painful[47]. When I read the accounts written by mothers, I could feel their frustration and fear. It leaps off the page.
The more frightened they became, the more of a 'nuisance' they became to professionals: the reaction is to discredit them. Then we see how the system gathers its power and takes to the 'we know best' pedestal.

There are several examples within the chapters where the law around confidentiality is misapplied to justify not sharing information with carers. Professionals huddle together under their cloak of power instead of

47 I recommend Catherine Seigal's book, *Bereaved Parents and their Continuing Bonds: Love After Death* (2017) if you are interested in parental bereavement.

thinking creatively about how to exercise their powers to prioritise safety. This is not always easy to do. As a social worker, I would rather answer questions about why I breached someone's confidentiality to keep them safe, than I would have to justify, in Coroner's Court, why I did not share life-saving information. One way forward would be to use advanced statements and advanced directives[48] more often, and adhere to them when someone becomes unwell. Robust and effective safety plans could serve this purpose but only if they are genuinely co-created and updated regularly.

Mental health professionals have to get better at working with families. We have to listen to the people who know the service-user best, those who are invested in them through love connections. We must work harder at identifying who is in someone's naturally occurring network and include them in plans to keep that person safe and well. In several chapters, the networks around the person who was unwell shrunk. Often to just one exhausted person, who was trying to meet the needs of a loved one when a support team was required. What is needed is for professionals to be proactive in extending the support network but also in improving the communication within it. Services are over-stretched and they want to discharge people whenever possible. Therefore, it is imperative that they build the relationships and strengths of people's support network. This is not about dumping people without support (as described in many chapters), it is about adopting a humble approach and genuinely working in partnership with carers.

Keeping people safe and well matters not just to them but to their entire network. The impact on those left behind cannot be underestimated. It is well known that people bereaved by suicide are at increased risk of dying by suicide themselves[49].

Research also shows that traumatic or parental bereavement can lead to becoming mentally unwell (including a risk of suicide)[50]. But our contributors describe unkind, thoughtless, or even downright dishonest and attacking behaviours from professionals and organisations towards them.

---

48 Information about Advanced statements and directives are on line: https://www.rethink.org/advice-and-information/rights-restrictions/rights-and-restrictions/planning-for-your-care-advance-statements-and-advance-decisions/

49 Open access to a journal citing research evidence about the link between being bereaved by suicide and risk of suicide can be found online: https://bmjopen.bmj.com/content/bmjopen/6/1/e009948.full.pdf

50 An American study into the long-term impact on parents who lose a child is available online: https://www.ncbi.nlm.nih.gov/pmc/articles/PMC2841012/

Throughout this book there are examples of traumatic bereavements that have been exacerbated by the associated additional stress and trauma relating to inquests and investigations, and how this has impacted on bereaved people in terms of their mental health, and ability to grieve.

When she introduced the concept of special deaths, Margaret Holloway said that these kinds of deaths were set to increase. Sadly, she was correct. Year on year deaths associated with mental illness continue to rise. It is impossible to get accurate figures because the statistics are confusing. However, the numbers are staggeringly high. If we count mental-health-related deaths in hospitals and the community, deaths by suicide, through drugs and alcohol, from eating disorders, or dementia, then tens of thousands die each year. The additional pressures brought about by Covid and the dramatic cost of living rise will be increasing people's stress and despair. There are examples throughout this book that bear witness to the way Covid has impacted on people's mental health and, in some cases, directly led to suicide. The rhetoric around 'underlying health conditions', which include mental illness, is stigmatising. Thus, many Covid deaths meet all the criteria for special deaths.

Although the concept of special deaths makes sense, and helps explain why certain bereavements might be more difficult to bear, I am not convinced 'special' is the correct adjective to use. To each of us, any loss of a loved one is special and a death in the family hurts. As you read the following chapters, I invite you to think about what words you might use to describe these uniquely painful losses.

When Time Runs Out
By Lynne

John's heart was made by his dear friend, Will, who says: "The heart is a representation of the way John could be such a put together, composed, confident, intelligent person, while hiding the fact he was struggling so much. For many years I lived with him, enjoying the beautiful man he was and trying to support the pained man he also was. He was incredible, so full of life, always full of wonder, and so emotional and passionate that his impact on my life will continue for the rest of my life. John's heart for this book was made by me. But my heart was made by John many years ago."

About Lynne

Since 2011, Lynne has assertively represented service users and carers at different forums, including scrutiny panels and suicide prevention action groups. She works in partnership with her local mental health trust and council to achieve positive change – making use of the negotiating skills acquired as a senior civil service trade union representative. Lynne is also involved in the co-productive design and delivery of training for mental health practitioners and other community service providers.

When Lynne was asked about contributing to this book, she identified an opportunity to get John's voice widely heard by including verbatim quotes from his notebook diary – to enable him, in part, to tell his own story, in his own words.

When Time Runs Out

As I write this, I am aware of John's presence alongside me and I sense profound approval from him. The people who loved John tried to help him access the care and support he needed – to enable him to reach the light at the end of a dark tunnel. Sadly, time ran out and, despite all of his and our efforts, we lost him. The ripple effect changed our lives from colour to black and white. We will always bear the scars of John's ordeal.

Going through a portal

John died suddenly, in 2015, at the age of 26 years. The inquest recorded his death as aspiration of stomach contents - which contained a combination of drugs and alcohol. The conclusion was: 'accident'.

Despite my representations, no mention whatsoever was made of the complex, long-term, and unstable mental health disorders that had, in effect, led to John's life becoming extinct. That omission camouflaged the root cause of John's death - his mental ill-health. The physical causes of death detailed on his death certificate relate to symptoms that had arisen from that cause. If deaths like John's continue to be inaccurately recorded, we will never know the full extent of the tragic loss of life that inadequate treatment of mental ill-health is responsible for.

If, at the first indication that something was wrong, early intervention and robust person-centred support had been offered, John might have been able to develop strategies to safely and effectively manage his illness. Without it, John passed through a portal into a tormented existence that led to self-harm, alcohol dependence, and substance misuse. Each aspect of John's dual diagnosis couldn't be treated in isolation, although this was repeatedly attempted, because as one monster was tackled and disabled, another one expanded to fill the vacated space.

Some months after John's death, I came across a notebook (a diary of sorts), in which John had made hand-written dated entries. These described his innermost thoughts, as if to a trusted friend, as he attempted to navigate the emotional roller-coaster journey that his mental ill-health had imposed on him. The notebook covers several years – with significant gaps between the dates of some of the entries. John's diary provides an insight into how mental illness took hold of his life:

6th July 2004:
"I saw other people with girlfriends and I often wondered why I hadn't got/ever had a girlfriend and then it hit me that I was gay and that I had known all along deep down but had denied it and convinced myself it was just a phase. I got depressed, real depressed. I'm not a crying sort of guy but boy did I cry – every night before I slept and when I woke tears welled. I was a mess."

"Depression hit me but I combatted this with food, boy do I regret that. I bottled up everything and did what most find impossible, ignored my heart. I now know what I should have done – talked to someone about how I was feeling. I turned to studying and that I don't regret, it made me smart."

"I am 15 now and I have just read a story on the net - the end was a bitch and I was devastated by it because it was so true to life. That story tore down the walls I had built up and like a bomb, it blasted through and hit my only weakness, my heart and it awoke all of things that I had kept hidden for years. I am more mature now and my overactive mind told me that my heart was empty and inside I felt hollow. I had lied to my friends and my own family. The emptiness is consuming me. I need someone to love and to be loved by. Well, finding someone is the logical answer to that but logic is no use because if I follow what I feel I would cause so much pain it would destroy me."

"I wish I could say [I am gay] to other people. Mum wouldn't show she minded – she loves me for who I am, so she must still love me if I am gay. Dad – ooo a tricky one this, that I can't predict. My brother - I have my suspicion that he knows more than he shows. Friends – mixed. I've managed to weave an intricate web of lies and use a female friend as a shield, to prove I wasn't gay and I regret that. I need to come out, I can't deny it for much longer."

7th July 2004:
"I have only eaten one meal in 2 days. I am starving myself so as not to be fat."

9th July 2004:
"I hope these feelings will go away soon – I can't eat and all I want to do is sleep. I feel in despair – this illusion cannot last much longer."

4th September 2004:
"Well out I came and very well it went too. Everyone (Mum, Dad and family) took it well. I knew they would, so why I didn't tell them earlier, I don't know!"

23rd September 2004:
"I feel more confident. I can't believe I have lost 4 stones (well three and a half after tonight's feast!). I must drink less alcohol (1.5 drunk in 2 nights) – far too much and I must fast for 2 days too - due to excessive feed tonight."

2nd November 2004:
"I'm so screwed up at the moment – my bulimia is out of control. I can't eat without being sick (making myself sick). I wish the voice would go away – it's constantly in my mind telling me how fat I am, how ugly – as if I don't already know! As awful as it is, I am drifting back into depression. I hope that if I seek help that maybe it won't be so bad – I hope."

6th December 2004:
"Dark thoughts enter my head again – wishing before I sleep that I shall not wake; hoping to be hit by the bus which doesn't stop or to be in the shop where the robbery takes place and get stabbed. I don't care anymore – I have no reason to live, so why not die? It would solve all my problems … Why should I put up with this? I never asked to be a freak, it's not my fault. I wish with all my heart, every day, that I was not still here and yet I still am. What to do? How to end? Why must I bear this – I deserve to live more and be happy. What can I do to bring light where only darkness now dwells?"

16th June 2007:
"Bulimia is a demon I still carry with me."

One June to January, John recorded his weight reduction on the last page of the notebook. The starting weight is in excess of 19 stones. Beside a 13 stones 9 pounds entry, John wrote, "I used to dream of this but now that I'm here, I feel worse than when I was 20 stones."

John's journey through services

The first warning sign, for me, of the emotional turmoil that John was experiencing, was the realisation that he had developed the eating disorder during his early teenage years. Towards the end of his life, John told me that when he left behind the small, sheltered environment of a combined infant and junior school, and transferred to a high school with over 1,500 pupils, he had felt overwhelmed and vulnerable. This was compounded by him being one of the youngest in his year.

John told me that when he began to face up to the fact that he was gay he had gone through a phase of related self-denial. To combat the related trauma, he began comfort-eating and excess weight then became a major problem for him. This led to him being bullied. John felt that bulimia appeared to present the ideal compromise solution. He could still make use of his comfort eating coping strategy, whilst keeping his body mass indicator within the desired range. Reflecting back, he realised that this was a technique designed to camouflage the emotional problems that he was facing. He initially used alcohol as a coping strategy and he acknowledged that, as a result, he had become alcohol-dependent.

John was regularly told, by clinicians, that he needed to take responsibility for his behaviour and, if he wished to be treated for his mental health disorders, he needed to sort out his problems with alcohol first. This approach ignored a basic fact: with a dual diagnosis, a robust, holistic approach is required to achieve a positive, safe, and sustainable outcome. Often this will be unachievable unless it can begin with a residential stay (with in-house peer support and a clinician present). A person-centred strategy is required which includes preferred and safe alternatives (ie: an activity timetable) and avoids generic, prescriptive time limits. All being essential to avoid a post-discharge relapse and the re-establishment of the dangerous default setting of alcohol and/or substance misuse coping strategies. A 'one size fits all' approach will never work.

Aged 18, John went to a Cornish university where he gained a degree in Geology. Naively, we all felt, John included, that a fresh start was all that he needed. However, mental ill-health doesn't stay behind in the wardrobe with your old school blazer, it accompanies you wherever you go. In 2010, John had to pause a Masters Degree course (which he never completed) and return home. As his parents, we were deeply shocked to discover how ill he had become – something he had managed to mainly camouflage, up to then. We felt completely out of our depth, about how to help him. Adequate guidance was not provided to us by mental health services.

During the last two years of his life, John regularly talked to me about the mental health challenges he faced and the profoundly negative impact that they had on his wellbeing, and ability to function in a stable and safe way, on a day-to-day basis.

John was diagnosed with an 'unstable personality disorder'. He felt this was responsible for his often erratic, and sometimes dangerous, behaviour. He viewed his bulimia and medication misuse disorder as forms of self-harm that had developed in the guise of a self-medication strategy. I recall being asked, by a mental health clinician, whether I thought John's mental health problems had arisen from his consumption of excessive quantities of alcohol and medication misuse. I responded that, as John's mother and carer, I could confirm that his mental health disorders predated, by several years, his alcohol use and medication experimentation.

Clinicians appeared to believe that John's high level of intelligence and wide range of skills must surely have enabled him to make informed decisions, relating to: 'taking responsibility and avoiding risk to life behaviours'. They failed to grasp the profoundly negative influence, on personal judgement and safety, of the brain malfunctioning. For John, this resulted in a lack of rationality and an inability to identify, or understand, his 'personal best interests' and act in accordance with them.

John participated in outpatient counselling therapies. He told me he found the after-effects of those sessions 'unbearably traumatic' and had specifically asked for them to take place on Friday afternoons - so he could consume a large quantity of alcohol afterwards, and remain in 'an induced stupor' over the weekend, to block the overwhelming emotional impact caused by the negative memories that were being triggered.

Although John struggled with his mental health, he aspired to help others. At the time of his death, he was undertaking a Mental Health Nursing degree at a nearby university. I recall him telling me about the course induction session, where attendees were asked to define a service-user. John said that he eventually put up his hand to share his thoughts, "a service-user is a person and an individual".

I spoke to John three times during the last week of his life. Each time, he was extremely emotional and tearful. On one of those occasions, he said, "The devil is loose Mum and I can't control him anymore". This was a direct reference to his perception of the negative influence of his personality disorder.

During my last ever conversation with John he spoke of, as he saw it, mental health services' 'determination' to discharge him. He felt that discharge appeared to be the home-based treatment team's sole objective. He had made it clear that he did not want to be discharged and go on a waiting list to access another form of community mental health support. He was still in need of urgent and significant help. He knew he needed help "*NOW*".

Nevertheless, John was discharged *over the telephone.* This was a direct contravention of the team's working policies and protocols. It is not necessary to have any medical qualifications to understand why telephone discharges should not happen. It is impossible to carry out a safe, robust, accurate, and effective mental health assessment by telephone! Less than 24 hours later, John's life had ended.

The baton passed from John to me

I feel that John's life ended tragically, due to the abandonment of the very team that should have been fighting for his life alongside him. This perception was reinforced by the findings of a referral that I made to the Parliamentary and Health Service Ombudsman. In their report, specific reference was made to "a likely abandonment perception", on John's part.

I sent the coroner lots of information - but I didn't attend John's inquest. I couldn't bear to listen to mental health practitioners 'defending the indefensible'. I felt the verdict of 'accidental death' hid the truth about the significant part that John's mental ill-health played in his death. I forwarded a copy of the Ombudsman's report to the Coroner because I wanted to see more probing questions asked at inquests and more context recorded. I had a letter back thanking me. I have noticed in media reports, about subsequent inquests conducted in my area, that this is happening.

Since John died, I have been committed to working with local service providers to improve support provision for family and friend carers. When John was experiencing a mental health relapse, he would often insist that his clinicians did not disclose any information to family members - myself in particular. He would also provide an edited version of the problems that he was experiencing – often omitting information that was crucial to an accurate diagnosis and the establishment of an effective treatment plan. Whenever I tried to become an equal partner member of John's care and support team, I was made to feel that I was perceived as interfering. There were times when clinicians appeared to derive a sense of satisfaction, and experience relief, when they could 'play the patient confidentiality card' to justify not engaging with me. I recall many occasions when I felt excluded from having any involvement in the multi-disciplinary team meetings about John when he was an inpatient on a mental health hospital ward. This was despite the fact that on discharge, John would be returning to live under my roof – with me being his main carer.

Things that John said were often taken at 'face value', by clinicians, without any consideration being given to the 'bigger picture', validity, or context. He was also adept at playing the different component parts of his care and support team off against each other - leading to a lack of trust, misunderstandings and, on occasions, conflict.

Many times, it became necessary for me to become assertive and insist on 'being heard', in order to ensure that the professional members of John's care and support team were informed about the relevant facts and not just the parts that John had elected to share with them. In the face of clinician statements along the lines of "I can't talk to you because John had instructed us not to tell you anything", my approach was to highlight that I wasn't subject to a legally binding 'confidentiality clause'. Therefore, I could disclose all of the information that I felt they needed to know in relation to John. I respected that clinicians would be unable to comment on what I said - but I still expected them to listen, note, and then have subsequent ongoing due regard to what I told them.

When delivering training and awareness sessions, I have often referred back to my negative experiences as John's carer. I invite clinicians to consider how they would feel if John was a patient on their hospital ward and they were excluded from the information sharing process. They would likely be reluctant to get involved in his care if they were being denied access to his medical records, including diagnosis and treatment information and care and support plans. I then point out that, by denying me that insight and information, they were creating an expectation that once John was discharged into my care, and was in effect on 'my ward', I would be required to attempt what they would probably refuse to do. Caring for John, without being aware of what I would be dealing with and how best to help my son, was like blundering around in a dense fog - with no idea as to where I was going or how to get there. I call my related lived experience training module the: 'My Ward Scenario'. It has proved to be a very powerful learning tool for many clinicians.

John and I were not living under the same roof when he died but he was storing some of his possessions in my garage. Amongst them, I found John's diary notebook. I immediately recognised its value as a powerful with-hindsight learning tool - but also the highly confidential nature of it. I spent significant time considering whether I should keep the contents private or whether I should share excerpts. I hope that introducing John, as he really was at specific points in time, in contrast to the person he pretended to be (hiding behind the mask of a smile and regular, reassuring 'I'm fine' statements), will lead to insightful learning.

John taught me the vast majority of what I know. He ran out of time - but it is not too late for others like him. My mission now is to try and ensure other patients and families and friends don't have to go through the same nightmare journey with its worst-case scenario ending. Mental health practitioners need to engage with service users and carers and really listen to them and respect their 'lived experience expert' insight.

I find it deeply concerning that there is little 'beyond reasonable doubt' evidence to validate the mental health diagnostic labels that are imposed on people. A cultural change is required whereby the question 'what is happening to you and how best can we help you?' routinely replaces the statement 'what is wrong with you – you need to pull yourself together'.

I sometimes deliver related presentations with the title, "I am not a pair of curtains".

Reflecting back, the best description that highlights how John came to 'die waiting' is that there was an ongoing clinical perception that it was possible to treat, with an Elastoplast, a wound that required 100 sutures – it was, quite simply, never going to work! For his memorial service, I wrote this tribute to John. Will and I still refer to John as 'Mr Brave'.

Darling John
You fought courageously against a powerful; cruel; destructive; devious and ultimately overwhelming foe.

Right up to the end, you remained in the thick of the fight and you were insightful and tremendously brave and I am so very, very proud of you – my wonderful and amazing son.

In the months prior to your death, you handed off to me your place on a number of mental health forums and when I pointed out to you that I saw myself as only caretaking those roles for you, your response was:
"No Mum – I'm handing you the baton now – don't drop it!"

My response to that John is:
"As if – just you watch this space!!

A Place of No Return: Lisbeth's Story
By Rose

Rose made this heart in memory of Lisbeth. It is made from Lisbeth's clothes. The carefully embroidered words show how she is loved and missed as a Mummy, sister, and daughter.

About Rose

Rose is Lisbeth's mum. They had a lovely, close relationship and her family was the core of everything Lisbeth did. The bond Lisbeth had with her family was the springboard of all the exciting things she did in her life. Things she loved to share and enable them to be part of.

From the onset of her illness, 18 months before her death, Lisbeth became highly dependent on the support of her family, especially Rose.

Since Lisbeth died, Rose has been trying to get justice and accountability from those responsible for her care. This account is her view of the causes and treatment of Lisbeth's illness and death.

A Place of No Return: Lisbeth's Story

Lisbeth was the second of four surviving siblings. The cot death of a younger brother when she was seven years old, and the birth of a sister when she was eight, culminated in the breakup of my marriage. Despite that, all of our children maintained regular contact with their father.

Lisbeth grew up to be a very empathic and caring person with a big heart and a fearless attitude to life. She could be stubborn and wouldn't give up on anything she thought worth fighting for.

Lisbeth always said that she had a happy childhood, with a great love of the big outdoors and anything adventurous, especially if it involved water! Along with her siblings, she was a strong club swimmer and loved sailing. School holidays usually involved visits to distant family members, youth hostelling, or house swaps. She participated in many trips offered by her schools. The most memorable was a three-year exchange programme to Africa run by her high school. All participants had to raise the money in the first year, go to Africa in the second, and to pay for students to come to England in the third. Lisbeth spent a week at an African high school and two weeks working in a school for disabled children. The following year each of the participants hosted an African student for three weeks.

Lisbeth was an accomplished clarinet player in her school orchestras in middle and high schools. Although she followed the sciences academically, she was imaginative and creative - bubbling over with ideas.

Following her 'A' levels, Lisbeth undertook a TEFL (Teaching English as a Foreign Language) course in London. Then she spent six months in an eastern European country living with a family while teaching English to young children in a local school. While there she also had holidays in Transylvania and Egypt. On her return, she taught English to foreign students until she went to university to study for a degree in Marine Biology. While there, Lisbeth learnt to Scuba dive with her partner, who was also a marine biologist. They both continued to build their PADI qualifications while working to support themselves eventually getting work as Scuba instructors abroad, with Lisbeth specialising in teaching young children. They both scuba-dived around the world and visited the elephants in Thailand (a long-held dream). When their relationship ended, Lisbeth came home.

Lisbeth drew people to her. She had a lovely smile, was always friendly, and a good listener. Everyone who knew her remembers her sunny personality and infectious giggle. Her caring nature, however, made her vulnerable. She saw the best in everyone and her tendency to see the world through rose-coloured spectacles blinded her to potential issues in her relationships.

When things started to go wrong, she was always convinced that she could 'put things right' by talking and searching for solutions. Not being able to recognise early enough that 'walking away' was the only solution, came at a high cost to Lisbeth and her well-being.

Following the break-up of a relationship, due to physical violence from a partner, Lisbeth got medical help for the trauma. This included low-dose medication. To help her recovery, she adopted a wonderful rescue dog and spent hours walking the local marshes. By the following spring, she was recovered enough to return to Bulgaria to live and work. When she came home, she worked as a carer. She was very popular with her clients, some of whom she maintained contact with after she had left.

Several years later, Lisbeth's relationship with her partner began to disintegrate. This impacted on their finances and her wellbeing. We helped as much as we could, and Lisbeth did her best. She left her partner and found alternative housing for herself and son. Close to the beach and sea, she was happy and started to make a new life for herself.

Lisbeth was devastated by the loss of her beloved maternal grandparents within three months of each other in the 18 months following the birth of her son. He was a lovely, energetic little boy but a very poor sleeper. So, I was often with Lisbeth to help out. Mistakenly thinking she was helping me, and against my wishes, Elisabeth enlisted the help of her ex-partner. It proved a disastrous decision. Lisbeth eventually told me that he had invaded every part of her personal life and had awful temper outbursts, although he never hit her. She said that she was very anxious and frightened for herself and fearful for her son, and she would frequently call helplines. After joining a group for mums who were living with anxiety at her local children's centre, Lisbeth finally managed to move. The children's centre funded a course of CBT (Cognitive Behavioural Therapy) with a psychologist. This focussed on the emotional abuse she had experienced and it helped her enormously. She regained her sunny outlook on life, spending time out and about with her son and her friends and making plans for the future.

Despite our warnings, that she needed time and space to help her fully recover from the trauma she had experienced, Lisbeth started a new relationship. A few months later she announced her pregnancy. She was overjoyed at the thought of another baby, especially when she discovered it was a girl.

For her birthday, during the third month of her pregnancy, Lisbeth, her sister, and myself had a celebratory weekend in London. We went to a show and sightseeing. It was a lovely weekend, although her sister remarked to me that she seemed a bit down. Lisbeth had started to exhibit a growing concern that she was experiencing adverse reactions to an increasing number of foods.

Over the following two to three months, her anxieties grew. Looking for causes, she continuously researched online for side effects of the medication that she had stopped, and then restarted, in early pregnancy. She convinced herself that her actions had caused her permanent brain damage. Damage that resulted in her being unable to connect to her emotions. For Lisbeth, this was the worst possible illness to happen to her.

Lisbeth's anxiety became so debilitating that she could not be left alone. I spent weekdays with her and covered the weekends with her when her partner was working. Following a severe panic attack in the seventh month of her pregnancy, I took her to her ante-natal clinic at the local hospital where she was assigned to a psychiatric paediatric nurse. This nurse was with her throughout her illness and became a trusted and wonderful support. Lisbeth was hospitalised a few days before the birth of her baby, when she was diagnosed with acute anxiety and kept on an anti-depressant/anxiety medication, a drug she had come to hate, until the birth. Because of her extreme anxiety she was sent to an out-of-area mother and baby unit (MBU), almost 200 miles away, where she was diagnosed with psychotic depression in the post-natal period. Her medical notes record Lisbeth's sensitivity to medication. The side-effects of the anti-psychotic drugs were so severe they were discontinued. During her time there, Lisbeth hid her medications until that was discovered. Both her father and I both asked that the medication be discontinued and psychological treatment started but were denied. Lisbeth was discharged home towards the end of the summer, after 12 weeks at the MBU, with no alleviation of her symptoms.

During the following five weeks at home, Lisbeth continued to be highly anxious with no change in her belief of being brain damaged. During this time, she researched methods of ending her life. Thoughts that she shared with a perinatal nurse.

As a result of frequent and persistent thoughts of suicide, Lisbeth was transferred to a local psychiatric hospital. Then, a few days later, she was transferred to another out-of-area mother and baby unit, this time 85 miles distant. Once again, we requested a reduction of medication and asked for psychological-based treatment but were, again, denied. Treatment by medication continued. Lisbeth was also given a course of ECT (Electro-Convulsive Therapy). Although she appeared brighter in mood, Lisbeth continued to be far from how she presented normally. She was constantly saying that, for her, nothing had changed and that she couldn't carry on feeling as though she was in a living hell. She attempted to end her life again which meant that she was separated from her baby when she was admitted to local acute psychiatric services.

To anyone who didn't know her, Lisbeth presented as normal. Responses to her children appeared affectionate and loving. She responded with her usual lovely smile. But to me and, when talking to her father, she continuously reiterated her inability to 'feel'. She believed she was letting her children down. She wanted to see them grow up but felt that she wouldn't be there for them. Nothing could shake her belief that she would ever recover from her permanent brain damage and the loss of her connection to the world around her. Always a great reader, she had lost the ability to engage with people, the written word, or any other media.

Both mother and baby units did try to establish a baseline of who Lisbeth was and how she normally presented, by talking to her and her family. The final medical notes from the second MBU recorded that Lisbeth was considered to be treatment resistant to medication.

From the information available to me, I question whether Lisbeth's prior medical notes were fully read when she was transferred to an acute psychiatric unit, for what would be her final stay. In my opinion, decisions made, and acted upon, appeared to show little consideration for Lisbeth's history, care, treatment, or recovery. In fact, it felt quite the reverse. I feel that Lisbeth, her family, her perinatal clinicians, and her GP were excluded and ignored. Other issues that, in my view, probably contributed to Lisbeth's demise included: a failure to follow her care plan; transfer to another hospital as a bed management decision; fast changes in medication; complete failure of communication with patient, other clinicians, and family; changing her diagnosis; and fast discharge (despite our warnings of the risk). At no point, to the best of my knowledge, did the final acute psychiatric services make any effort to establish a baseline. Lisbeth's attempts to flag up her low mood and risk of suicide were in my opinion, persistently ignored.

The result was a fast deterioration in Lisbeth's physical health and self-care. She was discharged to a crisis care team that did not seem to me to be fit for purpose in terms of Lisbeth's needs. Although she was not allowed to have her children without supervision, Lisbeth spent time with her son every day. He was living with me, and she put him to bed and, initially, took him and met him from school, until she became too tired and ill to do so. She spent time with her daughter (who was living with her father) three times a week.

During those last few weeks, until her death, I spent every day with Lisbeth. It was heartbreaking. She had lost her appetite, was unable to sleep, and didn't want to get up in the mornings. Although she felt completely disassociated from her emotions, she appeared most responsive to her children playing with them and putting her son to bed every night. To them,

Lisbeth appeared perfectly normal responding with her lovely smile and warm nature. However, her inability to emotionally connect exacerbated her deep distress. She persistently reiterated that she couldn't go on. She would use phrases like: *"the worst nightmare for me … I've been transported to a place of no return, where every second is hell … my head can't process anything … It's like a fog that has physical attributes … Thoughts are on a roundabout and come and go ... whirling around … on the periphery of my consciousness … there's no emotion".*

Hindsight is hard and difficult to deal with. It is my view that, had the correct diagnosis been made and the appropriate treatment been available, it is highly likely that Lisbeth would be with us today. Prior to her discharge, we had arranged for Lisbeth to see a highly reputable psychologist, who she saw three times before her death. Before the first meeting, I had a long conversation with the psychologist about Lisbeth's background and clinical treatment. At another meeting, the psychologist advised me that Lisbeth's mind was so clouded by drugs that it would take some time to start treatment. She was in no doubt that the cause of Lisbeth's illness was PTSD (Post-Traumatic Stress Disorder), which was rooted in her experiences of emotional abuse and triggered by her pregnancy. In the psychologist's view, treatment could take up to two years for a full recovery.

This confirmed what we had suspected. In my opinion, Lisbeth had been misdiagnosed from the start. Her symptoms were treated rather than the cause, resulting in her being subjected to a living hell until, in the end, she could only see one way out.

On researching her lack of empathy, I discovered that Lisbeth had been exhibiting all the symptoms of 'disassociation' and 'derealisation' which are linked to PTSD. It was all there, the language she used, her presentation, her 'foggy' brain, and her apparent resistance to drugs. Although widely documented within the medical community, there seems to be a national disconnect between those who promote psychological versus psychotropic interventions. My observation is that many psychiatric clinicians appear unable to recognise the possibility of a psychological cause of the symptoms they observe.

While Lisbeth was with us, throughout her illness, I was always concerned about her medications, knowing her sensitivity, to and hatred of, them. There seemed to be an over-reliance on medication. The justification for the refusal of her clinicians to adopt a psychological approach was that she was not ready. "When will she be ready?", we asked. "When the medications start working", they said. But they never did.

We became increasingly concerned during Lisbeth's final inpatient admission. As far as I am aware, the perinatal team, who seemed to really understand Lisbeth, were not consulted. It seemed that they were ignored when their psychiatrist tried to warn that she considered Elisabeth to be too high a risk for discharge. Lisbeth's hospital consultant felt 'invisible' to her family. Lisbeth called me, to say that a member of staff had told her that she was being discharged that day. I telephoned her consultant to question the decision because we considered her to be too high risk. He denied that any discharge plans had been made. That evening Lisbeth was transferred to a halfway house and then, less than a week later, sent home.

We were given only one day's notice that Lisbeth was being sent home. During a distressing phone call, my request to delay discharge by one day, because of family commitments, was refused. It left me in tears. Lisbeth was discharged home two days later despite our concerns. Her father had to travel 170 miles to collect Lisbeth. She died six weeks later after fighting so hard for so long against her belief of being permanently brain damaged and the debilitating side effects of her medications.

Lisbeth was desperate to live but she could not envisage recovering. Her last, long letter, appears completely rational and it demonstrates her deep awareness of the consequences of dying. In her mind, she had reached a place of no return.

As a family, we are learning to live with those consequences together, trying to do what Lisbeth would have wanted us to do. The worst outcome, from my perspective, is that her two children are living apart and not growing up together. However, both of them, each living with their respective fathers, are loved and happy. The eldest has wonderful memories of his mum and personal items. Both have lots of photos and other memorabilia. Although the youngest was too young to remember her mum, she has lots of photos of them both together

Our family ensure that her children frequently spend time together doing the things that Lisbeth would have done with them, mostly outdoors in all weathers. We have holidays together with at least one big holiday a year with all of us: Lisbeth's parents, siblings, their partners and cousins (12 of us!). Usually in the far north west of Scotland one of her favourite places.

Following Lisbeth's death in 2018, I have searched for answers and tried to make sense of what has happened. Such a devastating loss inevitably raises feelings of guilt and so many questions. How could this happen? What went wrong? And always, what could I have done to prevent it?

There were people who demonstrated good and, at times, exceptional practice. The perinatal team went above and beyond in their care of Lisbeth. They were the only team who had a continuous overview of all her treatment. From the information provided after Lisbeth died, I have formulated a view on how limited the perinatal team's options were following her precipitous final discharge. During her last inpatient stay, Lisbeth's medication had been changed quickly. The physical side effects of fast medication changes became all too apparent. As well as continuing loss of appetite and sleeplessness, Lisbeth began to exhibit blurred vision, headaches, and problems with her hearing. I discovered that one of her drugs was a key ingredient of an over-the-counter remedy for sleep, and to which, in the past Lisbeth had had a very severe reaction. To my knowledge, there was no care plan in place when she was discharged and the perinatal team had not been advised that Lisbeth's diagnosis had been changed. A diagnosis that would indicate a very different treatment pathway to the one she was on. The perinatal team started to reduce Lisbeth's medication but it was too little too late. Her physical health had deteriorated to such an extent that she had become anaemic and was finding it difficult to walk even short distances.

The publication of the Serious Incident (Root Cause Analysis) Report not long after we lost Lisbeth, brought to light more very serious concerns about clinical practice within the local trust. The risk assessment presented in the report showed little evidence that the concerns we had expressed had been taken into account. At our initial meeting with the facilitator of the RCA report, we discovered that the Trust was aware of the 'culture' of the ward where Lisbeth was a patient and discharged from. The implication being that there were known issues.

Immediately following Lisbeth's death, a solicitor friend of the family recommended a medical legal company who began a no-win, no-fee claim. Unfortunately, for them and us, the expert witness presented a report biased towards the use of medication. To carry on, we would have had to use another medical witness which we couldn't afford to do. But what it did mean was that we had extensive paperwork surrounding the case.

A year later, at Lisbeth's inquest, the written and oral evidence presented underlined our fears. It seemed to me that the Trust had taken no action at all on what appeared to be highly questionable clinical practice at the inpatient unit. From the Coroner's remarks, we summised there was a continuing high risk to acute psychiatric patients. Media reports, into subsequent deaths and inquests, have highlighted the same issues we raised about Lisbeth's care: not listening to families; failure to adequately assess and act on risk; poor communication between teams; and unsafe discharges.

I spent almost a year compiling a 12-page letter of complaint to the Trust. Because the evidence was so extensive, I used the four domains of the *GMC Guide to Good Medical Practice* to organise it. What followed was, in my opinion, a complete travesty of complaint procedures.

I have had to involve both the Parliamentary Ombudsman and the GMC (General Medical Council) in the search for answers to our concerns. This has been time-consuming and heartbreaking work that should not have been necessary. Now, over a year after the original complaint, this unresolved situation has caused anger, frustration, distress, and made it more difficult to grieve.

As I write, the GMC has already taken some action about the clinical concerns while the case is still under investigation. The Trust has, so far, failed to give us any information on the progress of their own investigation. Or, indeed, confirmed that they have even started one. We receive letters, at three-month intervals, advising of further delays with no explanation. We have made the CQC (Care Quality Commission) aware of our concerns.

The fact that the administrators of the Trust do not seem to have recognised and addressed the issues, which were reported to us as ingrained before Lisbeth's last admission is, in my opinion, a very serious indictment of their ability to oversee medical practice. We are aware of problems in mental health services and the extremely stressful conditions that service providers are working under. I was amazed at the care and compassion shown to Lisbeth in all her placements except the final one. At that institution, I was personally involved in some very distressing incidents in her care.

Since losing Lisbeth, the journey has been a long and very difficult one. It has helped trying to find answers to what went wrong. I know I would have felt worse had I not tried. Although it can't help my daughter it may help others. Along the way, I have talked to so many kind and helpful people: bereaved people; those who are there to help; and campaigns. And it does help to talk to people. Thank you, all of you.

Lisbeth died waiting for the right diagnosis and treatment.

Our beloved mummy, daughter, granddaughter, sister, and aunt. Always beside us.

Precious Boy, You Were Loved and Loved
By Lydia

Lydia created this heart for her son. She says - When he moved schools, he met a new group of kids who loved him (because he was loveable). I created a large fish for his entry in an art competition. It was so pretty. He won and shared his prize with his new friends. I agonised about making this heart. One day, I happened to walk into a shop and found this fish brooch. I really cried because it was virtually identical to the one I had created. The similarity took my breath away.

About Lydia

Lydia comes from, what she describes as, an autistic family. Members of the generations above her, probably herself, and her children, are on the autistic spectrum. She uses her professional skills and experience to advocate for children with SEND (Special Educational Needs and Disabilities). She is a fearless champion, fighting for children with SEND and their families to receive the health, education, and social care provision they deserve.

In this letter to her son, who died when he was just 19, Lydia shares an account of their experiences. She offers an insight into how professionals and services appear from a mother's perspective.

Precious Boy, You Were Loved and Loved.

I did not know what hit me when you shot into my life. One minute, I was working in the city with big plans. I was good at what I did. Confident. The next, I was in a small and alien hospital on a drip. I supposed that I would have you, drop you into a creche a handful of weeks later, and roar back to work. To the world that I knew. I would dress you up and send you to a great school and we would have terrific holidays. What did I know? Instead of returning to my desk, there was no going back. I found myself in the deep countryside with you. Money was not an issue, I had enough and I did a little work from home.

You were the most beautiful thing I have ever seen. I will not see this kind of beauty ever again. I promised you a fabulous life. The kind of life that my late, autistic, brother could never have. I promised it to you, and then to my other children, because of him. Although I never spoke of him to you, his loss made me cherish every second and take nothing for granted.

You screamed from the moment that you were born and I could not put you down without you screaming. You were a curious, cross, but extraordinarily bonny, baby. Certain things made you delirious with bliss. Light streaking around the sky, soft textures, water. Just dressing you could take a half-hour because it all seemed to hurt you. You banned me from playing my piano. I could not vacuum. It never occurred to me to question or complain, about how hard things appeared to be. Or consider that it was not this way for others.

If the doorbell rang you would race upstairs and pour bottles of milk down the stairs. It would cascade dramatically down and you would be delighted by your handiwork. A waterfall. Then you would move on to my shampoos and shower gels from Liberty that I coveted. Things were smashed and broken all of the time. There was nothing that could not be replaced.

You had a mop of caramel curls and the beauty of a mixed-heritage child. Neither white nor black, you were the world. The only time that you could bear to be touched was on a Saturday evening when, in the darkness, I held you as you sat on the window ledge and we watched the weekly fireworks from the theme park nearby. I have never felt closer to you, as we laughed and laughed. That pleasure part of you was like the most expensive perfume. You lived for thrills and loved rides at the park. Your eyes came fully alive. A part of you, that was concealed at all other times, was unlocked. Usually, I was with you but you were far away.

The time came for us to visit a paediatric team. You were diagnosed with classic autism with an IQ of 58. The paediatric report was long and detailed. Your needs were understood. With SEND support, including a full-time assistant, in place, you headed to mainstream school. On the way to school, you counted and named all of the street lamps and you would sob inconsolably if any of them were not working. As I stood at the school gates, I felt no connection with the other parents. You would come bursting out and I would have to run with you to the car. I longed to speak to the mothers but I was spared seeing the world through their eyes. There were things I wanted to say. To explain why I always looked so stressed and had to run. I was not sure that they would understand me. I began to lose my confidence. And to feel ashamed.

At home, I always knew to check up on you when you left my side for a handful of seconds. The quietness was an omen. I once found you'd painted your entire face with my Chanel lipstick. You turned, and you beamed at me. The most extraordinary, joyous beautiful force of nature. I kept a little purse around my shoulder, containing keys/phone/cards, in case you managed to circumvent our home security and make a dash outside. Once, while I was cooking, you somehow made it. The doorbell rang and there you were, outraged but mute, with a kind neighbour. He told me that you refused to speak to him but that he knew roughly who you were and brought you back.

I laid side-by-side with you until you were eight. There was no other way that you could sleep. It was my privilege. I parented solo. I never drank and had no typical life. This would have been too much for you. You needed routine and to be able to trust in the world.

As you grew older, I would take you to the park and you would race around the perimeter, stopping gingerly now and then to gently approach another child to say, "Cashier number three please". You had learned this in the queue at the bank.

There was never a time when in your life that your love of all things was not apparent. I learned everything about you through years of perseverance. I tried so hard to ease your journey through life. To translate it all for you until you could. I was scared to keep speaking out for you. And when I did, I was not understood.

Sometimes, you struggled in school but you loved it. You gave it everything that you had. You were loved at primary school. High school was not so great. You found yourself in a small group of kids with additional needs, some of whom had serious behavioural issues, and they were not a good example.

One day, when you were about 13, I took a phone call from a concerned lady telling me that you had 'collapsed' in the street near our home. I raced off to find you. No. You had decided to simply lie down on the pavement because you wanted a pit stop. How I loved you. You gave me a massive smile and you climbed into my car. You were my delight. My luxury.

Puberty changed you, from plump and ungainly into a tall, athletic but elegantly beautiful, tousled-haired god. You were shy. Then you found an outgoing and chatty friend and the world was your oyster. You fought for the right to have a little independence. I would let you get the bus home after spending time with your friend at the park.

As you got older, things became more difficult. Sometimes, you would come home with cigarettes stubbed out on your arm or bruises. But you would tell me nothing. Many times, you would not make it home and I would need to track you down.

My mum and extended family were the centre of your universe. You seemed to cope so well when mum and two close relatives became ill at around the same time. They lost their battles with cancer. Their homes had been your stop-off places. They'd all had freezers full of your favourite ice creams and dogs that needed walking in the evening sun. You doted on them but you had lost them. You had also been forced to confront the vicious, random unfairness of death. You secretly considered the possibility of joining them so that you could be reunited. My heart broke for you because these were the people who had loved you the most.

Aged 16, you added epilepsy to your list of diagnoses and we learned how to keep you safe. I was desperate to make it all bearable. But you were being bullied at school. The child next to you would say, "I am glad that your family are dead. Why don't you kill yourself?" This child was not your only bully. You only told me all about this after your first suicide attempt, which seemed to come totally out of the blue. On a rainy October morning, you were apprehended by a security guard and taken to hospital, where an appointment was made with CAMHS for a full assessment. It also became clear, in the wait for that assessment, that you had been smoking a little cannabis. For years, the foods you ate were carefully chosen by you to be 'safe'. Now you had stopped eating and developed a target weight of 1lb. And you were self-harming. Because of your autism and learning disability, CAMHS cancelled your assessment. I discovered that the risk of suicide completion is nine times higher for autistic people and four times higher for people with epilepsy. These risks were ignored and I feel that they left you for dead. This was not really a surprise because I had been warned of this on the SEND community grapevine. I went to our GP and I asked for a higher referral, which never materialised into anything. We waited for an appointment letter for months. It never came.

Your school career ended abruptly, in year 11, when you set off the fire alarm. I finally realised that school was a major source of your agony. We were broken. It felt like there was nothing for you and that this had been accepted, with a careless shrug, by those who ought to have been ready to meet your needs. I felt such anger and terror.

You spent some time away with your father abroad and then with my father abroad. When you returned, the sun had warmed your soul and you were so much better.

Meanwhile, your younger brother became unwell and was also diagnosed with autism and depression. He had been equally stressed by our bereavements. Gaining access to any basic services again proved terrifyingly futile. The grief that we all felt was paralleled by the realisation that we were in danger and alone.

I feel that I was subjected to the most vicious two-year ordeal while we all fought for our lives. As a family, we were badly failed, and maligned, by every service tasked with supporting us. The 'mother-blaming' was relentless. I learned that when services were failing, they cover up with personal attacks and threats against parents. There was nobody to help us. We existed only in a cold and toxic void.

I was so outraged about the way we were treated. This made me stand up and oppose it. I started a local charity to support other SEND parents because we were far from alone both at home and nationally. Young people like you should be able to receive basic support under the law.

Time passed, and you enjoyed being at college and becoming independent. Your freedom was carefully supported by your friends and family. A gentle, beautiful friend accompanied you everywhere. Girls told me that you were the one they ran to for a hug and they liked to sit next to you in the large cafeteria. You were the one to stand and speak for them when they were suffering with anxiety.

Sometimes you would end up in hospital again. I can remember visiting you and returning home at 3 am. Your anxious brother, who could not cope without me showing him that he too was a priority, wanted me to roast a chicken for him. I did. I was so exhausted. There were no carers to support us. We seemingly occupied a space where we had to look after ourselves, while other families seemed reasonably well catered for via their attendance at a special school.

I felt vilified when I asked for help. I was even accused of Fabricated Induced Illness. Instead of help I was 'investigated' for months on end. It was punitive. I wondered how humans could treat others this way.

January 2020. One freezing night, I got a call from your friends saying that they could not find you. We found you sitting in a photo booth in town and we had to drag you to the car. Your poor brother and I were terrified for you. The next morning, you said that you had not known where you were and that you had not known how to get home. You promised that you would never take anything again. I realised how much danger you were in and that I needed expert advice and support for you. But you, and your needs, did not exist in professionals' eyes. I told them about your risky experimentation with prescription drugs, and my fears for you. They gave me a Princes Trust form and an appointment to see a careers advisor.

When you finished college, I hoped that you would be able to return abroad. You had fallen in with a group of friends in our town using drugs. We didn't make it before Covid struck. Then it was too late.

I tried so hard for you all. I was ignored because the message I needed to convey was not one that professionals wanted to hear. I didn't give up because I couldn't. I deeply resented those who left us to stumble along without anything available to meet your needs, and those of your brothers, who also needed help with their mental health. There was nothing for us to cling to. No security and no peace for us. No reassurance.

When Covid lockdown began, it was terrible for you. You didn't cope for long. Walking outside daily had always helped you to regulate your emotions. You were still smoking a little weed. I hated that but it was everywhere in our town and other anxious young men like you had grouped together to smoke it.

Over a few weeks, you were in and out of three hospitals, like a ping pong ball, due to multiple terrifying attempts upon your life in the brief times that you were home. The question that I agonised over every night in the months before you died was "when? When would those responsible for your care outwit me and let you die?" I felt your life-force ebbing away.

Even though you gave your permission for information to be shared with me, I was barred from all planning meetings. There was so much that I needed to know. You could not tell me, and your 'care' team told me next to nothing. Their mantra was, "let's hope that this works out." I told them all I knew of autism and risk. They ignored me. I was told that you had the 'capacity' to kill yourself if you wished and that this would be up to you.

At no time were you with anyone who understood you. I wasn't allowed to visit. You couldn't see or hear me but you loved me, and I loved you. Beyond all words.

And then the countdown began… April 2020.

You were discharged from hospital into a care home. I was assured they could keep you safe. I was told it was a wonderful place where you would have 1:1 support and the rehabilitation you needed. I was sold heaven but, in reality, you were placed in a glorified bedsit. A place you could just walk out of.

One seemingly benign morning, I was racing through a draft Ombudsman report, which ruled our family had experienced systemic multi-agency neglect. I had been given a short time to read and make my observations. The pressure was huge.

You were having your therapy session and I was due to collect you. I was unaware that the timings had been changed and you had been let out earlier than expected. The phone rang. It was one of your childhood friends. He had seen troubling reports on local social media. Someone had died. He knew that it was you. I knew.

It was the most exquisitely beautiful sunny day. I had been running from a tsunami with my sons in my arms and it had finally caught us all. This was not a surprise to me. I could not feel emotions. Nothing about the human condition was open to me. I remembered my brother's death and I knew that I had to hold on. Having to give your brothers this devastating news was bad enough, without my collapsing in front of them. I would not do it to them or to anyone. I wanted to rip the heavens open but I could contain this agony for their sake. I only broke and screamed when I was alone in my car.

Six weeks after you died, your brother was found at the scene of your death and saved by a member of the public. They physically clung on to him and kept him alive. I will never know this man. How do I get to thank him? I owe him everything. Your brother was taken to hospital. The policewoman, who had taken me to identify your body a few weeks earlier, was there. She was devastated to see us like this. She told the nurse to 'section' your brother because she was so worried that he too would die.

Your brother and I were treated better than when you had hospital admissions. There was no question of hiding behind confidentiality. The nurse pulled me aside and broke your brother's privacy to warn me of his earnest intention to die. She reasoned that this was the priority. It was poignant because with you there was so much that should have been shared. Your life might have been saved had the professionals worked with me rather than against me.

The contrast between you and your brother's inpatient experiences were vast. The staff were warm, open, and honest. They were empathetic and driven. However, when it was time for discharge the same difficulties appeared. Meetings, with up to ten attendees, resulted in the usual nods and promises but nothing materialised in the 'discharge package'. We were written up for 'extensive support' but I had to wait almost a year, and go to court against our local authority to win your brother the EHCP (Education Health and Care Plan) he so obviously needed. I represented him against their well-resourced legal team and I won on all counts. You died because your needs were not met, yet health and social care professionals were resisting meeting your brother's very similar needs. I was grieving for you whilst having to fight to keep your brother alive.

Care and support for people like you rests entirely on family and friends. When your brother was discharged, three of your mutual friends moved in to help keep him safe. They stayed for over a year. They lay either side of him when he had flashbacks and could not sleep. They cleared his airways when he got hold of alcohol and vomited at 1 am. They saved his life.

I feel invisible. Months later, still nothing is in place for your brother. I am trying. *I am trying.* We are so broken and so alone. The agony of your loss is so great that I cannot work. But I will carry on fighting for what your brothers need in order to recover and to survive.

You died waiting for your mix of autism, learning disability, and mental health needs to be understood and provided for. You died waiting for those who knew and loved you to be included, listened to, and supported.

When you died, we yearned for you. It was unspoken. We had all breathed for you. You were our blessing and our privilege. My graceful boy who walked so lightly on this earth, you are loved and love

Bridget made this heart for Danny. It is full of hidden meanings that relate to their shared childhood or adult lives. The French words translate as 'a spider and its web'. Bridget feels Danny was trapped in his web.

About Bridget

Bridget is a trained therapist and she has spent many years working with adults experiencing various difficulties. She also has over 30 years of experience working in the field of education with children and young people. She describes herself as a survivor of a chaotic, abusive, and dysfunctional family system.

The Best (and Worst) of Brothers

Danny was the sunniest of babies. With his blond hair, blue eyes, and a smile that filled his face, he lit up the world. I am guessing that Danny was born with a sensitive nature. As a baby, his mother adored him; he was one of her 'golden children'. He was smothered with love and affection and there are photographs of him being held and cuddled in which he is laughing and smiling. He responded well to this attention, as any baby would.

Danny loved music and he had the voice of an angel. He struggled to read but loved Roald Dahl. He had an incredible imagination, which wasn't always helpful to him. Danny adored football but he was frail and not especially athletic in his early years, which must have been very hard for him. His older brothers were sporty and especially his closest sibling who excelled in various sports. Danny was always in the street kicking a ball with his best friend and partner in crime, Stevie.

One thing that Danny and I had in common was a profound love of animals. We were forever finding sick and injured birds and beasts and bringing them home to look after. Danny once found a kestrel with a broken wing. We took the bird to an elderly woman who was famed for her ways with animals. She set the wing and the kestrel came home to convalesce. The bird would sit silently and still on the back of the couch, always close to Danny, and would consequently alarm strangers who would sit down only to realise that a hawk was right behind them. The kestrel recovered and was released, probably to make way for the next injured creature that needed Danny's attention.

As an adult Danny learnt to fly, fulfilling a dream by gaining his pilot's licence. He transformed his physique through weight-training and became fit and strong. He was tall and good-looking and had no shortage of women on his arm. He was funny, charming, quick-witted, and kind. If you had a problem that was within his power to sort, he sorted it. He was my baby brother and I loved him dearly.

I think that Danny's story is a good example of how the environment can shape and mould a child's personality. Danny was born to a family which was already too large for the parents to cope with and resources were stretched to breaking point. Born at a time of family turbulence and upheaval, his first year witnessed the stress of family violence, separation, and a move across the country into cramped, temporary accommodation. His cheerful demeanour was not enough to protect him from the ravages of an adverse environment. This sunny baby was surrounded by chaos, violence, uncertainty, poverty, and overcrowded living conditions. He was born to parents who lacked any real parenting skills. A little more than a year after his birth, the family was joined by another baby. As he grew, Danny became needy and awkward, lost in a sea of dysfunctional siblings who were all trying desperately to get their needs met. There was quite simply not enough of anything to go around and Danny stood very little chance.

From an early age, Danny was looked after by a string of fairly incompetent and neglectful childminders, until an exceptional lady was found, because his mother had to work. I don't think that was a career choice although she was highly educated and intelligent. It was because her husband was erratic - an alcoholic who spent most of his money down the pub. She worked so there was usually food on the table. The downside was the neglect that accompanied a lack of time. Danny became clingy and 'needy', craving his mother's attention. He became whiny and whinged constantly. This behaviour had the effect of further diminishing his chances of getting his emotional needs met. He suffered from severe separation anxiety. He was 'naughty' and unable to sit still; 'hyperactive' before hyperactivity was understood. He just could not stay still. This upset him as well as everyone around him. It was hard to relax with his constant movement and fidgeting.

As an adult, Danny firmly believed that he had ADHD. He could not focus at school and he slipped through the net. This was before the days of 'special needs' assessments and widespread understanding of learning difficulties. Danny was a severe asthmatic and lived in a household where both parents smoked. He became increasingly badly behaved, failing to achieve academically, and he started to display antisocial behaviour.

Danny suffered abuse; emotionally, physically, sexually, and through neglect. In his family of origin, there was little understanding of the importance of attachment and a culture of ignorance around child abuse and its impact. Danny was unable to behave in socially acceptable ways and no-one seemed to understand that he was exhibiting his cognitive dissonance through his behaviour. In the 60s and the 70s 'family problems' were rarely spoken about. Shame and denial prevailed and no one thought to ask, 'why?'. There was no Childline, no safeguarding, and no real understanding of domestic abuse. Many child survivors, of the abuse which went on during these years of denial, became the walking wounded adults needing the support of mental health services today.

Danny was the best and the worst of brothers. He could be funny and hugely endearing, loving and kind. He was a live-wire, never sitting still or resting for long. He irritated his siblings as they tried to watch kids'

TV or some other activity, with his fidgeting, shuffling, and his infernal sniffing. He could also be incredibly naughty; he probably had some version of compulsive defiance disorder. As one of the oldest, I was often left to babysit, at an age where I was incapable of taking on that adult responsibility. I didn't have the tools. He refused to go to bed. He would be put to bed, and he would be downstairs again five minutes later. This could be repeated 30 or 40 times - I kid you not. Eventually, I would lash out and smack him, desperate for him to stay in bed. As children, we were used to physical violence and at the time it just seemed like the thing to do. As an adult, reflecting on past memories, I was mortified. I apologised profusely and Danny, quite naturally, forgave me. I am not proud of this, but I was a child myself without the necessary skills to cope with an increasingly maladjusted boy. I was just five years older than him. I feel that I was just one more influence that helped him towards his downfall.

Danny's father died when he was a teenager. His behaviour was already out of control and he was getting into trouble with the police for delinquent activities. The sudden death of one of his parents certainly didn't improve things. Danny left school without any decent qualifications, destined to make the best he could of his life. He was sent to the other side of the globe following his father's death, by a mother unable to cope with his extreme behaviour. He was away for a year, living with a branch of the family that he hardly knew, feeling pretty unwanted, and ultimately left to survive on his own wits. He did, however, have a gift for selling and could read people so well - all that hyper-vigilance does come in useful for something! He had an answer for everything and that, coupled with a quick wit and a lively mind, provided the skills to sell sand in a desert and have people thinking it was the most amazing and innovative thing that could have happened. Danny returned to England and much of his working life was spent in the sales industry and, when he was on form, he was quite brilliant.

Danny grew into an adult with what might be considered an insecure-anxious attachment disorder. Unable to access the help he needed, initially because he didn't know he needed help, he self-medicated to alleviate his psychological pain. He dealt with his pain with alcohol and with drugs, following a familial pattern of alcohol abuse. When sober and not on drugs, he was plagued by his demons - the memories of his abusive, chaotic, damaging childhood. Devoid of any model of a stable relationship, he lacked the tools needed to maintain adult relationships and was unable to remain committed to one woman for any length of time. Naturally, this had far-reaching consequences for those who loved him.

Danny needed help, but he was terrified of facing his past. He knew that he needed to talk about his childhood but he didn't have the words. His profound sense of shame prevented open disclosure to all but the most intimate of his tribe. He would reach out to those closest to him when he was drunk or high, and was consequently unable to process any help that was offered. He was also enmeshed in a familial culture in which disclosure resulted in ostracism, denial, and scapegoating. While his agonising reality was denied by those who he needed the most acknowledgement from, money was thrown at him (because finances were no longer a problem). He had at least two lengthy inpatient stays at private detox clinics. Short-term fixes didn't provide solutions in the long-term. Danny belonged to Alcoholics Anonymous, on-and-off, and had a sponsor who gave him real support. He joined a lively church and said he gained much from attendance there as well as from the support of the pastor and the congregation. He was supported by family members in finding accommodation and meeting his basic needs. Sadly, nothing seemed to endure.

Danny would ask for help through various avenues for his ADHD and for counselling to understand his behaviour. When appointments came around, he would be too drunk, high, or hungover to attend. In the climate of an overburdened NHS, long waiting lists, and budget cuts, his failure to attend was read as Danny not wanting to engage. He would be referred to the substance abuse service, and back to the mental health services, each wanting the other service to take responsibility and each claiming that the other service was the more appropriate. The game of human ping-pong, which seems so common, was to have fatal consequences.

I tried to help. Other family members tried to help. At times we enabled his behaviour because we didn't know what else to do. Danny would threaten to kill himself but pleas from his family for mental health intervention were denied. The reason? Danny did not want to engage with services. We begged, pleaded, got angry, talked about the failure of duty of care, but we felt unheard by services. Danny would say one thing to us and then deny he had said it when he had sobered up and was faced with a health professional. Danny would lie through his teeth and then, later, admit that he had lied because he wanted to get out of hospital and drink. We knew he was a danger to himself but he was one of many who are desperate for the dregs left of services. He was trying to survive while services were treating rising rates of addiction and adverse mental health conditions with ever-decreasing resources.

One of the consequences of a life lived through alcohol and drugs is that the user tends to mix with others who have similar addictions. Danny was no different. A party of sorts, at his home with two of his associates, went that bit too far. A bottle of wine and shared prescription drugs were followed by vodka and marijuana. A plan was hatched to obtain some harder drugs and the shopping list included cocaine and crack cocaine as well as a substantial amount of alcohol. At some point during the evening, Danny's girlfriend went upstairs with his friend leaving Danny in a drunken state on the sofa. During the night he vomited and subsequently suffocated on his own vomit. He suffered heart failure. In the morning his friends looked in on him and decided he was sleeping and they went off to have breakfast together. Upon their return, they realised that all was not well and attempts were made to resuscitate Danny amid arguments about calling the emergency services. Apparently, there were worries about the police finding drugs.

Eventually, an ambulance was called and Danny was transferred to intensive care at the local hospital and put on to life support. The medical team did everything they could but they were fighting a losing battle and Danny was experiencing multiple organ failure. With some of his family at his side, life support was withdrawn and Danny was allowed to die. He hadn't even reached his 50th birthday. His friends, meanwhile, were robbing his home.

A couple of weeks before he died, Danny called me. He was very low and was struggling to understand the abuse he had suffered and to get a grip on his constant anxiety. He told me he had reached rock-bottom. I gave him my thoughts, told him of a book I thought would help and assured him that I loved him. I told him that I would make time for him soon and we could talk about his 'stuff'. Sadly, we never had that time.

Danny was my champion. He was the one person who saw only my good points; I think we all need championing by someone. Danny looked up to me, sought my counsel and advice, and overlooked my shortcomings. He believed, erroneously in my opinion, that I was the person who could bring cohesion to our fractured family. He would call me late at night and beg me to take up this mantle. I would tell him it was a futile, pointless exercise, but he never stopped believing. I miss him beyond words. He believed in me totally, absolutely, without reservation. That unconditional positive regard is so very rare, especially when one comes from such dysfunction. His yearning for a loving, cohesive, and functional family was never realised.

Danny's life was not a life well-lived. It was a life of pain and psychological torment, of demons and monsters too big for him to deal with. He was severely damaged by the people he loved and he never got the chance to heal. I am not sure that we are always aware of the damage that we inflict on others, often as a result of our own damage. The damage that Danny inflicted on others was a direct result of the damage that had been inflicted upon him. I am not excusing his sometimes appalling behaviour, but I do believe that as a society we have to change our approach to those who are crying out for help. We condemn the behaviour and fail to see the person or the underlying reasons. There is a conversation that needs to be had; a conversation in which listening is paramount and blame and shame have no part.

When I think of Danny, it is not the alcoholic adult that I see, but a smiling, happy baby with potential stretching out in front of him. I want Danny's death to mean something. Until there is global recognition of the importance of mental health and the need for this to be nurtured from birth, the walking wounded, like my brother, will continue to undermine the security of our communities. We have become hardened to problems, atrocities, genocides even, and we have become blind to the people populating those events; the wide eyes of innocent babies and children born to people ill-equipped to nurture them appropriately.

I want that conversation. Education is at the heart of everything. I want parent-craft classes instead of Pythagoras (although I am sure that this has its place). Childminding classes should be valued above the current emphasis on STEM (Science, Technology, Engineering, and Maths). Those things might be wonderful for the advancement of society but are pretty useless if the people in our world are too damaged to play a part or participate in that advancement. No-one should be bringing a child into this world without an understanding of the needs of that child, and grasping the true meaning of responsibility. They need insight into sleepless nights and crying that goes on and on and on. I want housekeeping and nutrition taught in schools with the same focus as literacy and numeracy. If I had my way, physical exercise would be a daily occurrence in our schools with a total ban on sugar (more addictive than cocaine) and fizzy drinks. In my view, children need to move, not be chained to desks for hours on end learning things they have no interest in and that will have little real meaning for their lives. School is the only time that members of our societies are incarcerated without having committed a crime! So many young people are alienated from education because that education is mostly irrelevant to their lives. Instead of labelling children because they fail to respond or to comply with outdated norms, we should take a radical approach to educating our young. Schools are amazing places and teachers are, wrongly in my opinion, blamed for so much of society's failings. They are generally incredible people, undervalued, working long hours earning far less than other professional colleagues.

I want our governments to stop paying lip service to the health of our children and young people and to start taking the appropriate responsibility for future generations. Poverty should not be a part of a child's lived experience whilst billionaires are allowed to increase their assets. My ideas are not new; they have been mooted before. We are failing our children and they are our future

I miss Danny so much. I miss his laughter, his charm, his warmth, his smile, his hugs. The last message he left me was one wishing me a happy birthday. Less than 24 hours later, he was dead. I can't bring him back, but I can highlight his story in the hope that something will change.

Danny died waiting for someone to engage with him, to meet him where he was at, to really listen to him. I hope you have found your peace baby brother.

84 Symptoms and Loving Notes by Sheila

Sheila made her memory heart for her son, Leo, from silk. She chose colours that were 'not too sad'. The words are traced from one of his loving notes to her. Every careful stitch in this heart reflects Sheila's love for Leo and his for her.

About Sheila

Sheila retired from teaching in 1999. When her son, Leo, became ill she became involved with her local mental health trust. She continues to represent service-users and carers' views and remains an active member of a mental health campaign group.

Like his mother, Leo liked to write. He said:

> *"I am starting to write everything down, in case I ever receive counselling or need to explain myself and understand what is going on or has happened. I have to write everything down because my memory is so bad and I get so lost and confused."*

Leo kept a diary and wrote '84 symptoms', a note to his psychiatrist, which give insight into his perspective. Quotations from these are included in Sheila's account.

84 Symptoms and Loving Notes

Leo was born in 1977, second son to a Jewish father and a mother who converted to Judaism. It took ten years for the conversion to be agreed by the Beth Din in London, but days after that acceptance it was withdrawn when my husband was seen carrying an umbrella on the Sabbath[1]. When my conversion was rescinded, I changed my mind. However, at seven months pregnant, I was convinced by Leo's father to travel to Israel to complete my conversion there. Leo's birth at eight months was by caesarean section.

As a child, Leo fought furiously with his elder brother. While I worked as a designer and his brother was at nursery school, Leo was cared for by an adoring housekeeper and a nanny. During his early years, he witnessed all the bitterness and anguish of my divorce from his father. When he was six years old, I trained to be a teacher and moved to Norwich with the boys to take up a design and technology post. I entered a department of men who found it difficult to accept that a female could do the job. Without familial support, and with a new career in a new place, I found it a challenge to manage my two little boys, who seemed to be at war. Our house was near my workplace and the boys' primary school. Although I rushed home at the end of the school day, arriving shortly after the boys, I twice found the glass on the front door smashed and my sons angry and disgruntled on the doorstep.

I struggled on until I was advised by a colleague to consult a psychiatrist and social services. After months of unhelpful family psychotherapy, I agreed to put Leo's 11-year-old brother into temporary care. This resulted in losing him forever to a judgemental care system that did nothing to help us. The social workers seemed to show no understanding of my predicament. The rigorous timetable they set for me did not work for a single parent trying to hold down a job.

In the hope of Leo's brother returning home, I enrolled Leo in boarding school so that I might manage both boys' needs. When Leo came home from school on holidays, he spent most of his time sequestrated in his bedroom with the curtains closed against the outside world. I thought this was due to needing privacy after boarding school life. But I was wrong. In retrospect, it was the first sign of schizophrenia. Leo's brother was 13 and living with foster parents. He sent me letters, writing that his foster parents advised him that, if coming home to live with me did not work, he might end up in a children's home. He decided not to come home to our family

---

1 At the time this happened to Sheila, the idea of observing the Sabbath Day to keep it holy was strictly adhered to be some orthodox Jews.

or to involve me in meetings about his future. He never returned to us, so there was no need to send Leo away to school but, as he was settled, I left him there. Ultimately, social services judged me to be an unsuitable mother. Involving them was the worst decision I have ever made. For years, I fought to get my elder son back but he remained in care until he was 16 years old when he returned to live with his father.

I moved to a new house with a new partner. I confided in the social worker that I was pregnant but that I was not intending to have the baby. However, she told the foster parents, my ex-husband and his wife, who in turn told Leo and his brother, that I was pregnant. I have never regretted having the baby and in 1989, I gave birth to Leo's sister. When Leo saw her for the first time he said "Mummy, she's magic". He loved her and as they grew up the feeling was mutual.

It was during the first term of Leo's sixth form that he phoned me to say, "Take me out of school, or I will get myself expelled". I brought him home and enrolled him in the school where I taught. He completed a year there. But, during the summer holidays, he disappeared without warning, jumping from his bedroom window with his belongings in a black bin bag. Leo went to live with his father in Sheffield who supported him to gain top grades in his 'A' levels. Leo did not contact me during these two years. However, despite the bitter divorce, I had confidence that my ex-husband would steer Leo in the right direction and care for him.

One day, some of my students came to tell me that they had seen Leo at the university. I was delighted when he phoned me to say he was living in the students' accommodation nearby. When Leo got in touch, he invited me to his room to tell me that he had been in hospital that Christmas and that he was mentally ill. We visited the university doctor and Leo was 'sectioned' for the first of many times. At the beginning of his illness, I had no idea about the diagnosis or the terrible prognosis of schizophrenia. Leo described his frightening symptoms:

> *"I am not in control of my body, thoughts, actions, senses, reactions and my life in general. I am certain that trickery is involved with everything I think, do or know, see or hear. I have severe, unexplainable nightmares: never get a good night's sleep and always wake up feeling disturbed, worried and confused. I am always tired and when I cannot sleep, I lose my sanity and all perspective of what is happening or has happened … I hear normal voices and almost robotic voices too. These cause a lot of problems for me and I feel that they control or bully me…. Sometimes the voices that I hear deliberately keep me up at night and scare or upset me which is a living hell."*

The inception of Leo's mental illness was a watershed, not only for him but for the family too. Leo, his sister, and I, went on the journey together. From that time onwards, I devoted myself to trying to learn everything I could about mental illness and its treatment.

I spent nearly 20 years in voluntary roles relating to mental health services. I became a Chair of a patient and public forum for mental health. The forums were a government initiative, designed as a watchdog to provide the public with a platform to offer 'constructive criticism' on the design and delivery of NHS services. There were 572 forums, one for each NHS trust. An editorial in *The Times* newspaper, *Death of the Forums* (15th April, 2006), described them as, 'at best tokenistic' and 'at worst non-existent … dominated by the well-meaning but professional busybody'. The article stated that "a public that does not understand the Government's health reforms could turn ugly". During its existence my forum produced a report on older people's mental health services, challenging the reduction of 'dementia' beds from over 250 to 44. We did '*understand*' and yes, we did become *'ugly'*. For me, this was the start of my monitoring strategic and operational so-called 'reforms' and, to this day, I challenge inequitable and inadequate NHS mental health and social services. The forums morphed into Local Involvement Networks and eventually into Healthwatch.

I chaired the carers' council at my local trust, until it was axed when two counties amalgamated into a single Foundation Trust, for which I served nine years as a governor. During this time, I have delved into every orifice of local mental health services – finance, safety, the law, ethics, integration with the care system, recovery, crisis services, dual diagnosis, bed management, and commissioning. I would like to write the thousands of meetings I attended over many years trying to improve services were well spent, but they were not.

In 2012, the Trust implemented what I believe to be a most damaging local mental health service reform, which became known as 'the radical redesign'. This was introduced by the then head of operations who announced that the Trust were:

> "*…taking out intensive services to protect other services, even though locally there is a lower number of available beds than anywhere else in the country and the need for beds and services is statistically rising*". (I took notes verbatim.)

Staffing would be reduced as well as bed numbers, which would be replaced by 'recovery innovations'. One of these was to be a wellbeing service that would be available in primary services only. Improving Access to Psychological Therapies (IAPT) would offer Cognitive Behaviour

Therapy (CBT) - a government initiative designed by an economist to get the unemployed back to work. I was not alone in realising that the result of the planned redesign would be disastrous - the beginning of the decline in services and a drastic rise in unexpected deaths of the Trust's service users. Vulnerable people like Leo, needing regular clinical intervention and support, would receive fewer visits by community nurses and reviews with consultants. The cost of this 'reform' in redundancies of clinicians who subsequently the Trust would be seeking to re-employ was reported as reprehensibly high.

I challenged this plan vociferously everywhere I was able. I chose to represent public opinion and the views of those who, like Leo, could not speak out, for example, at the local Health Overview and Scrutiny Committee. I wrote and met with the Trust's succession of Chief Executive Officers, Chairs, Directors, non-executive Directors, as they came and went. I have appeared on local TV news programmes, and been on the radio. In 2014, I was interviewed by the BBC, and I talked about Leo. At that time, over 300 people were waiting for a care-coordinator. I described the crisis in mental health services and said, "They need to listen. There needs to be a regular, meaningful interface between service-users and the Trust." I have made public presentations, met local MPs and members of the House of Lords at Parliament, and attended endless strategy and operational groups at the Trust and its medical council. I have even spoken to a crowd from the steps of the Town Hall.

Meanwhile, Leo continued to be very unwell and he did not feel listened to. One day when out driving with him, Leo told me that he was in constant torture all the time. My heart sank. He wrote down and described 84 symptoms and gave them to his consultant. At a subsequent meeting, she said "I suppose I should read them". Leo felt so afraid and unsafe:

> *"Sometimes I am unwilling to go out since I feel I am always picked on and victimised.*
> *I am claustrophobic sometimes and I have a fear of drowning.*
> *I believe I am being stalked by cyber terrorists and will be murdered soon [by] 'Techs' and also anti-semitic people and I feel I am a 'pogrom' victim or like one.*
> *I feel that when I go out people are constantly watching me and talking about me which is upsetting and frightening.*
> *I feel constantly bullied and undermined."*

Leo's life, from the moment of diagnosis until his death, age 39 in 2016, from an overdose of cocaine, followed the tragic trajectory of many people with schizophrenia. Over the years, for my daughter and me, it meant being ready at a moment's notice to help Leo through his many crises, his many 'sections', financial problems, and house moves. At the beginning of his illness, Leo hoped he would be able to re-establish his planned life, returning to university, and having a successful career. To see this hope fade and his ambitions obliterated was heart breaking. I used to look at young couples realising that my son would probably not enjoy the joy of a loving relationship, marriage, and children.

In the early days, I felt I had an understanding, helping hand supporting me in my caring responsibilities. Support from mental health care co-ordinators was a comfort until the radical redesign took hold. Leo's first community nurse used to end his week by bringing Leo to see me where I lived in the country. We would sit drinking orange juice in the garden. A full caseload then was 12 to 15 people. Now it might be over 40. Each time Leo's community nurses changed I was saddened. Initially, I thought times in hospital would improve Leo's condition, but I remember going to a meeting where the concept of 'one step forward, two steps back' was explained. I wish I had been told the brutal truth about the prognosis of schizophrenia at the beginning of Leo's illness. I retained hope where really there was little. I thought the hours I spent with mental health providers would help not only Leo but others too. But I was as powerless to prevent the decline in Leo's condition as I was over the years in preventing the deterioration in local mental health services.

I have no idea when Leo began taking drugs. I assume it started with cannabis, but towards the end of his life, he progressed to hard drugs. Sadly, and for no reason that I know, the year before his death Leo began to exclude me from his care and his care co-ordinator could not confide her suspicions to me due to confidentiality. She tried to hint that Leo was visiting an area on the bus which I know now is a place known for the supply of drugs. At the very end of his life, Leo's flat was taken over by some young drug dealers. Leo kept a diary until the day before he died. He wrote he hoped they would stay away. He wrote about his delusions, his financial problems, and his daily life.

Leo died waiting for a visit from his care co-ordinator. He usually received a visit every two weeks. The Trust had redesigned its outreach services to make care co-ordinators' travel distances to their caseloads more efficient. Sadly, two months passed before the handover of Leos's care co-ordinators was discussed between the new and the old. This conversation took place on the Monday after the Sunday Leo died. If he had been visited, maybe the co-ordinator would have become aware of how Leo was being controlled by drug dealers and the deterioration in his mental health.

Leo took great pride in his flat. When we cleared his possessions, excluding furniture, comprised over 80 large moving boxes of books and DVDs. Whoever was around Leo when he died stole his money and his telephone. The only food left in his flat was a Happy Shopper tin of chicken soup.

Many people must have had that knock on the door by two hatless police persons asking to enter the house. The shock is terrible. Immediately, I telephoned Leo's father who was in New York. He insisted that I arrange a Jewish funeral in Sheffield, which he was unable to attend. I regret not burying Leo close in the Jewish cemetery in Norwich where I could visit his grave.

Following Leo's death, I continued working with the Trust. I have consulted the Ombudsman for mental health, members of NHS Improvement, visited the Department of Health and met with the police. I have consulted with the Care Quality Commission (CQC). I have become the epitome of *the well-meaning professional busybody* referred to in the Times editorial. And, in some circles, I have become very unpopular.

In my opinion at the time of writing, after years of being in 'special measures', a hubristic, intransigent culture pervades within the Trust's leadership. People who dominate large organisations should be competent to lead and succeed. I question whether people within the Trust are sometimes promoted into jobs they are not competent to do. In my view, the power structure needs disrupting - values and mission statements revisited and upheld. Local mental health services seem to have become a crisis only service. As a member of a group campaigning for local mental health services to improve, I remain driven by the passion to prevent the unnecessary deaths of people with enduring mental health conditions, like my dear son Leo.

The knowledge I have gained over the past 20 years convinces me that the way mental health services are delivered have been mismanaged. 53 unexpected deaths were recorded in the Trust's annual report from 2012 to 2013, rising to 184 from 2016 and 2017 - the period when Leo died. In 2018, the contract commissioned for the Trust to deliver a drugs and alcohol service was lost to a private company and statistical data on deaths of service users were computed differently. At the Trust's 2018 AGM, the figure of 137 unexpected deaths was described as 'an improvement'. I pointed out this was an insult to the 137 service-users who died and their families!

My experience of involvement is that contributions are received with obsequious and suppressed hostility. Suggestions and involvement by service-users and carers should be welcomed but I am not alone in feeling we are not listened to. Just before Leo died I was approached by the then

CEO who challenged me, saying, "you need to make a choice about whose side you are on". I replied, "I think about this every time I attend a meeting like this and my answer to you is that I am on the side of the service-users".

After Leo died, I took part in a BBC Panorama programme that exposed the high number of deaths at the Trust. Whilst being interviewed in Leo's flat, I relayed this incident with the CEO to the journalist interviewing me. I said, "now perhaps the CEO will know whose side I am on as I am sitting on the chair my son died in". This was not broadcasted.

The inquest on Leo's death was one year to the day after he died. A barrister provided by INQUEST represented the family. Both Leo's sister and I read out our witness statements. The people who were with Leo when he died did not attend, but I received some kind words from some of Leo's neighbours. In his diary Leo wrote he would miss his nurse. After the inquest, I purchased a compact disc of the proceedings. I was warned that I could not use the recording in future legal proceedings. I have not yet taken the CD out of the envelope. I cannot bear to relive that horrible experience.

When asked how many children I have I answer, "I've lost two of them" because I have never got over the loss of my first son. Years later, I found him on Facebook - such a shock to see the son I had last seen when he was 16 - as a man in his late 40s, living in the United States. He continues not to want to know me or have contact with me, and I can understand why.

One the Mothering Sunday after Leo died, I received an email from Leo's father. He wrote, "you know it was your fault that Leo died". A question I ask myself daily is, "what more could I have done to prevent my son's death?"

Leo was the kindest, most intelligent, caring, affectionate, loving son. I remember him holding my hand when we were out until he was a teenager. He used to leave me loving notes, which I treasure. Losing him has broken my heart. It has also encouraged me to empathise with all people who suffer loss.

Leo died waiting – waiting for his regular visit from his community mental health nurse, waiting for his father who visited him once a year, and waiting for me, his mother who sensed the danger he was in but failed to convince mental health services of that. I am left feeling his death was preventable if I had been listened to and Leo had been protected when he needed it most.

May Leo rest in peace, he is remembered always as a loving son and brother by his sister and mother.

Peggy: Not 'Acting Up' But Dying
by Nick and Maxine

Maxine made the heart for her Mum: The red is the sparkle jumper she always liked to wear. Red is the colour of Christmas which she loved. Red like the roses in the garden at the cottage where she lived with her husband. The golden heart because she had a heart of gold.

About Nick and Maxine

Peggy's daughter and son-in-law, Maxine and Nick, have been seeking answers and accountability on behalf of her family. Nick, a soft-hearted man who cares passionately about his family, is vociferous in his views about failings in mental health care. Maxine is a quieter and more private person who is devoted to caring for those she loves. Together they have been strong advocates for Peggy, their family, and their community.

Peggy: Not 'Acting Up' But Dying

Peggy knew her husband, Neville, from their schooldays. They became neighbours and fell in love. They remained happily married for over 60 years. Neville describes Peggy as "the love of my life". Maxine was their only child and they were very close. Peggy was family-orientated, and every Sunday she liked to be with her family for a roast dinner. She worked locally in a baker's shop and Woolworths where she was well known in the community because she was kind and liked to make others happy.

When Maxine was three years old, Peggy had a nervous breakdown and she was diagnosed with schizophrenia. Over the decades, Peggy had a range of treatments including medication and electroconvulsive therapy. Mostly she was kept stable on medication and she got on with her life. Though she did have three relapses and needed hospital stays to help her recover.

When Peggy was young she used to cycle into town to go to the cinema. She loved the glamour of Hollywood movies. She was a fan of stars like Elizabeth Taylor and Doris Day. Peggy took pride in her appearance, she liked to wear fashionable clothes and she had beautiful hair. Even as an older lady she was stylish. She had a wonderful smile and her fun side can be seen in photographs of her. One that captures Peggy's character is her in a party hat, with a cheeky grin, raising her cup of tea.

Peggy was happiest in her own home. Neville worked long hours as a farm worker but in his spare time, he enjoyed gardening. Peggy loved to spend time in the garden admiring the flowers and vegetables he grew for her. She would say he was a 'professional' gardener and everyone else were amateurs by comparison. She was a very private person and she would get anxious if people visited but once they were through the door she would always offer a cup of tea and some cake.

Peggy found it difficult to be outside her home. Nevertheless, when Maxine was younger, every September the family would go to the Yarmouth on holiday. Although this was not far away, Peggy would get travel sick and call out in distress. Once she had settled in, Peggy would enjoy the variety shows and going into the shops. As she got older, Peggy preferred to be in her cottage where she felt safe.

Peggy and Neville were a beautiful couple who were devoted to each other. She would see to his every need and, in return, he cared for her in a gentle and calm way. He never raised his voice and he was accepting of her frailties. He knew what to say and never pushed her boundaries.

Peggy became more frail, so she moved to a care home that was within sight of her house. Every night Neville would go to the window and say goodnight to his beloved wife. Every two weeks, Maxine would pick up Peggy and take her to spend time at home with Neville.

In 2017, Peggy's medication was changed and the care home started to struggle because sometimes Peggy became confused and aggressive. In December 2019, Peggy became unwell and the mental health trust tried to find a specialist bed for her. The nearest one, who could care for an older person with schizophrenia, was 280 miles away in Somerset. Peggy had never left Norfolk before. Knowing how distressed she would become, when travelling even short distances, we were appalled to know she would be enduring such a long journey. We were not informed of the imminent move because it happened earlier than expected, so none of us had the chance to say goodbye to our dear Peggy. This is something that we cannot get over. She was whisked away and we never saw her again. If we had known what would happen we would have taken her home with us.

The journey must have been horrendous for Peggy. An ambulance with a stretcher had been requested but she was transported upright. Such a long journey without rest breaks. Two days after she arrived in Somerset, Peggy was diagnosed with a urinary tract infection and she was prescribed antibiotics. We wanted Peggy home but we made it clear she needed to be well enough to travel before she was moved. Our concerns were ignored. We would find out later that the hospital had not given Peggy adequate fluids. They described her as 'acting up'. It seems only one nurse took the time and care to try and encourage Peggy to drink. We feel so grateful that someone cared and was kind to Peggy in her final days.

Four days after arriving in Somerset, Peggy was again put in a private ambulance for the 280-mile journey back to Norfolk because a bed had been found locally.

The shocking CCTV images of Peggy leaving the hospital were deeply distressing and they will stay with us forever. She was slumped over to one side, almost falling out of the wheelchair. She looked so very unwell. How did anyone think she seemed fit to travel? The 'ambulance' was a converted transit van. The staff were not medically trained and there was no defibrillator on board. Peggy was not transferred onto a stretcher, or even a comfortable seat. She once again travelled upright in a wheelchair.

The first we knew anything was wrong was when we had a phone call to say the ambulance had pulled over on the motorway but we were not told why. We were desperate to know Peggy was okay and we called every local hospital asking if she had been admitted there. Maxine was so worried that Peggy would be frightened. But Peggy had died. She died at 3pm but we were not told until 7.20 pm.

The escorts had noticed Peggy was making grunting noises but they thought she was snoring. They failed to notice that Peggy was having breathing difficulties and had become unresponsive. When they did realise, they pulled over on the hard shoulder of the motorway. Emergency services were not called until after they had made calls to the private hospital and the private ambulance service. Only one of the escorts had CPR training and this was not started until the escorts were instructed by emergency services to do so. However, this was ineffective due to Peggy's position.

In a Regulation 28 Prevention of Future Deaths report, issued to the private ambulance service, the coroner, said that an expert witness was "of the firm view that the staff transporting [Peggy] did not recognise she was in respiratory distress and/or cardiac arrest and that she had effectively died whilst sat between them". Our adored Peggy had died sitting between people who did not even notice she was dying.

The inquest was gruelling. A friend came with us for support. We had managed to get some legal representation from INQUEST and they did their best for us but the power imbalance is unequal. We had to sit in Coroner's court for four days listening to evidence that was devastating. It was really upsetting that the Trust did not attend in person. They remained in their offices a few miles away and participated over video link. The other legal teams came from London and Wales but the Trust, who were the nearest, didn't have the decency to be there. Listening to all the witnesses and the things that came out. It was so hard to hear about the poor quality of care Peggy received. There were times when we wanted to call out 'liars!'. We found it hard to believe all the things we heard. The mental health trust, the hospital, and the private ambulance service all seemed to be trying to avoid blame. I don't know how we got through it.

Afterwards, we complained because, in our opinion, the Trust had been economical with the truth about whether the practice of sending frail older people out of county had stopped. The coroner decided to accept the Trust's account which rested on an argument over who might be considered an older person. This felt like another kick in the teeth. By this point, we were feeling so angry about what happened to Peggy and the way we have been treated since. We feel that we have had to fight for information. Fight for the truth. Everything has been a fight and so much more painful than it should be. People tell us they care and that they are committed to making things better but it is not how we have been left feeling.

Our concerns relate to all parties involved. In our view, ultimately the Trust were responsible for Peggy's care. Their bed management has led to a long-standing shortage of beds. This means that very unwell patients are being transported long distances. This is something they have been picked up on by the CQC. The Trust made the decision to send Peggy and to recall her. They did not ensure she was checked as medically fit to travel or that the ambulance was suitable, or adequately staffed, for a frail older person. In our opinion, they should be held accountable for that.

We feel that pretty basic stuff was missing from Peggy's care. Diagnostic over-shadowing meant that Peggy's mental health diagnosis resulted in her physical health needs being overlooked. Peggy was ill and she was put in the back of a glorified mini-bus for a 6-and-a-half hour journey. Would anyone want that for their grandmother? What happened in the back of that ambulance should never be allowed to happen again.

We have become increasingly critical of the CQC because they seem unwilling, or unable, to bring registered organisations to account in a timely manner. It took two years for the CQC to remove the licence of the private ambulance service and the Trust have been in 'special measures' for years. As we see it, there is no sense of urgency to change.

Losing Peggy in such awful circumstances has devastated our family. We are all struggling to come to terms with what happened. Maxine wears a heart necklace with Peggy's fingerprint on it. She visits Peggy's grave every Sunday with her father but we should be enjoying a roast with our beautiful Peggy.

Nick feels it is his role to be strong for the family. He's the one that speaks out loudly and demands answers, justice, and actions. He can get a bit heated and swear about things. This is just his frustration and hurt spilling out. Nick often struggles with feeling like he has failed his family because he has not made any difference. After the inquest Nick said that he had never felt so bad in his life but he felt he couldn't break because his family need him to stand up for them. He feels that he has let his family down because the outcome did not result in Prevention of Future Deaths reports for all involved. But we are just ordinary people up against a powerful system.

At times, what happened to Peggy, and all the things that happened in the aftermath of her death, has really impacted on our mental health. We both suffer with nightmares now and can find ourselves waking up sweating and shaking. It's not really surprising because we have been through such a traumatic and stressful time.

After Peggy died, we were put in touch with someone from a local campaign group. A wonderful chap, called Terry, took us under his wing and he helped us navigate the system. He supported us through some terrible times. He would have been at our side through the inquest but, sadly, he died from cancer. However, other members of the campaign continued to support us.

As well as striving to get answers for Peggy, we are trying to get actions to prevent other people losing their lives. Nick is an active member of the campaign now. He has lost close relatives to suicide and we have struggled to get mental health support for our son. We know other people who have lost someone or who cannot get the mental health support they need for a relative. One voice is not enough to get heard and force change. We think it is important to campaign as a group because together we might get listened to.

We have been negotiating with the CCG and the Trust to get a local mental health walk-in centre set up. This is a frustrating process and at times we have wondered if they genuinely want to support this venture, or whether they were trying to keep us sweet. We, but particularly Nick, have made a lot of noise. We have made a nuisance of ourselves because we want to see more accessible, safer, and more caring services for older people. We will carry on trying to get this established.

We have needed help to get noticed. The media have reported on Peggy's story numerous times since her death[2]. Without their help we suspect what happened to Peggy would have been swept under the carpet.

We have tried to work with the Trust but it's hard because we feel so raw and angry still. We are not always reasonable, in the way some professionals think we should be, because what Peggy suffered was not reasonable. It was horrendous and our anger is justified. Two years on, there are still things happening that trigger our feelings of grief. For example, the news that the private ambulance service had been de-registered coincided with the second anniversary of Peggy's death, which is just before Christmas. When other people are preparing for celebrations we are re-living the trauma of losing Peggy.

After Peggy died, the then CEO of the Trust suggested creating a scholarship in her name. We felt this would be a good thing to come out of this dreadful situation. The first year's scholarship was awarded for specialist dementia training for an older people's inpatient team. We initially thought Peggy would be proud to think people would get training to improve patient care in her name. We are proud of Peggy and we want her to be remembered for the lovely person she was. But as time has gone on, we feel that this is probably virtue signalling and a PR exercise. Rather than honouring Peggy, we have started to feel this was not perhaps something we want Peggy associated with. In the end, we decided to withdraw.

---

2 This BBC report by Nikki Fox sums up what happened to Peggy: https://www.bbc.co.uk/news/uk-england-norfolk-57575298

Peggy meant the world to us. She was unique and special to everyone who knew her. We are devastated that she died in such awful circumstances. She was 81 years old, ill, and she needed kind and effective treatment. Instead, she was transported hundreds of miles in a so-called ambulance. Her last hours were spent sitting between two strangers who failed to respond to her physical distress. No frail older person should die on the hard shoulder of a motorway. In our view, Peggy was failed by everyone who was responsible for her care. We will never forgive those responsible. We will not stop fighting until we know that no one else's elderly relative will be treated the way Peggy was.

Peggy deserved to be treated with dignity and kindness. She was a wife, mother, and grandmother who was very precious to us but she was treated as human cargo. We have to live with the heartbreak of being denied the chance to tell Peggy how much we loved her when she was dying. All the family have suffered heartache because of the way dear Peggy died. We are angry and upset but, more than anything, we are absolutely heartbroken.

Our dear Peggy died waiting for a bed near home. She was a beautiful, gentle, kind, and loving wife, mother, grandmother, and mother-in-law, who was tragically taken from us.

Love Will Find a Way

by Heidi

Sam's mum, Karen, hand-crafted his memory heart. She describes her choices: a rainbow, butterfly, and white feather because seeing these comforts us because they are signs he's still around; oak leaves for his beloved Brimmon tree; a daffodil for Wales; and the red guitar which was his shield and protector - he always had one slung on his back ready to play a song for anyone who asked.

About Heidi

Heidi went into adulthood determined to help people, first training to be a midwife, then a mixture of ophthalmology and diabetes care, and latterly as the manager of a care home for adults with learning disabilities. Heidi was working as an activity co-ordinator for elderly residents with dementia when Sam, her younger brother, died. Since his death, Heidi has been involved in raising suicide awareness and prevention.

Love Will Find a Way

I write this, sitting at the kitchen table, nearly three years after Sam left us. I was born first, then Sam came along. Although we later had other siblings, we had spent our formative years as a team of two. We are a close family, which I describe as being built of the same Lego bricks but assembled in different orders. We all can interpret each other's idiosyncrasies and we are not afraid to show our love for each other.

Sam's story

Sam was funny, sensitive, kind, cheeky, and a showman. He excelled at sport and was quietly determined to follow in our dad's footsteps as a successful musician. We grew up surrounded by talented musical artists who visited dad's recording studio. I was the nerdy, but creative, big sister with limited sporty or musical abilities.

Sam had a wonderfully colourful life. He was scouted by a professional football club in his youth. After scoring a goal, Sam once said, "I feel like something marvellous". He undoubtedly was. Sam wrote his first song in primary school which was recorded by the school. When he was about ten, Sam accidentally burnt down a series of barns because he and his mate tried to cook sausages near some hay bales. They tried to put out the fire with lemonade. It didn't work. Fortunately, the police saw this as an error of judgement by two young boys.

As an adult, Sam continued to be something marvellous. When he left school, Sam had a job as a milkman for a bit. He took the offer of 'borrowing' the milk float literally and broke down on the M6 (on his way to Manchester's Hacienda). This was not the only unexpected thing Sam did. He turned up once outside our family house, driving a London cab with a drum kit fully set up in the back. On another occasion, he sat in the village square playing his guitar, wearing only his underpants, as if it was the most normal thing in the world to do. Sam ran away and joined a circus, as a fire eater and juggler, and he went to Europe. The funniest medical letter I ever saw, was one where the doctor had written, "… this gentleman failed to attend his appointment because he has run away with the circus". It was true, Sam had done exactly that.

There was a serious side to Sam too. He helped to campaign to save a tree and wrote a song to help with the fight for its preservation. A whole town bypass was re-rerouted to save that precious ancient oak. There is a plaque for Sam under its boughs.

Sam's mental health first started to wobble in his early 20s. His life was full of shitty curveballs. The first was being abused by a neighbour which Sam, at the time, claimed hadn't happened to him. Finally, conceding years later that it had. Then Sam fought off blood cancer but this changed him physically and mentally. He was left with a permanently broken leg, caused by radiation therapy, which could lead to falls.

Sam moved from Wales to Holland to pursue a career in music. He became very well known in the town on the German border where he lived with his girlfriend (and their dog) for over ten years. By day, Sam set up events marquees and stages. By night, he performed. He was interviewed frequently by television and radio stations. Recently, the Dutch town civic society sent us a page from their annual town chronicle which marked Sam's life there. They noted his musical ability and the love people had for him. Eddie van Halen was also recognized in the same book and Sam would have been so proud.

While Sam was in Holland, he was diagnosed with bipolar disorder. Some of Sam's songs give insight into his experiences of mental illness. In the lyrics of songs like *Inside my head*[3] or *You didn't listen,* Sam conveyed how lonely and hopeless he sometimes felt. In *Cyber bully* he sings of trying to make sense of his life, which felt like 'walking on a tightrope, pulling me from both sides', and 'holding onto sanity'.

Sam made repeated cries for help but it seemed that he had 'too much mental capacity' and, in our opinion, he was not taken seriously as a suicidal person. On one A and E visit, Sam had things he could use to harm himself in his washbag which he described as his 'insurance'. I gave these to the mental health assessment nurse for disposal. Despite the clear risk that I thought Sam posed to himself, he was sent home. Then, he self-harmed in an attempt to be 'sectioned' because he felt safer with his thoughts in hospital settings. Sam liked the routine of the psychiatric hospital, the warmth, food, safety, camaraderie, and friendships. He enjoyed the music therapy classes and took up jigsaws which helped him to relax his mind.

One day, Sam fell in the street. He hadn't fallen because he was drunk, he fell because his leg gave way and he wasn't wearing his splint. In A and E, once again, he was treated like a nuisance. He smelt bad and looked awful and was writhing and gurning. His trousers and pants were sodden with urine and faeces and he had trench feet from not removing his boots for weeks. He was covered in bruises which I noticed when washing him and he also had burns from the ammonia in his urine. I read the transfer note from the acute emergency doctor to the psychiatric unit. It was as if Sam was a criminal and it claimed he was repeatedly attending A and E because he had alcohol issues and he stunk of it. He did smell but not of booze.

---

3 Sam's songs are on YouTube. *Inside My Head*: https://youtu.be/r8A0r9UPJQI *You Didn't Listen*: https://youtu.be/jgePINpZynU *Cyber bully*: https://youtu.be/xCPgMsPiYVg

I was in two minds whether to even hand that letter over due to its judgemental, discriminatory, and frankly defamatory tone.

Sam lived on the Welsh border. There appeared to be cross-border hiccups and a lack of joined-up thinking and communication between the agencies. The local mental health hospital was newish but did not seem to have enough beds. Being sectioned became a regular battleground and Sam was twice sent to a unit two and a half hours from his home. While he was there, it felt like Sam was told off for wasting resources, "could you try not to be so crazy and do crazy things because it is expensive!" A figure was quoted to him for the previous two weeks-worth of manic behaviours. Sam told us they made him catch a series of buses to go home alone which frightened him. It seemed like it was all about the bottom line, the cost of care packages and services.

Sam had mostly been manically high with his bipolar disorder but this dramatically changed to terrifying levels of anxiety and depression for the last few months of his life. After he died, we made a timeline of the months before his death which, when pieced together, paint a picture of a family desperately trying to get him well and keep him alive and protected. There were meetings, appointments, letters begging for someone to help him, and a gazillion phone calls.

The last time I visited Sam in a psychiatric hospital, I could see his light was fading. I took a black and white photo of Sam playing the grand piano there. His light had dimmed so much during the wait for the help he needed.

I fought so hard for Sam. I begged A and E staff to get him assessed by a psychiatrist or the mental health team prior to discharge. I left him during the night knowing in my heart that without intervention it was probable that it would be the last time I saw him. I couldn't bear to use the word, "goodbye", as I left his bedside.

If I was to pinpoint the main reason for his rapid decline, in my view, it would be the poor care plan set in place by a previous social worker. Sam had not been happy at all with the plan and he felt bullied into agreeing to it. He wanted to go into supported living accommodation so he could be looked after but there were no places available. So, Sam was to be sent home to his flat with carers coming in a couple of times a day. Sam was so anxious about going back because he was scared of his neighbours, lonely, and it was a miserable existence for him. Sam was so scared that he often slept in his car instead of his flat. Sometimes he would sleep in the GP's car park. This gives an indication of his psychological state. Yet he was deemed to have capacity and be fit to live on his own in the community. As a family, we will never understand that. His flat was a long distance from any family members and we had asked for him to be re-housed nearer.

We managed to get the social worker changed but not the care plan. At our insistence, Sam's GP called for a meeting to discuss it. The meeting was to be held with all involved agencies and was delayed many, many, times. It was scheduled for a Thursday in early June but Sam died on the Monday of that week. He had given up hope.

Sam tried so hard to stay alive but he believed that there was no hope for him and that he was a burden. He was just 43 when he left us. Sam had shone so brightly and he didn't really want to die. Tragically, during the last weekend of his life, he made numerous outgoing calls to services but the help he felt he needed did not come. We would have helped Sam if we had known how desperate he was feeling. Sam didn't leave us a note. I think he hoped that we would know why he did it and understand.

Sam was buried in a willow coffin in a natural burial field. Cows graze there among the wild flowers. It overlooks the Welsh hills and the spot is marked by a simple, large pebble. A Serious Case Review of Sam's death has been undertaken. The outcome of which we have no idea.

Sam's legacy is his music. During his last psychiatric admission, Sam wrote a song in music therapy and left a video of him singing and playing it on his phone. *Love will find a way* is truly beautiful, full of meaning and one of the best songs he ever wrote, so we want to release it. We would love his song to be recorded by top artists and orchestras and be used as a fund-raising and suicide-awareness tool.

Making sense of things

As a health professional, it somehow cut deeper knowing what was supposed to happen, what could have been done and what are, in my view, staggering failings in mental health services. What happened to Sam appears to be happening to many people. I have a friend whose son is facing the same struggles that our Sam did. It is heartbreaking to see the same patterns emerging. In our opinion, there are fragmented services, a lack of communication between agencies, and lack of supported living.

The struggle to get anyone to listen was real. You would think it would cross professionals' minds to value the input of his family repetitively painting a picture of Sam. But we felt they had this 'we know best attitude' and we needed to shut up. Some staff seemed to project a fixed idea and would not contemplate another way. What was most galling is that they didn't actually know Sam at all. They saw the latest version of him and not who he really was. On one occasion, we were only listened to because someone came past, who knew Sam from a previous admission, who made the comment "mate this isn't you".

Our family feels that, over the years, Sam was subjected to unfair judgements and cruel or unthinking comments. Sam said after one hospital visit, "I am a machine", such was his feeling of dehumanization. The weird thing is that all this appears to be seen as an acceptable way to treat people.

In my opinion, the issue of whether Sam had mental capacity got in the way of keeping him safe. In a meeting, which we attended with the psychiatrist and the social worker, it was suggested Sam had capacity and that if he didn't sign off (agree to) his care plan then the social worker would have to become his legal guardian and agree to it on his behalf. I pointed out that this would mean that he was being deemed to lack capacity whilst simultaneously also have capacity. No wonder Sam felt bullied.

I feel Sam's housing played a part in his decline. He should have been in supported accommodation. He needed companionship whilst he dealt with the unwelcome thoughts in his head. He was so lonely and isolated, we discovered that he was writing messages to himself on Facebook from two different accounts which was heartbreaking. Sam wasn't eating and we don't really know if he was taking his medication as the documentation seems so scant.

In my opinion, the risk of Sam dying by suicide was not taken seriously. Sam's carer noted, on more than one occasion, that Sam said he was going to take his own life but that wasn't fed back to us, nor was any action taken. It is really quite astonishing. Sam had been discharged by the mental health crisis team because, in their words, he was "becoming too reliant" on them. They did not inform the family of this and no other help was set up for him.

We feel Sam's care plan did not match his needs. It should have had some contingency measures in it and some safeguarding built in. Clear communication pathways should have been created and action plans of who to refer to and when. We don't believe that there was information within the plan, to help people who didn't know Sam, spot changes in his behaviour and mood. We feel that these omissions cost Sam his life.

After Sam died we raised concerns that he might have been being bullied and exploited. His debit card was gone, so was his ring and wallet. He was £900 lighter in his bank than the month before. I asked the police to investigate this but they did not seem interested. I explained that Sam was classed as a vulnerable adult but they said there was nothing suspicious. Sam had two mobile phones which was very weird. It feels like people like Sam skirt the periphery of society and don't quite matter as much as the rest.

The impact on our family

We are still waiting for answers and conclusions. There is so much we know but also so much we don't. We have had some advice from the organisation, INQUEST, that supports bereaved families. They helped us find legal representation.

Mum and Dad had counselling after the funeral but they felt going over and over it all was making them feel worse. Sam's brothers and the wider family have all been devastated by his disappearance from their lives. Christmas, birthdays and other family events will never be the same again. He was our 'go to' entertainment guy and it feels weird not to hear his chuckle or his beautiful singing voice.

I haven't been able to work since Sam died. I am left frightened of letters, phone calls, and texts. I am afraid to answer the door in case something bad has happened to my family. I know Sam would not have wanted me to be scared like this. I joined a suicide support group but haven't met any other members in person yet due to the pandemic. Counselling made me upset that I couldn't change anything by talking about it. I am very proactive and like to be actually doing something tangible and find purposeful to manage my feelings. Mum captured in a poem the way we feel:

I see you everywhere, flying high in circles.
Darting, diving, in the sky,
I see you everywhere,
In rainbows, in the sun, the moon and the stars.
I see you everywhere.
I love you so, I wish you didn't have to go away,
I understand that living in your head, was just too much for you to bear.
I see you everywhere.

Sam wrote a song, *Rainbows*[4], in which he sings about chasing rainbows and hoping they will come his way[3]. Sam has a dedicated bench in the woods where we played and rode our bikes as kids, it reads 'Forever Chasing Rainbows'. It is the After Life[5] bench of our small hometown.

In memory of Sam

I am determined to use Sam's voice to get the message out. Society is cushioned in a way because suicide remains a taboo subject of conversation for many. There seems to be little input in preventing suicide and, as no one feels comfortable talking about it afterwards, then nothing is learnt and nothing changes. I want to fight to end the stigma, the shame, and the taboo surrounding mental health and suicide loss. Sam was important and he should still be here.

4 *Rainbows* by Sam Gomm is on YouTube: https://youtu.be/MnUjWFxYHW8

5 After Life is a television drama written and directed by Rick Gervais.

Money was raised by our family for our local mental health charity MIND. There is now a dedicated service to offer a place of refuge and support to try and reduce A and E pressure in our local hospital. However, you have to be referred there, rather than drop in, which seems counter-intuitive to me. There is also a room within the hospital for patients who are having a mental health crisis. One room doesn't even touch the surface for the geographical area that the hospital covers.

In one of Sam's songs, *Waiting for the Sun,* the lyrics describe 'waiting for something good to happen' for 'the sun that melts the snow'. I want there to be somewhere for people who feel like Sam to find hope. Somewhere that people who have been bereaved can go to find a sense of peace. I am currently working on a memorial for persons who died by suicide in my county. It will be a place where relatives, friends, and the public can visit. This will be a hexagonal oak structure with seating. Each seat with have a message engraved on it such as, 'there is hope', or 'there is help'. Metal chimes, with the names of those who have died written on them, will jingle on the breeze. The louder they sound, the bigger the problem that needs to be fixed. The memorial will demonstrate both the scale of the suicide crisis, especially in young people, and also offer a place of hope and support. Somewhere the public can post messages of kindness and words of wisdom. A place where the sun can melt the snow. I will be sharing the design and hope to see similar memorials in every town and city across the UK[6].

Sam died waiting for the sun. Afterwards, I wrote him a letter and asked for it to be placed next to his heart in the coffin along with locks of all the family's hair. He was buried in a smart suit lying on our childhood bedroom curtains (Paddington Bear) and tucked in by the flag of his homeland of Wales. In the letter, I made him a promise that I would fight for people like him and for things to change in the mental health service provision in the UK. Part of that fight is sharing his story with you.

Sam lives on in our Lego bricks xx

Love will find a way into your heart and soul,
Minute after minute, hour after hour,
You've gotta know'
It's true.

Sam Gomm, 2019

---

6 You can contact Heidi via Caroline – caroline.aldridgesw@yahoo.com.

Part Three - Holding On To Hope

Caroline made this heart from a card that Siobhan Maclean (who wrote the foreword) sent. It landed on the doormat on the day Caroline was planning to make the heart for this section. It contained a thoughtful note that recognised the emotional impact of editing a collection of trauma and loss stories might be having on her. It reminded Caroline of how important the people in our network are when we are holding on to hope and the way other people's encouragement can make a difference. Holding on to hope can be difficult but together it is easier.

Holding On To Hope
By Caroline and Emma

Hope is powerful. It strengthens, inspires, and brightens. If we hope, the impossible can become possible and we can hold on through the most difficult times. Hope cannot solve every problem, neither does it erase pain, but it can carry us through dark places. Sometimes people who are in mental distress, grieving, or depressed can lose hope. These are the darkest times when no way forward is visible. This is when we need people to hold hope for us. There are numerous examples in this book of people holding on to hope for others.

In this section, stories of hope abound. We begin with chapters that explore what people need to be mentally well and keep safe.

Caroline: Hope Theory

Hope is part of our everyday lives from the smallest of desires and wishes to our dreams and aspirations. Yet the concept is hard to pin down. Whether hope is an emotion or cognition is debatable. However, there is agreement about the importance of hope in terms of wellbeing and feeling happy with life.

Charles Snyder[7], who created Hope Theory, defines hope as "the perceived ability to produce pathways to achieve desired goals and to motivate oneself to use those pathways". According to Snyder, the three main components to hope are: having focused thoughts and goals; developing advance strategies to achieve them; and being motivated to put in the required effort to achieve them. It is no surprise that this theory has found favour among the positive psychology and coaching community.

The flip side of hope is the deep sadness and despair of hopelessness. Hopelessness features in many of the stories of loss in this book. Whether it is associated with a despair of being stuck in the depths of mental illness, fear of losing a loved one, or rooted in grief, hopelessness can be debilitating. I doubt that many of the contributors to this book would relate to Snyder's motivational and cognitive elements of hope. In *Angry of Bury*, Rebecca articulates how the attitude that she was somehow supposed to put more effort into overcoming her raw grief caused her further distress. I know motivational conversations made me feel even worse after my son died. I was thrown a lifeline of hope - my first grandchild was about to be born.

---

7 Charles Synder is an American psychologist. He devised Hope Theory in the 1980s.

My whole family clung on to this symbol of hope - the promise of a future with joy in it. Even so, there were times when I lost sight of the hope of ever feeling better. From my many conversations with similarly bereaved people, I recognise that for some all hope is stripped away. Hopelessness prevails and their mental health, maybe even their lives, are at risk.

The word 'hope' features in the names of many suicide prevention and postvention groups or initiatives because it is critical to survival. The statistics presented by contributors to this book, regarding the risk of suicide for those bereaved by suicide, are stark. Research findings suggest that hopelessness presents a 'stronger risk factor' than depression for suicidal ideation when people have been bereaved by suicide[8]. Many postvention initiatives provide solely for those bereaved by suicide. The wisdom behind this is clear; this particular type of bereavement brings a layer of pain that is specific and perhaps best understood by peers. However, I worry about the lack of postvention and support for those bereaved due to mental illness where the cause of death is not clear or the death is stigmatised for some reason. These people also need to be supported. I know that I needed people who had gone before me to demonstrate that at some point it would be possible to move from existing to living again. I found my peers, my beacons of hope, via social media. These small interactions brought much comfort.

I would like to propose a definition of hope that might feel more relatable to those experiencing hopelessness. 'Hope in Hopeless Situations' might be defined thus - a belief, of one's own or of another who is offering emotional support, that, contrary to one's current circumstances and emotional state, things can get better, albeit in tiny steps and with setbacks along the way. The three main features, as I see it, are: holding on and going through the motions even if you don't feel it; taking baby steps and keeping expectations realistic; having the emotional containment and support of someone who understands.

Critical to holding on to hope when hopelessness overwhelms is having someone who can hold on to hope for you. Professionals have a part to play in this but each of us as citizens can do this for the people in our networks.

Emma: Holding on to hope for people.

Holding on to hope was vital in my clinical practice while trying to work safely alongside people who were feeling suicidal or hopeless about whether their distressing thoughts or frightening psychotic symptoms would ever

---

8 Grafiadeli, R.,Glaesmer, H., Hofmann, L., Schafer, T. and Wagner, B. (2021). 'Suicide risk after suicide bereavement: the role of loss-related characteristics, mental health, and hopelessness. *Journal of Psychiatric Research* **144.**

abate. I was not necessarily explicitly aware of the role of hope in the moment but, as things slowly became more bearable for people, we were able to reflect together on what had helped at the time and build this into future safety plans.

The ability of someone else to hold on to hope when the person was feeling devoid of any was essential. This was important for the individuals experiencing mental distress but also for their families and wider support networks. I often encountered people who had received unhelpful and doom-laden messages from other parts of the 'helping' services. Just imagine being told that all was lost and everyone should just lower their expectations for the remaining 70 years of life they, or their loved one, had to live. It always staggered me how some professionals, who hold a significant amount of power, predict with an entitled professional arrogance their vague hypotheses as 'certain facts'. Some people seem to unashamedly present themselves as accurate predictors of the future.

Hope meant different things to different people: the gentle reassurance that I had confidence that they could get through the next hour, and then the next hour after that; an acknowledgement that the pain and overwhelming feelings, that are in that moment intolerable and unbearable, will pass, even temporarily, to allow a small window to do one small thing together; the reassurance that goals that they had in life could be achieved, albeit via a different path to the one they had initially imagined. It was being kind to someone in a way that they could tolerate when they could not be kind to themselves. It was helping people unravel what felt overwhelming and trying to puzzle out what is within their control and what is out of their control. And to try together to put our limited collective energy into the things within their control.

I would argue that hope is only useful alongside safety. Although a lot of my work meant taking calculated risks, it also meant stepping in when necessary to maintain safety. Of course, there is a professional duty of care but, on a basic human level, it is important to send a clear message to a person that their life is of value and that you will act to protect it. So, that meant having direct and calm conversations (although I may not have felt calm inside). I gained the confidence to say things like, "I am really worried you are going to kill yourself so I'm going to take this action, you might disagree with me but we can argue about that later once I've made sure you are safe".

It was important to allow people to disagree with me, or be angry with me, and for me to show that it is something that will not lead to abandonment because we can work it through. So many people were justifiably terrified of rejection if they revealed their honest thoughts and feelings because that was their experience to date. These feelings are laden with shame which is such a powerful and debilitating emotion.

Shame, which can be prompted by criticism, can be turned inwards and manifest as self-loathing or even self-harm. It can also present as behaviours (denial, minimisation, blaming others, or rage) that might lead to further rejection. In her 2013 book, *Attachment in Common Sense and Doodles*, Miriam Silver uses the analogy of a shield of shame as a tool to help people work from a belief of 'I am bad' to 'I did something that had a bad effect on someone else' (p150).

Building trust, to hear the most traumatic and abusive things that had been done to people and not responding in the way that they predicted, was critical in many of the relationships that I built with people. Being able to allow someone to take a risk, and test their prediction that I and therefore everyone else in the world will feel disgust and revulsion and ultimately reject them, was a turning point in many relationships. A glimmer of hope that if I didn't feel those things and respond in that way, then it is possible that there are others out there too.

To hold on to hope as professionals, we need holding by those around us. In the initially well-resourced team that I had the privilege to work in, I had an inspirational team leader who was emotionally intelligent and very attuned to the needs of her team. It meant access to regular restorative clinical supervision with a fantastic clinical psychologist and amazing peer support from a committed and skilled team of colleagues. Our workload was manageable and we had the capacity to step in and help colleagues when they were particularly worried about someone, or feeling overwhelmed by the situation they were trying to safely contain. The stories throughout this book lay bare the consequences when these things are not in place and individuals and teams cannot safely deliver care. We also need the support of our own friends and family outside of work to provide that counter-balance of hope and joy outside of work. I had the complete support of my family and friends to leave mental health nursing, despite being the main wage-earner.

Emma and I are not immune to feelings of hopelessness creeping in. There have been times when we have despaired of mental health services ever improving. However, we remain positive that things can change, but that change will need to be relentlessly fought for. We invite our readers to join with us because, if enough people stand together, we can gain strength from each other and hold on to a collective hope.

Day Follows Night
By Sam

Sam wrote, *Day Follows Night*, which explains the heart they made.

The damaged heart is patched up
Behind is the barrier to services
Strewn with irritants and harmful experiences
Ahead the sun shines bright, high in the sky
The barrier behind rejected
This is my vision and reason to carry on
The sun is for every person who died waiting.
I knew some of you.

About Sam

Sam is an experienced nurse in a mental health community team for older adults. In this chapter, Sam reflects on the way a patient, Barry, was failed by services. This is Sam's account of undertaking 'heart work'[9].

9 See the chapter, *Heart Work*, by Emma and Caroline.

Day Follows Night

Let me begin by telling you about myself. I live on the coast in the south of England. My lifestyle is fairly typical. I am married and have children, pets, and elderly parents. I work as a senior nurse in a community mental health team for older adults. I have no burning desire to manage others. For leisure, I like to run, and walk my dogs. This is all that I feel able to disclose about myself because I harbour anxiety about 'whistle-blowing'. I am fearful of becoming unemployable because I hold views that would be deemed negative or disloyal to my employer. I am not sure if my anxiety is disproportionate to the consequences that I would be subject to in reality. But I am not prepared to risk it.

I want to tell you about Barry. His story is still quite raw for me despite the events occurring over a year ago. Barry lived with his wife, Susan, in a bungalow near the sea. Barry was a surveyor. Like many people, they retired in their mid-60s to a coastal area. They were an active couple who were very content.

Following a minor car accident, Barry was referred for a memory assessment. He seemed disorientated and Susan reported that he was becoming vague and short-tempered. He was not his usual self.

I visited Barry to assess his mental health and, after talking to both him and Susan, we decided to formally assess his memory. This showed a mild cognitive impairment. However, this was not a clear picture because in conversation with Barry, I detected that he was depressed, anxious, and very pre-occupied. He was prescribed anti-depressant medication which seemed to significantly reduce his anxiety.

In a sad and unexpected turn of events, Susan collapsed and died suddenly from a major stroke. This was deeply shocking for Barry. His distress was apparent when he described to me how she had been cooking a meal and then complained of a terrible pain in the head. In a instant Barry's life changed without warning because Susan dropped to the floor and was gone in moments. Barry was blind-sided by this catastrophic loss.

An immediate concern for me, knowing Barry and his relationship with Susan, was the risk of him harming himself. He 'ticked' many of the 'red flag' boxes that indicate a risk of suicide. He was an older man, with a history of depression and a chronic illness, who was traumatically bereaved. Without Susan's care and protection, he was isolated and would struggle to meet his own basic care needs. Barry agreed that I could refer him to a crisis service for some short-term support. I approached the adult's crisis service and explained how concerned I was about Barry. They declined support on the grounds that he had a 'cognitive impairment'. So,

I approached the crisis service for older adults. I explained his issues and the risk he could end his life. They said that their expertise was more with dementia crises rather than 'harm to self' and in any case, they couldn't see him for several days due to staff shortages. Eventually, they agreed they would accept the referral on the proviso that I would continue to visit until they could start working with him.

When they took over from myself, Barry was seen by the crisis team for just two weeks. He never saw a psychiatrist in that time. He was discharged back to my care. In the crisis team's view, he was coping. They told me bereavement was a 'natural distress' not a mental illness. Whilst I would agree that grief is not a mental illness, Barry was someone with an underlying mental health condition who had experienced the sudden loss of his wife who was also his carer.

I was really shocked to discover that the older people's crisis team had not sought a social care assessment. Susan had been compensating for Barry's difficulties and he had significant care needs. I made a referral to social services and was informed that their waiting times had lengthened. Due to staff shortages, they could only offer temporary support where there were 'serious care deficits'. I felt that I was met with a coldness and lack of empathy for Barry.

I continued to visit Barry several times a week and I felt anxious about his lack of support. What I was able to offer did not meet his needs. However, Barry assured me that he had good neighbours who helped him out and that I need not worry he would harm himself.

Barry and I often talked about Susan. I sensed that although we had developed a good rapport, there were things Barry was not prepared to share with me because he found it hard to articulate his feelings. I tried hard to conceal my stressors but, despite his impairment, Barry was astute enough to realise that I had many more patients requiring my attention. More than I could manage. He said he did not want to add to my burden or take my time and attention away from others who needed my support. He was a kind man and he cared about other people's wellbeing (including mine).

In assessing and managing the ongoing risk of suicide, I was dependent on Barry's candour. I relied on his inherently gentlemanly tendencies. When I requested he carried on with his life, he gave me his word that he would continue living.

Christmas loomed and my concern for Barry deepened. He was understandably saddened when he envisaged the festive season without Susan. They had not had children so his options were limited. I told Barry about two open access events in his town that he could attend on Christmas

Day if he wished. The volunteers running these events would transport him to and from them if he wanted. He told me that he would 'think about it'. However, when I returned to work in the new year I discovered he had not attended either. He had stayed at home alone.

It was now more than four months since I had made the referral for a social care assessment. Barry still had not even been considered for a care package. During this time, he was sinking further into clinical depression. Barry appeared more confused and he was frequently tearful. He was neglecting himself and would say, "life is meaningless for me now". My concerns were heightened, and the risks of suicide had escalated. So, I discussed with Barry whether he would consider admission to a local older people's mental health ward. His agreement to this was a reflection on how low Barry was feeling.

Like many areas of the country, bed shortages have been a long-standing issue in my locality. I really hoped that Barry would be lucky enough to be offered a bed near to home. In fact, he was not offered a bed anywhere at all. When I asked for a bed for Barry, on the grounds of his severe depression and suicidal ideation, I was told there was already a 'queue' of people waiting for beds and Barry would need to join a waiting list. As if this was not bad enough, I was told that most of the people on the waiting list would be people who had been assessed under the Mental Health Act as requiring detention. It was likely that Barry would never reach the top of the list to qualify for admission because new bed requests for detained patients would 'piggy back' over Barry. He would be perpetually at the bottom of the list. The reality being that it is almost impossible to get people informally admitted to hospital because the patients detained under section would 'trump' them. I knew things were bad but I was shocked to hear this.

I had to go back to Barry and ask him to hold on because I couldn't find a bed for him on a local ward. There were no older people's beds available anywhere in the country at this time. However, that was irrelevant because Barry would not agree to leave his town. I felt helpless.

Despite my ongoing support in the community, Barry continued to deteriorate. He lost weight and muscle strength. When the social care assessment was eventually offered, he refused. In my view, he had lost momentum and motivation during the long wait. I was informed in a phone call that Barry had 'capacity' to make that decision. I challenged this by highlighting how the Barry I first met, who was relatively well and did have capacity, would not be refusing care. He had wanted support and a care package but he was now so depressed, and disregarding of himself, that he was unable to see any hope. I explained that Barry was malnourished, he had become accustomed to only eating snacks and biscuits. He would no longer accept any ready-cooked meals. Barry was often cold and he had started worrying about the bills even though money was not an issue. In my view, his thinking was on the verge of delusional, his ability to self-care was slipping, and he could no longer tolerate the idea of asking for help (particularly as this involved repetitive questioning). This was unsurprising given his pleas for help had been disregarded. I had got to know Barry well but my opinion was ignored.

In February, Barry fell. He fractured his hip and was hospitalised. I was not permitted to visit due to the pandemic visiting restrictions. He had a hip replacement but caught Covid in hospital. This quickly turned to pneumonia. He died without returning home.

I feel really angry about Barry's death. It was preventable and avoidable. With the right support, he could have lived a more comfortable and happier life. Instead, like many older adults, he was increasingly isolated and he died without the comfort of those who knew him. The chain of events are, in my mind, a series of barriers and multi-agency failings. The lack of interagency cooperation meant doors were closed at so many points when help might have diverted the downwards spiral.

Barry did not die by suicide. He died of organisational apathy. He died waiting for the support that he deserved as an older, vulnerable adult.

Ahead the sun shines bright, high in the sky, the barrier behind rejected. This is my vision and reason to carry on. I shall not forget Barry. I mourn his untimely loss. The sun is for every person who died waiting. I knew some of you.

If Only We Knew…
by Billy and Caroline

Billy chose bright colours and a lively pattern for Karen's heart. The vibrancy and swirling patterns reflect her personality. Karen loved music from the 60s and 70s and Billy felt the fabric captured that vibe. Billy added the words, "If only we knew…" because nobody understood what struggles Karen was dealing with and, if they had, there might have been a different outcome.

About Billy

Billy was married to Karen for over 20 years. When his children were teenagers, Karen died of a heart attack associated with alcohol toxicity. Billy describes himself as 'a bit old-fashioned and a stereotypical bloke'. He is not generally comfortable talking about his feelings. Caroline interviewed Billy about Karen, his experiences following her sudden death, and how bereavement counselling helped him.

If Only We Knew…

Could you begin by telling me about Karen?

Karen had a really big heart, she was loving and kind. She enjoyed socialising and she had lots of friends. She loved cooking, dancing, and singing. Karen was fun to be around and everybody loved her. I worked hard to provide for our family. Most of Karen's time and energy was spent at home and looking after our children because I was working long hours.

Looking back, I can see that things had happened to her when she was young which affected her mental health. Not that either of us would have thought about it in that way. Mental health was not talked about. I thought people with mental illness were dangerous and needed locking up, I didn't think mental illness applied to a housewife and mother. Even when Karen was prescribed anti-depressants, I didn't think she had mental health problems. I just thought she was a 'bit low'. My view was based on the way I was brought up. I thought you just have to 'get on with it' when you feel sad or worried.

In our circle of friends, there was a culture of drinking alcohol for pleasure and as a way of lifting our spirits, having fun, and shaking off our worries. I suppose we accepted binge drinking. We worked hard and played hard. At the weekends we liked to go out for meals and drinks. On Mondays, I would get up and go to work but Karen would keep on drinking. But I just didn't see it. I knew she would have a few glasses of wine when she met her friends for lunch but I honestly didn't realise she had begun drinking every day. Or that her drinking was a problem.

How would you describe your relationship with Karen?

I absolutely loved her and whatever difficulties we had I was totally committed to her. Our relationship was hot and cold though. There were good times but sometimes she would shut me out and stop being chatty. We did all the usual family things like days out, holidays, or visiting relatives. Like all couples, we argued sometimes. Occasionally, if she had been drinking, Karen would lash out at me.

Things got harder when the children became teenagers. Karen had been brought up in a family where there was a lot of freedom but my upbringing was strict and traditional. So, we didn't agree on what our children should be allowed to do.

Karen kept a lot to herself. We had been married for years before she told me that she was abused by a relative from age 13 until she left home. She tried to tell someone but was not believed. She was called a 'liar'. When I think of that, it makes me feel so sad for her.

How do you think what happened to Karen might have impacted on her?

Because no one (by that I mean her own family) believed Karen had been sexually abused, she was made to feel like she was the problem. I think she drank sometimes to escape her unhappy feelings. I don't think Karen's drinking was just self-medicating though. She came from a middle-class background where alcohol was freely available and used recreationally. Everyone drank wine - even the children did with meals. Karen had learnt from a young age to hide her problems behind socialising.

What might have helped Karen?

Looking back, I can see she needed help like counselling to support her come to terms with being abused. She needed to realise she was the victim, not the cause.

I probably didn't help the situation either. I would have a drink with her but I could stop. Sometimes I got annoyed with her when she was drunk because I couldn't get my head around why she couldn't control herself. Right up until the very end, I didn't realise just how big a problem her drinking was. I think I kept my 'head in the sand' in the hope everything would be okay.

Could you tell me what it was like for you when Karen died?

I think the shock was awful. I knew she had been drinking heavily over a few days but I didn't expect her to die. It was total devastation. That night, when I was alone, was the first time I have ever cried.

I couldn't allow myself to grieve because the issue of how we were going to survive was so pressing. How was I going to hold down a demanding job and bring the children up alone? I didn't even know how to cook or do laundry, let alone deal with the children's emotions. They were all over the place because their world had imploded. I was far too busy trying to contain them to worry about myself. I can see now that I was all over the place too and that I made mistakes. I still struggle with feelings of guilt about the thoughtless things I did when I was overwhelmed with grief.

The feeling, that I could have done something about it – something to prevent it - stayed with me for years. I wanted to understand why Karen had died but there didn't seem to be any rhyme or reason. I kept thinking, "If there is a God, why has he taken someone so lovely?" I was bereft.

When something like Karen's death happens, blame is a factor. Everyone was blaming everyone else. The children were blaming each other for their bad behaviour, "It's your fault because you stressed Mum out" type of thing. I was so desperate to make them feel better, and to keep us together as a family, that I told them to blame me. Which they did, and sometimes still do. All of this was not helped by some unkind and critical things Karen's family and friends did. Someone started a rumour that I might have murdered Karen because the police investigated her sudden death. I suppose that they didn't know the police always investigate when someone dies suddenly in the community.

There was an inquest which just made everything even worse. We had been told that the post-mortem had found Karen died of a heart attack. But when I went to the inquest, all this stuff came out that I was not prepared for. It was another shock. The toxicology tests found high levels of alcohol and this was put as a contributory cause. It went into the local papers. You cannot imagine what this triggered. None of Karen's friends or family wanted to accept her drinking was a problem. They just saw Karen as someone who was great fun and liked to have a drink. I was accused of lying about Karen's drinking and sullying her character.

I was very lonely. I had a few close friends who did what they could to support me with practical things but I still felt so empty. No one talked to me about the emotional stuff but that was partly my own fault.

You have mentioned how difficult Karen's death was for the children. Was there any help available for them?

Some of the help wasn't very helpful. Karen had so many friends and while some of them were great, others interfered and caused more hurt. The children's school was pretty useless. They didn't make any allowances for what the children were going through. I seemed to be always being called in to be told off about their behaviour. They even suggested I took one of the children out of school for a year but they were not offering any educational or emotional support for them.

The children were the wrong age for any bereavement support. Too old for one service and too young for another. A local youth project did offer some support and counselling even though it was not in their remit. I think they could see we were desperate.

One thing that helped was being advised about some benefits that we were entitled to. I did not realise that we could have been claiming Working Tax Credit and Widowed Parents Allowance. Getting some financial help took some pressure off.

What led you to have some bereavement counselling?

Moving forward with life was hard. I really struggled with being alone. Fast forward a few years, and I met my current partner, Sally. I joke that she is as broken as I am because she has been through similar heartbreak. When you have lost someone close, and you are going it alone, you get stuck in your own little rut. Self-doubts creep in about whether you are good enough. Getting over this fear is quite something. I was lucky to meet someone who had some understanding of my issues. Sally could see that I was traumatised by Karen's death and the way I blamed myself was standing in the way of our relationship. She suggested I went to Cruse[10] for some counselling. I did not want to go because I couldn't see how talking about this would help.

Eventually, about ten years after Karen died, I decided to give counselling a try. It was so helpful. Things I described, that I thought were unique to me, like the guilt and difficulties in forming a new relationship, the counsellor reassured me were quite common. She asked me questions that made me look at myself and think about why I was stuck on blaming myself. In one session she asked, "If you could go back in time, knowing only what you knew then, what could you have done differently?" This was like a weight being lifted from me. I realised there is nothing I could have done, without knowing more facts, to prevent Karen's death. That doesn't mean I was the perfect husband. I was acting on limited knowledge and nobody can control someone else's alcohol consumption.

All through her life, Karen was let down by people who didn't recognise how unhappy she was. She was surrounded by people who loved her but just couldn't see, or were not willing to believe, what she was dealing with. That is so sad.

Have you got any advice for others?

It's good to talk to friends and non-friends who come from different perspectives. You cannot benefit from counselling when you are in the aftermath of a sudden death but a few months down the line it is a good idea to talk to someone outside your situation. Someone who is not grieving too. I wished I had gone sooner. The sense of grief and loss will get better but it probably won't go away. With the right counselling problems can be mitigated.

Is there anything else you would like to say?

I was lucky to meet Sally. I am grateful that she pushed me into getting some help with my grief. Together we have managed to iron things out. She understands how I feel about the past. We have formed a strong and unquestionable bond of love and companionship which has helped me.

---

10 Cruse is a national organisation who provide support for bereaved people. Their help line is 0808 808 1677

I have changed over the years and learnt from my experiences. I don't drink much these days and I hope I am more tolerant of people who do drink too much. I have been able to support other people who have been bereaved and help them through difficult times. I know I am much more understanding than I used to be. I have even considered training as a bereavement counsellor.

I just wish that I had a greater awareness of mental health. Back then we were so blinkered because it was a taboo subject. People are more open about these things now but there is still such a stigma. Openness is the key to preventing these tragedies. If I had been more equipped, maybe I could have helped Karen to get the support she needed and there could have been a different outcome.

Karen carried burdens and secrets from a young age. She did what she could to manage those things. Nobody recognised it. Not me, not friends, family, her GP, or maybe even Karen herself. If only we knew then what we know today about mental health and alcohol use.

When I think of the wife I lost, I will hold sadness and love in my heart that won't go away. Karen died waiting for someone to recognise and understand her problems. If only we knew what could have been. My deep love for her will be with me always x

We Need to Talk About Death and Dying
By Frances

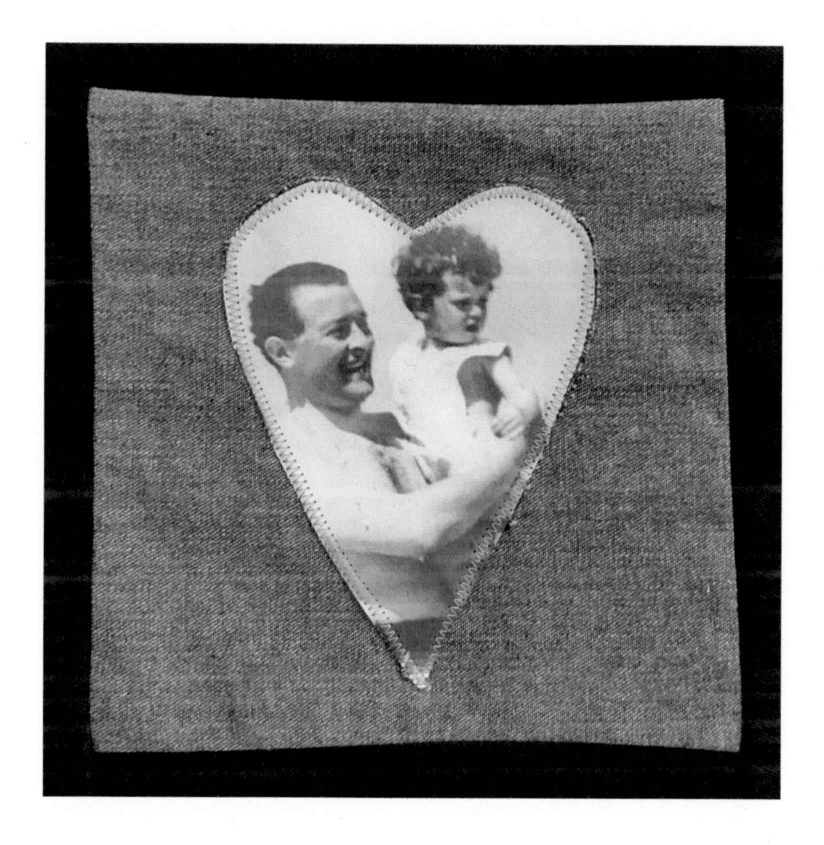

Frances made this heart in memory of her father. It was made with – "no sewing, just love and missing after 55 years".

About Frances

Frances has a background of many years of helping people. Since she retired from social work, Frances volunteers for a charity, where she offers 1:1 support sessions for bereaved people.

Caroline interviewed Frances about her role, her observations of common issues bereaved people might face, and how they might be supported.

We Need to Talk About Death and Dying

Would you like to explain what you do?

Essentially, my role is to give people (who are in great emotional pain) the opportunity to talk, be listened to, and above all be heard. Like everyone in the organisation I volunteer for, I've been trained to support bereaved people. Some people are trained counsellors but they don't have to be. Bereavement counselling is different from social work because I do not offer advice or need them to meet certain expectations. I'm not trying to get people to fit into society. I take my direction from the bereaved person that I am supporting without judging them. I feel passionate about the importance of providing this service because, in the past, I received counselling following a bereavement and it helped me through a painful time.

Could you tell me a bit more about what motivates you?

It is not essential to have experienced a bereavement to be able to support people who have been bereaved. However, I decided to become a volunteer because I had experience of losing someone close. I wanted to give something back. I have had two significant bereavements and I know the difference being able to talk to someone made.

When I was 11, my father died. Nobody explained what had happened. He suddenly went into hospital and did not come back. I didn't go to the funeral because our family and friends thought that was the best thing to do. I was discouraged from crying or showing I was upset. I was told I needed to look after my mother, who was distraught. I found it hard to believe my father was dead and, without information, I made up an explanation that I could cope with. It felt easier to believe he had left us. Without the right support, my mother, sister, and I found it difficult to process our grief. I believe that not talking about our grief at the time, and subsequently, had a lasting effect on all our lives.

Nearly 30 years ago, my partner died from cancer. We had been able to talk openly about death and dying which was positive. After she died, I was struggling and I phoned a bereavement helpline. I remember saying, "I can't deal with all of this" and a lovely person replying, "we can help you". It was the most frightening thing I have ever done. I was connected with a counsellor who supported me for months. She gave me the tools I needed to manage my grief.

Losing my partner when I was quite young has made me mindful that bad things do happen. So, I try to live a good life every day. I tend not to take life for granted. I think my bereavement experiences help me to be empathetic and compassionate. I can still get in touch with the feelings I had then. Feelings that can resurface, ten or even 20 years later, when something reminds me of my loss.

How do you think bereavement counselling can help people?
We live in a society where talking about death is not the done thing. We shy away from it. When someone dies, people might help in the beginning but after the funeral they often fall away. People can be left unable to talk about what happened or share lovely memories. Bereavement support can help people talk about the good and the bad times. They can share the things they feel stuck on.

An important part of my work is normalising people's grief. Almost always, the people I see begin by asking me something like, "am I going mad?", or, "this is really weird isn't it?" I can reassure them that what they are feeling is common. Helping people to understand that they are not losing their minds, and that the things they are experiencing are a normal part of grieving, is often all people need from me. Sometimes, just one session is enough.

Grieving is like a piece of work that we have to do. There are lots of ways to do it - there is no one right way. Theories about grieving can help but not always. Sometimes they get in the way. For example, if a person feels that they are doing their grieving wrongly because they don't fit into a theory they have read. Sometimes people need to cry. Or to laugh. It can be really important to laugh but people often feel guilty when they do that. They can feel really bad about it because it feels disloyal.

What common themes do you encounter?
Many families become fractured after a bereavement. All families have their fault lines and everyone in a family will have had a different relationship with the person who died. Even if the family all went through the same things, they will all experience and remember it differently. If they are lucky they get through the aftermath.
Blaming each other is very common. When people are hurting they might blame someone else for the death. "Why didn't you do ...?", or, "You were supposed to have taken better care of [the person who died]". Of course, people often blame themselves. In their head, people might know they could not have prevented a death but, in their heart, they feel it should have been possible.

People within the same family might need to grieve differently. One might want to visit a grave every day whereas another cannot bear to go. It is common for people who are grieving to not be able to understand and accept each other's behaviours. For example, funerals can collect tension. Families can disagree over the arrangements and fight with each other because they need different things. Things like what to do with someone's ashes can cause disagreements. One person might want ashes interred and other family members want them scattered. It is not uncommon for each person to take their share of the ashes home to keep.

Sometimes the person who died was the one who held the family together. They were like glue and without them everything falls apart. It's really hard to repair if you have not got your central glue.

When someone loses their partner it can be hard. For example, people who are widowed are expected to continue caring for their children and put them first. But they have needs too. Other people can be intolerant of this. The cumulative effect of being strong can really take its toll. As I became older, I was able to see the death of my father, in the 1960s, from my mother's perspective. As a woman, in her 30s with two young children, she had to adapt to a significant change in circumstances and re-build all our lives.

One of the things that can happen is that bereavement triggers financial or other practical difficulties. The person who died might have been an important source of income to the family, or the person who is bereaved might lose their job because they are unable to continue working. Carers can lose benefits, such as carer's allowance, which they rely on. Overnight, their finances might be reduced but their outgoings have not changed. Having your standard of living compromised on top of bereavement compounds people's grief. There might be other difficulties that are triggered by a death. For example, people living in social housing might discover they cannot stay in their home because they were not on the tenancy agreement. These things can cause additional worry and stress.

Families, communities, and society make assumptions about who has the right to grieve and how they should do that. I see incredible amounts of pain where people have what the theorists call 'disenfranchised grief'. This is where people feel they are not allowed to grieve. Maybe they are seen as 'not the right person' or it wasn't the 'right kind of death'. There might have been a complicated relationship or situation and the person grieving is perceived by themselves, or others, as having no legitimacy to grieve. It can be as simple as having been a friend, or work colleague, of the person who has died and feeling that you shouldn't express your grief. Or, it could be the way someone lived or died is stigmatised. For example, when someone's death is alcohol-related it is not viewed as an acceptable death. When someone dies by suicide it can be difficult for the bereaved person to openly grieve because of societal taboos. When grief is disenfranchised, bereaved people can feel unable to speak about their loss or feelings.

Many people have complicated relationships and bereavement can bring all that up. For example, someone might have been abused by the person who died. They might feel the additional loss of what they could or should have had. When someone dies the opportunity to put things right can be lost.

What might somebody who is struggling with their grief find helpful?
It can be really useful to write a letter to the person who died. You cannot have the conversation in person but you can still say what you wanted to say. You can be angry, sad, loving, or whatever it is you need to be. This is not a complicated or expensive thing to do. If someone doesn't want to write they can speak into the audio recorder on their phone, or just say what they want to say out loud.

I often suggest keeping a journal as a way to help people process what is happening between their sessions with me. Taking notes and thinking about what comes up can act as a reminder of what people want to discuss. They might find it helps them make sense of things too.

To be effective, the support I offer needs to be rooted. I always ask people "who knows you are seeing me?" It's important that it is not a secret and I encourage people to tell someone. By acknowledging out loud that they are finding bereavement difficult, it can open up conversations with people in their life. Ideally, people can talk to someone between sessions about what they are exploring.

The most important thing is to be open and honest with people. We are all going to die: it's a 100% fact. As a society, we need to be open to that as a thought and start having conversations about death and dying. Death might be a shock but it shouldn't be a taboo.

How has Covid-19 impacted on bereaved people?
In terms of bereavement support, Covid is going to have an impact for years to come. For people who did not have a chance to say goodbye, or the last time they saw their loved one was on an iPad screen from a hospital, there will be additional pain. The issue of blame is more visible. I see people who are blaming themselves for not managing to protect the person they cared for from catching it. This is really acute when people have shielded someone for months or years but they have still caught Covid and died. I'm observing the premature fracturing of families because people are blaming each other for bringing Covid into each other's homes. Funerals became even harder for people to manage because they might have had to choose who attends and forego the usual ceremony or wake rituals. Getting over

this will require people to be more forgiving of themselves and of others. Something that has made bereavement particularly hard for people during Covid, is the way that all the things people can normally do, to get support or distract from their pain, just disappeared. In lockdowns, people couldn't pop into their local library, or visit their community groups. People have been more isolated in their grief and people have simply not been able to access the normal forms of support. People's grief has been hidden away behind closed doors. More people than usual will be finding it hard and unable to move forward as a result.

Covid has changed the world. We are seeing increased numbers of people struggling with their mental health. At one point, I think we all had to face the possibility of dying. We all had to face our fears. It was an existential crisis. For those who were bereaved, their fears were realised but within a society that doesn't want to talk about it.

Thinking about the rituals that surround death, how important are they?
The rituals we were familiar with stopped; this has been very hard for many people to manage. There are multiple reasons, aside from Covid, why people are excluded or unable to find comfort from things like funerals. There are a multitude of ways in which a life can be celebrated or mourned after a person's death. You don't need to go to a funeral to say goodbye – you can make your own ritual. For example, planting a tree or plant (maybe a favourite of the person who died) is something many people do. Likewise, lighting candles or going to a special place to reflect can be a substitute for visiting a grave.

I often suggest people make memory boxes as a tool to manage their grief. It might feel overwhelming to clear away someone's possessions. Putting some things that have special meaning into a small box, or even a big box, can make it easier to let go of the other things. People might put rings, letters, a daft gift they received, or anything that is significant. They might never open the box and look at these things again or they might bring it out when they need to. There is something quite therapeutic about physically putting something into a box for safekeeping.

Some people like to have tangible reminders of the person who died. I have supported people who have had memory bears made from the clothes of the person who died. These can bring great comfort because they can be hugged. There are other things, like quilts or cushions, that can be made.

We should remember that what is comforting to one person, might feel horrific to someone else. For example, people can have lockets made with some of their loved one's ashes in. There is no right way of doing these things yet people are judged. We need to stop doing that. We need to allow bereaved people to do what they need to do to manage the pain.

How can bereavement impact on people's mental health?

Grief is not a mental illness but it can lead to people becoming unwell. I see a high proportion of people who have been diagnosed with depression or anxiety. This perhaps reflects that most people manage their grief, with the help of their families, friends, or communities, but the people who seek support from counselling are probably finding it too difficult to manage by themselves. Bereavement doesn't happen on a blank sheet, we are all complicated individuals with our attachments and histories. Bereavement is another layer on top. Statistics suggest that at least one in four people will experience mental illness. If one in four of the people who seek bereavement support have some level of pre-existing condition, they already have a vulnerability and this could be exacerbated by their bereavement.

People with serious or longstanding mental health conditions, who become bereaved, are likely to find the two things compound. Mental health support is increasingly difficult to access because of dwindling or non-existent resources. Bereavement counselling is not a substitute for mental health services. Mental health practitioners have overwhelming caseloads and there is a temptation when someone mentions a bereavement to signpost to a bereavement support service instead of offering an intervention. These may be inappropriate referrals because organisations may be only able to offer a few sessions and volunteers are not necessarily equipped to support people with complex needs.

When I do get someone referred for support who is mentally unwell, I do what I can but I can be left feeling concerned because what I can offer is limited and may not be all they need. It worries me that some people might be left feeling worse. For example, if they already struggle to build trusting relationships, they could find it difficult when the sessions have to end.

What do you think needs to change?

If only society was more open and forgiving and could acknowledge the inevitability of death, then it would be easier to have conversations about grief. For a while, it seemed as if the pandemic prompted people to share their experiences. For example, the Covid memorial wall in London was fantastically helpful in showing people they are not alone and that people care. I felt hopeful that this would be a pivotal moment and things would change. However, as time has gone on, it seems that society has reverted to not talking about death and bereavement. People still tell me about friends and neighbours who cross the road to avoid them. Most likely this is because they don't know what to say. But it really hurts people who are already suffering. When someone dies there is often a flurry of activity and support in the short-term. But some people are conspicuously absent when there is a bereavement. That can hurt for years. People want to talk about their loved one, to mention their name without being shut down. I hear people saying how they have been criticised for not 'getting over it' within a timescale.

Bereavements happen in a world that can be a worrying place for people. Things like the climate crisis, the cost of living rises, or the war in Ukraine sit on us. They are hard to manage. When people are bereaved, we all need to do something, some individual actions to show that we care. Simple acts of kindness can make a difference. Small things can be big things.

There is a place for political protest too. Government policies impact on the way people might die and on the experiences of bereaved people. For example, the pressures on mental health services might mean people die prematurely or in ways that are traumatic for the bereaved. Another example, are the changes in government policy on bereavement payments which have adversely affected many people. There are important campaigns against these changes. Collective effort can lead to positive change.

We are changed by bereavement. I support people through the process of acknowledging that change and thinking about how they will live their life as a changed person. We have to hold hope. The act of going to a bereavement counsellor is an act of hope. It means the person is open to the idea that life can be lived – albeit in a different way.

What should people look for in a bereavement counsellor?

We can all learn ways of helping bereaved people and how to be compassionate to people. Giving bereaved people the opportunities to talk is different from the help offered by a bereavement support service. It is really important to choose an organisation that trains and supervises their volunteers. People are vulnerable when they are grieving. Therefore, things like background checks and robust safeguarding procedures are vital. Some organisations, such as faith-based ones, can provide excellent support but there may be those who have their own agenda. People can choose to get support from sources, which might concern me in case they are exploited, but I will not judge. If something feels helpful to them then that is their choice. When people come to the end of their sessions with me, I try to identify where they might get support if they need it. Before making any recommendations, I check carefully to see what an organisation or individual is offering, and what training, supervision, or safeguards are in place. I am looking to see what their standards are and that they are reputable.

Thinking about the bereaved people you have supported, what would you want them to know?
I genuinely care about the people I see. It is a privilege to be a bereavement support volunteer. People trust me to help them with their abject pain. They are making a brave act because it takes courage to admit you need help and to confide in someone you have never met before.

I hope that people feel supported, that they feel that they have been listened to, that their grieving has been taken seriously. I hope that people find the tools, often already within themselves, to deal with a horrible reality. I hope they are able to continue with their lives positively, whilst taking the memory of the person with them.

In Solidarity With Those Who Have Died and Those Left Behind By Duncan

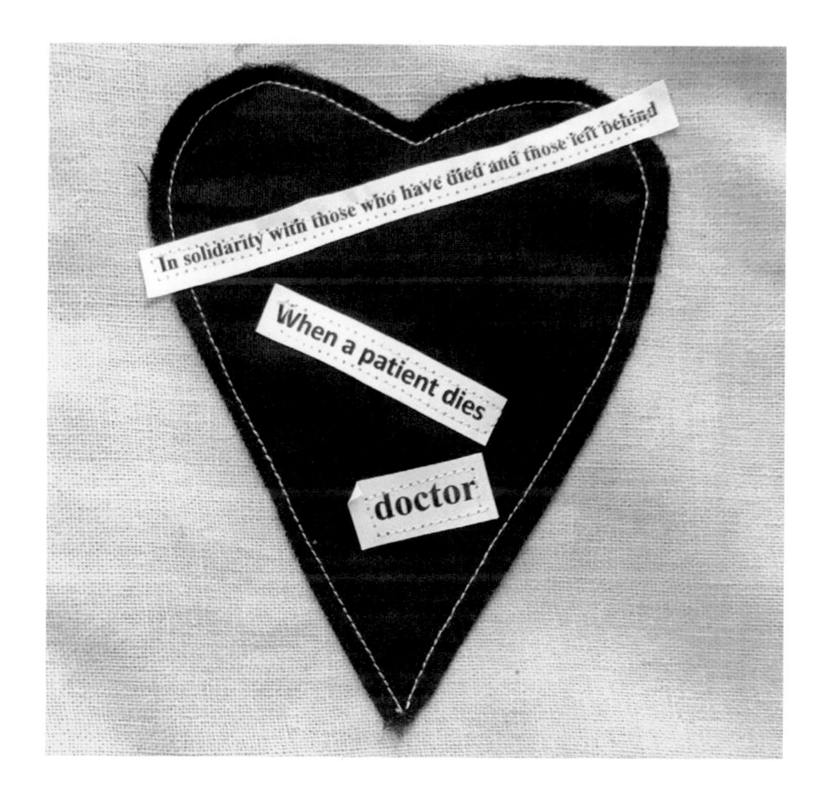

This heart represents the emotional impact on a doctor when one of their patients dies by suicide. Within the heart, things are out of kilter and solidarity, with those who have died or been left behind, cuts across it. The zig-zagging of the words is a nod to broken hearts.

About Duncan

Duncan worked for over 27 years as an NHS consultant psychiatrist. He does not view himself as a 'typical biomedical psychiatrist' who believes that mental illness is due to brain disease. Duncan was a founding member of the Critical Psychiatry Network[11]. His emphasis was always on the relational aspects of psychiatry, and he continues to blog at Relational Psychiatry[12].

Duncan's critique of psychiatry leads to him wanting it to be more rights-based in its approach. With this theoretical orientation, he approached the difficulties and limitations of mental health work in his clinical life. In this context, suicidal patients challenge professional responsibilities for life and death.

The suicide of a patient can impact on a practitioner's existential being. This chapter contains Duncan's reflections on this. He presents some information and facts about suicide and links these to his practice experience.

11 More information is on the Critical Psychiatry website: http://www.criticalpsychiatry.co.uk.

12 Duncan Double blogs about his views about mental health services and psychiatry: http://criticalpsychiatry.blogspot.com

In Solidarity with Those Who Have Died and Those Left Behind

When a patient dies

An inpatient died on weekend leave from the ward on which I was working in my first week as a psychiatric trainee. That was in 1984 and I have now been retired as a consultant psychiatrist for nearly three years. In my working life, I had several patients under my care who have died by suicide. I hesitate to call the experience of a patient dying by suicide an 'occupational hazard' of being a psychiatrist, but the reality is that it happens sometimes. Patient deaths have an impact on people working in mental health care, as well as obviously the people more directly involved in the life of the person who has died.

I remember being in that staff handover meeting, on that Monday morning, when I learnt of the death of the man. I was new and naïve in psychiatry. On hearing of his death, I crossed his name off my list containing the notes I was making of the patients that I had been getting to know since starting the job less than a week previously. I was still trying to get to grips with the circumstances of the patients who had been assigned to my care. The man was in his 60s and had become depressed in retirement. My initial thought was how unfortunate his death was and regretted that we had not been able to help him.

I was unprepared for the subsequent reaction of ward staff. I was working for a consultant psychiatrist who specialised in dealing with people with suicidal intent. He had not been happy with the argument, behind the then NHS directive, that all people who took an overdose should be assessed by a psychiatrist. Self-poisoning by overdose is a very common reason for acute presentations to doctors and hospitals, as are other forms of self-harm. My consultant's position was that doctors in general should be skilled in dealing with people who self-harm. He would help organise training events for all the new doctors in the casualty department of the hospital every six months when they rotated in their training. Such training was also made available to medical trainees working on the wards who looked after patients admitted following an overdose. Many such patients are only kept in hospital overnight. In his view, with which I agree, doctors should have general abilities and do not always need specialist advice to manage patients who self-harm. Assessment of suicide risk should not just be reserved for identified specialists such as psychiatrists or mental health workers.

Interest in managing suicidal patients had been sparked in that consultant by his sense of responsibility, which I share, created by the service need to prevent suicide and self-harm. This is not always an easy task to manage but it is an important role of mental health services. Staff deal with many patients who have expressed suicidal ideas, made attempts on their lives, and/or are regarded as at risk of suicide. Mental illness may be thought to diminish suicidal patients' responsibility for their actions through loss of mental capacity. Prediction of a person's behaviour, however, is not always straightforward or easy. Warning signs may be apparent, particularly with hindsight. But of two patients with seemingly similar symptoms and signs, one patient may act on their suicidal urges and the other may not. The question of blame for a patient's suicide, if it unfortunately happens, is inevitably raised.

Being new to psychiatry in that first week, I was unprepared for how these issues of responsibility and fear of being blamed would come to the fore. Someone being treated on an inpatient psychiatric ward might be thought to be in a safe place. But those admitted to a psychiatric ward may well be at high risk of suicide and that is why they have been admitted. However therapeutic the ward may be, that risk still has to be managed.

Questioning staff's integrity in trying to manage these problems, though, may not always be the most immediate factor to consider after a death. I'm not suggesting staff should be absolved of responsibility. They need to act in good faith and with competence. I'm not being protective of any negligent practice. But governance of untoward incidents, such as a patient suicide, needs to be fair, open, and properly informed. In reality, such investigations can be destructive at times. It's important that those providing mental health services are not unfairly attacked because of unfortunate incidents such as the death of a patient. They can have a serious effect on staff morale if they reach incorrect conclusions because of, for example, poor methodology or their inquisitorial nature.

In the weeks that followed, anxieties about being investigated or blamed were raised in the minds of staff. Over the years, I have noticed how, understandably, these thoughts and feelings can create a defensiveness amongst practitioners. Issues about whether they could or should have acted differently are raised, even if not discussed openly. The same kinds of thoughts and feelings that are left after death with relatives and others who have known the person can be felt by staff. But the reasons for human action, including suicide, are complex. However much we may think we understand why we do what we do, any explanation is not a linear cause and effect relationship. We constitute ourselves in our relationships with others and our environment. This circular self-creating aspect is central to life and includes the possibility of taking one's own life.

The primary focus should be on what's needed for patients rather than necessarily protecting staff from criticism. Patients need to be able to feel they can express their suicidal urges to staff without provoking an overreaction. Practitioner responses need to be appropriate. Just having suicidal thoughts and feelings heard, and accepted for what they are, may itself be therapeutic. Good communication is essential. On a ward, this also needs to happen between staff. The work of prevention of suicide should not be driven by staff anxieties about accusations of responding inappropriately. In my experience, expectations that all untoward incidents can be avoided may create intolerable pressures for staff, which will almost inevitably damage the therapeutic atmosphere of the ward.

What does the data on suicide tell us?

Over recent years there has been a national strategy to reduce suicide and other deaths of psychiatric patients. A guiding influence has been the National Confidential Inquiry into Suicide and Safety in Mental Health (NCISH)[13].

NCISH has collected data on deaths by suicide and homicide by psychiatric patients. It makes recommendations on clinical practice with the aim of reducing the risk of suicide and homicide. Its Director, Professor Louis Appleby, was also the National Director of Mental Health, an important advisor to the government.

NCISH 2022 Annual Report[14] provides findings relating to patients who died by suicide between 2009 and 2019 across all UK countries. Many patients who died had a previous history of self-harm (64%), meaning that the act which led to their death had been preceded by attempts to take their life from which they had survived. There were high proportions of those who died with a history of alcohol (47%) and drug (7%) misuse and more than one mental health diagnosis (53%). Nearly half (48%) lived alone. Although this kind of information is of interest and can be considered in assessing suicide risk, in practice, everyone has to be treated as an individual. People may not always fit into these categories. Such factors may not necessarily apply in assessing the risk in an individual case at all.

29% of people who died did so in acute care settings, including inpatients, post-discharge care, and with the crisis resolution/home treatment team.

Nearly half (46%) of all patients who died by suicide had been in contact with mental health services in the week before their death. Interestingly,

13 NCISH website: https://sites.manchester.ac.uk/ncish/

14 NCISH 2022 Annual Report https://documents.manchester.ac.uk/display.aspx?DocID=60521

the majority (84%) who died were viewed by clinicians as at low or no short-term risk, which highlights how difficult it is to assess suicide risk. Relevant to the patient who died in my first week in psychiatry, half of the inpatients who died were on agreed leave.

Nonetheless, rates of inpatient suicide fell by 42% between 2009-19, maybe related to the reduction in the number of people being admitted to hospital. 30% of inpatient suicides had been detained under the Mental Health Act and over a third of detained patients who died were under a medium or high level of observation. Of all patient suicides, 18% had recent economic adversity, 25% had a comorbid physical illness and 9% had a history of domestic violence. It is important, of course, to understand the reasons for suicide in a social context. This includes the current pressures on services nationally with staff vacancies and too many patients being admitted out of the local area.

The characteristics of people who die by suicide in the general population show that a majority (66%) are male, 13% are aged 65 or over, 73% are unmarried, 47% unemployed, and 7% are from an ethnic minority group. Again, although these can be considered risk factors, they do not necessarily apply in an individual case. Suicide assessment has to be done on a personal basis considering complete individual circumstances. 13% (excluding unknowns) of patient suicides had only one contact with services[15]. New referrals to services, therefore, can be at risk of suicide. Sometimes that one contact with services does not seem to be enough to prevent suicide.

Overall suicide rates in the general population in the UK rose between 2009 and 2012 and then fell, rising again between 2016 and 2018 before a slight fall in 2019. Over the longer term, rates have generally decreased since 1981, although rates are higher in 2019 than they were in 2009. Over the longer time frame, it is particularly in the older age groups: over 60s for men and the over 45s for women, where the reduction is apparent. Suicide, as are mental disorders in general, is associated with social deprivation. How much the reduction in suicide rates since 1981, especially in the older age groups, is related to an improved standard of living is unclear.

A particular focus of the NCISH 2022 report was on suicide in young people. In the UK, despite having a low number of deaths overall, rates among the under 25s have generally increased in recent years.
The readiness to use antidepressants in children has also increased in the same time period as the concept of childhood depression has expanded.

---

15 This was the case with Shirley in the chapter *She Wasn't Fine* by Laura and Caroline.

It's often suggested that any increase in suicide rates in young people means that they should be receiving more psychiatric treatment. But public mental health strategies should not be driven by exaggerated claims of effectiveness of psychiatric treatment, whether in young people or anyone. Wider solutions to help suicidal young people are needed because mental health interventions should be holistic.

Creating safe services

There has always been a tension between implementing control and being open and therapeutic in mental health services. Traditional locked asylums were replaced because of consternation about the conditions, including the potential for abuse, of psychiatric patients. Opening the doors had striking benefits: tension reduced, violence declined, 'escapes' were no longer a problem and staff were able to give their attention more to therapy rather than custody. Although the traditional asylums have closed, bureaucratic practices still exist in modern community mental health services.

In my view, anxiety about the numbers of suicides in the community and hospitals creates an incentive for mental health services to reduce their number. We live in a 'risk society' that has encouraged a target culture towards reducing risk. An increasingly technological society creates higher expectations of what can be achieved. The tendency has been to introduce an ever more rigid and bureaucratic interpretation of risk assessment. Policies and procedures are introduced by services that are designed to improve patient safety. However, these might make patients' experiences uncomfortable. For example, adaptations in inpatient settings to remove ligature points might also remove privacy. Conversely, privacy is maintained by the use of ligature-resistant toilets, but these can lack the basic comfort of a seat.

There is always a debate about the balance between risk-taking and risk-avoidance. The concern for safety in mental health services needs to be understood for what it is. Although the risk of suicide should always be taken seriously, taking a risk might be an opportunity for growth, as overcautious behaviour can be counterproductive. Quantification of risk is unreliable, and the uncertainty of risk assessment needs to be accepted. Merely knowing about risk, even if this can be measured accurately, may not necessarily improve practice, which needs to be centred on the person. Inappropriate psychiatric treatment could potentially increase the risk of death by suicide, for example, if the person does not feel understood.

The danger is that the fear that things may go wrong in mental health services is distracting services from the task of how to make things better for people. Guidelines and procedures cannot eliminate clinical judgement in practice. Helping a suicidal patient is more than a case of following rules and procedures. Procedures and policies may be designed more for the purpose of protecting the organisation than helping patients. It is one way that organisations think they are demonstrating that they are responding to the issue of suicide.

Mental health services do need to be improved and accountability also needs to be applied sensibly. Attempts to make professionals more accountable, though, have led to a crisis of trust in their practice. In my opinion, increasing regulation of practitioners has created a climate of fear and a culture of defensive practice. The belief that clinical errors are necessarily manifestations of incompetence, carelessness, or recklessness for which naming, blaming, and shaming are appropriate responses can be an obstacle to improving patient safety.

A learning culture is needed, with excellent leadership, that provides an ethos where staff are valued and supported as they form partnerships and relationships with patients. Few mental health services have the courage to provide such an environment when they are overly concerned to protect themselves against criticism. The complexity of mental health services means that staff should be helped to bridge the common limitations and problems of mental health care.

Risk by definition is about uncertainty and we cannot avoid relying on professional trust. Therefore, risk management is the management of that uncertainty. It can't be about creating a fantasy of absolute control in the prevention of suicide. But the treatment of suicidal people must be improved, and ironically, it appears that services becoming overdefensive can made that treatment worse.

From 1984 to 2022

I've come a long way in my learning about suicide from that first week in psychiatry when the man I had only just started to get to know died by suicide on weekend leave from the ward. I had probably never been aware of suicidal feelings within myself then but have had them since for a time, although never acted on them. In fact, dealing with suicidal patients is likely to bring practitioners up against such feelings within themselves. Death is the inevitable end of life, if that's not too trite a thing to say. We are all damaged, vulnerable and finite. That's actually what makes us human. We have to accept the human condition and its inevitable imperfectability.

Psychiatry is a relational practice, as medicine should be in general. Relationships and interactions create our experience which gives meaning and substance to life. When people lose that meaning, psychiatry should

have a role in helping them to recover their life situation.
Mental health services need to act in solidarity with those who have taken their own lives and with those that have been left behind. In my working life, I'm sorry I was not able to do more for people despite my best efforts, including preventing more suicides.

She Wasn't Fine
by Laura and Caroline

Laura's memory heart reflects her Mum's love of football. Shirley regularly went to Carrow Road to watch Norwich City play. 'Thinking of you' refers to the way Laura and her family hold Shirley in their minds and the way Shirley was always thinking of others.

About Laura and Shirley

For several years, Shirley ran a successful dog-grooming business. She lived in the countryside with her husband and her daughter, Laura. Shirley's younger son lived nearby. In 2020, Shirley died by suicide. Laura wanted to contribute to this book in the hope it will help other people who are going through similar experiences.

In this chapter, Caroline reflects on discussions with Laura about her experiences and what has been helpful to her and her family. Laura's words are in italics.

She Wasn't Fine

Shirley

Laura describes her mum as: *Very much a stereotypical Northerner. She was blunt and 'straight-talking', if she didn't like something you would definitely know. The thing I loved most about her was her straight-talking. If I had a problem, she would sit down and talk to me about it. People might have seen a hard exterior but inside she was a complete softie.* Shirley was also very caring and enjoyed supporting others. She would help neighbours with shopping and cleaning. Her caring nature meant that sometimes she took too much on. Reflecting on this, Laura said: *Looking back, she was always helping other people but actually she couldn't manage. Mum didn't want to let them down so she carried on.*

In her youth, Shirley tried her hand at hairdressing but anyone who knew Shirley would know that making polite 'small talk' all day was not for her. However, it did help Shirley hone skills which came in handy as a dog groomer later in her life. Laura and Shirley shared a love of animals. Shirley worked for many years for local kennels where she was well known and respected. Laura says: *She was brilliant with animals and brought home every waif and stray. Even though she was wary of large horses, she would still come and help me with mine.* Shirley enjoyed long walks on the beach with her beloved dog, Lottie.

Until a few months before her death, Shirley had never presented with any mental health difficulties. However, she would have a drink in the evenings to manage stress. Laura describes what that was like: *There was no pattern to it. Sometimes, she would binge for a day or two but then not do that for months. There was no building up, she was up and down with it. It never got to a really bad point but it never stopped.*

It was something of a shock to the family when, in late 2019, Shirley attempted to end her life whilst visiting extended family. She texted her friend asking her to look after the dog, and was found in a distressed state. Shirley was treated in A and E where she was properly assessed by a mental health liaison nurse. They recognised she was depressed and at risk of suicide and recommended Shirley's GP made a referral to mental health services.

Just before the pandemic struck, Shirley saw her GP. From Shirley's notes it did not seem they had recognised how unwell Shirley was. Instead, it was agreed she would go to AA[16] for some help with her drinking. Shirley attended a few meetings before the first Covid lockdown began. She began

16 AA is Alcoholics Anonymous who hold support groups in local communities: https://www.alcoholics-anonymous.org.uk/

to trust others in the group but when the meetings became virtual she stopped attending. Laura says: *Mum hated computers. We were all at home so there was no privacy for her to have the conversations needed for the AA group.*

Covid exacerbated Shirley's difficulties. Laura describes how: *Mum loved her work, she usually did it with her best friend. But at home, without the routines of work and seeing friends, everything was in the air. Her motivation to do things started to slip. She was very worried one of us would catch Covid. She was especially concerned for my step-dad.*

Laura had become worried about the risk of Shirley dying and she phoned her Mum's GP. However, due to confidentiality, this proved a fruitless discussion. Laura remembers saying: *I know you can't tell me anything, but Mum will have told you everything is fine when it's not.* Laura feels this was a missed opportunity to save Shirley's life. *I was not allowed to even tell them what I knew. Those of us who knew her would know Mum would say she was fine. I wanted the GP not to accept that at face value. I often think, 'would they have been as dismissive if it was their own family?' Until you have this sort of experience you don't know the warning signs. I didn't have a clue what to do to help Mum.*

Due to Covid, the planned follow-up appointments for Shirley with her GP did not happen. As the country entered the winter lockdown of 2020, Shirley died by suicide.

What this meant for Laura

My son told me the sad news and asked for my help to support Laura. Having experienced the loss of his brother in traumatic circumstances, he understood the grim processes that follow an 'unexpected death'. He was worried that none of Laura's family were receiving the support they needed emotionally. They were also trying to prepare for Shirley's inquest without an understanding of the process.

Covid made everything so much harder. Laura and I had conversations in my freezing-cold garden, standing six feet apart in the dark. I feel guilty about that and wish I had not been so anxious about breaking the rules. I remember listening to Laura stoically telling me about what had happened and all the practicalities she was dealing with. All her concern was for her step-dad and brother. But my concern was for her because she had just lost her mum in traumatic circumstances. I just wanted to hug her.

I can remember asking about what support had been offered and Laura saying: *Nothing really, the only people that have offered anything are the funeral directors. They have given us a number of a suicide support group.* Of course, the group was not meeting in person due to Covid. I reached out to my contacts and was able to give Laura some information about other possible sources of support.

My experience of funeral directors had been they were kind but functional. I found research evidence that suggested funeral directors are viewed by bereaved families as the most helpful and sensitive professionals following a traumatic bereavement. I remember being surprised about how much support some funeral directors offer to bereaved relatives. Laura reflects on her experience: *There was lovely lady who was so helpful and friendly. It felt as if it was as important to her to give mum a good send-off as it was to us. She helped us understand the restrictions and juggling who could attend. She supported our extended family to say their goodbyes. She supported us as individuals. We were all under stress and she would speak to my step-dad and then phone me to make sure I had the same information. Before the funeral, she phoned every day to see if any help was needed. She organised all the details for us. After the funeral, she phoned me several times just to catch up and ask, 'How are you?' or 'Is there anything you need me to do?' Usually, a suicide bereavement group would meet at the funeral home. I was offered phone support with that group but I needed to be face-to-face to have those conversations.*

Laura describes the pros and cons of a funeral restricted by Covid: *We were only allowed 30 people. It was shit only being allowed 30 people. Trying to work out who the most important people were to Mum was not easy. It took the decision away from people who would have liked be there. Some people got upset about that. But the funeral directors live-streamed the service for people who couldn't attend. Mum's sister and her family in Australia, and my dad and step-mum who live in Spain, were able to watch from their homes when they wouldn't have been able to come over.* Even with the restrictions, Laura organised a funeral that felt personal. One of Shirley's friends made the order of service cards which included a scan of a hand-written poem that was found amongst Shirley's possessions[17]. A friend of the family wrote a lovely eulogy.

Laura and I discussed what had helped in the aftermath of Shirley's death and what had been disappointing. Laura valued the kindness and support from friends and the community: *We had lots of people just turn up leaving food or cards. No one was intrusive. I dreaded being asked questions that I didn't have the answers to. I didn't realise how many people Mum knew. We had phone calls and messages. Through Facebook, some of Mum's friends from her teenage years connected with me. They sent daft memories of mum, like funny stories of her hen do. That was comforting. We had no contact from our GP. We were pretty much left to deal with it. I was really worried about my step-dad and brother and there didn't seem to be any help I could get for them. We didn't know what we were doing. There was no guidance.*

A few months later, the family received the bundle of paperwork relating to the inquest. Laura asked me if I would help her formulate the questions she wanted to ask. She was upset by the contents: *It was an envelope full of*

17 There are various versions of this online without sources. The words Shirley wrote are at the end of this account.

random documents, they were in no order and made no sense. They were full of technical language that I had to Google to find out what they meant. It was written in such cold and impersonal terms. It didn't seem to be about Mum, it could have been about anybody. The dismissive language, minimal information, and lack of professional curiosity in the reports from health professionals and emergency services were all too familiar to me.

The police report was minimal. Yet Laura recalls the police involvement very differently: *The older man who attended when we found Mum was kind. He asked the questions he needed to in a gentle way. Because Mum had been moved, in an attempt to save her, the police launched an investigation to check it was suicide, not murder. I know they have their job to do but it didn't need to be so aggressive and insensitive. This young lad came breezing in accusing my step-dad, who was already devastated by finding Mum. I thought 'How dare you! After all that, their report was literally half a page of meaningless information.*

I felt angry that Shirley's death merited so little attention. I was disappointed at how little evidence was in the inquest bundle. Somehow, Shirley had slipped past mental health services altogether. Even though risks had been highlighted, these had not led to any suicide prevention support for Shirley.

I knew from my own experience, that there is very little help for families caught in the aftermath of suicide unless they can afford legal representation. I can remember talking to Laura about how difficult attending an inquest can be and how important it was that she, and each member of her family, did what was right for them. I also prepared her for the possibility that the inquest might not provide the answers she needed. It was my privilege to be able to help Laura make sense of the inquest process and to help her ask the things she needed to. I put together a chronology which helped Laura identify the gaps. Laura says that without my advice she would have remained unaware of what to expect at an inquest and how to ask questions. This reflects a general lack of support for bereaved families trying to navigate the system after an unexpected death.

Laura sent a letter to the GP with her questions. They replied with some non-answers stating they would answer questions more fully at the inquest.

Shirley's inquest was held virtually. At the last minute, it was cancelled because of Covid. My heart went out to Laura and her family because they will have been preparing themselves. I wonder if the people who are involved in coronial processes have insight into just how stressful it is for families in the run-up to an inquest. By the time the inquest was re-scheduled, Laura felt that the impact on the family of being held in suspense was just too difficult. So, when the GP did not attend, and therefore any opportunity to have questions answered would have required an adjournment, Laura felt silenced. The virtual inquest was over in half an hour.

What Laura had wanted from the GP was for them to reflect on their practice, learn from Shirley's death, and put things in place to stop, or lessen, the possibility for other families to lose their loved ones to suicide. A recurring question for Laura is: *If one of their friends or family was in this situation, would they be this dismissive? It felt like their attitude demonstrated that Mum's death was not hugely important to them. But we had questions and things we wanted to say to them so they could learn. Because this is huge and life-changing for us.*

Laura and I thought about what helped in the 18 months since Shirley's death: *Grief can pop up without warning. Random things can trigger a panic attack. Often these things are not directly related to Mum. I really wanted to do CPR*[18] *training for work but it was triggering and I couldn't do it. I had some virtual counselling sessions through work. But they were not able to recognise that I needed other support. When I asked to re-schedule a session, so I could take a last-minute opportunity to visit my Dad in Spain, I was told I wouldn't be allowed to continue with the counselling if I cancelled. I had not cancelled, I had simply said it might be very expensive for her to phone me abroad. My main support has been my friends and Mum's friends. I find having people who are prepared just to be with me while I watch TV or go for a drive together helps. There doesn't need to be a conversation. I really valued being able to do things that distracted me from the grief. Like coming to yours to have a meal and play board games and not talk about sad stuff. At first, I would feel like I shouldn't laugh or be happy. But then I think Mum would not want me to be sad.*

I asked Laura what she would advise bereaved people: *We are all different. You shouldn't feel you must be sad a certain way or meet other people's expectations of what grieving should be. It doesn't matter whether you laugh or cry. No one has the right to tell you what to think or feel.*

Laura is the most courageous and loving young woman. She held on to her own grief because her priority was ensuring the people she loves got through this traumatic experience. She worries that in some way she might have let her Mum down. She has, in fact, done her Mum proud.

Shirley died waiting, for her mental health difficulties and the risk that she could die by suicide to be acknowledged and addressed. Shirley's eulogy included these words: We cannot escape the fact that Shirley had some deep unhappiness within her and she increasingly suffered in her own dark place that she wasn't able to get out of no matter how people tried to help. But Shirley gave love and she was surrounded by love. We want to remember those happy memories and hope she is at peace.

---

18 Cardio Pulmonary Resuscitation

I thought of you today
But that is nothing new
I thought of you yesterday
And will tomorrow, too

I think of you in silence
And make no outward show
For what it meant to lose you
Only those who loved you know

Remembering you is easy
We do it everyday
Its the heartache of losing you
That will never go away.

Thinking of you, Mum. Love Laura x

The poem Shirley had written on a page torn from a notebook.

The Beast of Grief
By Lucy

Lucy made this embroidered memorial heart. She says it represents: *"The dove of peace which to me symbolises hope. When you are supporting anyone who is grieving, or suffering from poor mental health, they need hope. The heart shows the love. I cannot see you with my eyes or touch you with my hands but I will feel you for eternity in my heart."*

About Lucy

Lucy is a Community Ambassador for a group of funeral homes[19]. She is a Mental Health First Aid Trainer and is ASIST trained (Applied Suicide Intervention Skills Training). Lucy participates in suicide prevention and awareness initiatives. She is a Bereavement Support Facilitator who delivers training on grief and loss, supporting those bereaved by suicide, and bereavement training in schools, locally and throughout the UK. Lucy is a volunteer for Nelson's Journey[20] and she is passionate about supporting bereaved children.

For more than a decade, Lucy has worked within the funeral industry and helped support many bereaved families. Lucy feels that she has learnt more about loss and grief from the families she has served over the years than from anything she has read.

19 Lucy's profile is available online: https://www.rosedalefuneralhome.co.uk/our-people/lucy-coote/

20 Nelson's Journey offers bereavement support to children: https://nelsonsjourney.org.uk/

Most people die at the right time for them, be that because they are old or ill. This doesn't necessarily make the grief easier to bear. The depth of grief relates to the depth of the love. Acceptance of bereavements can depend on the circumstances of the death and on the relationship to the person who has died. Some deaths, such as those by suicide or because of drug and alcohol use, are recognised as being particularly hard to bear[21].

Grief effects our whole being, it can consume us. Only when someone is able to process the reality of the death, and been able to accept the reality of their loss, can they truly start on the grieving process. There is no time frame, no one grieving process fits all, like a snowflake or fingerprint, everyone's grief is unique. Some grieve for the person and the relationship that's been lost and some for a relationship they never had, and subsequently, will never have.

Bereavement support

Many years ago, I realised there was very little support locally for bereaved people and, having worked with hundreds of families and gained some bereavement qualifications, I wrote an eight-week bereavement support programme[22]. Many hundreds of people have now been through the programme, and I have come to realise there is no hierarchy to grief - the worst grief is yours. For this reason, anyone who feels the need to, can come to a bereavement support group, no matter what their relationship to the person who has died was. I have had partners, children, neighbours, and friends attend the groups.

Grief has many facets. Theories, such as Kübler-Ross' five stages of grief, might ring true in some ways for some people. However, when a person has a sudden death, there is also trauma and numbness which can take many months, and for some many years, to accept the reality of the death. This is why I never put a time frame on when someone can participate in one of my groups.

Some people might be ready only weeks following the death. The bereaved person may have done much of their grieving before the person died because the death is expected, for example, when a person had died from dementia or Motor Neurone Disease. They might feel ready to process

---

21 See Caroline's chapter, *A 'Special Death' in the Family*, for more information about this.

22 Lucy offers training to other funeral homes who wish to run the 8-week programme. The details are online: https://www.rosedaletraining.co.uk/services/running-your-own-bereavement-support-programme/

the reality of the death when the person dies. This is not true for everyone. On the other hand, when someone dies unexpectedly (which is often the case with mental health related deaths), or maybe the person attending the group has not been able to see or be with the deceased person (which has been a real issue during Covid times), the bereaved person might struggle to process what has happened. Accepting and processing the death can take many, many months, and for some, years.

Grief can be supressed. Sometimes, circumstances at the time of death mean that the bereaved person has 'blocked' or delayed'[23] their grieving. Grief may come out years later, perhaps when another death occurs and then the 'domino effect' of grief allows the individual to grieve for past losses. This can lead to complicated or prolonged grieving and some people may need additional support[24]. For example, EMDR (Eye Movement De-sensitisation and Re-processing), CBT, (Cognitive Behavioural Therapy), or trauma-based counselling might help them manage and overcome any psychological distress.

People often look upon grieving families and say how well they are coping. This is often not true because the bereaved person might be masking their pain and pretending to be okay for the sake of others. Whilst wider networks might hear about a death and accept it, the immediate family may be numb to the reality of the situation. This is the body's protective mechanism kicking in, enabling them to function whilst blocking the emotional side of things. Often bereaved people go into survival mode - fight, flight, freeze. While in this state it is difficult for the bereaved person to begin processing their situation and grieve for the person that has died.

My belief is that no one owns anyone else's grief and that people need to find the right support for them, at the right time for them. This may be one-on-one counselling or group counselling and some people may need both. It is vital people find what works for them and, as professionals, we have a responsibility to be able to signpost people on to appropriate support.

Many organisations offer counselling services within restricted time frames, some provide support for the first few months following a bereavement but stop offering their services after a year and others will not begin counselling until several months have passed. I am an ambassador of the At A Loss[25] charity which is a national signposting charity. People

23 An explanation of blocked or delayed grief: https://www.griefrecoverymethod.com/blog/2017/09/delayed-grief

24 An explanation of complicated grief: https://www.cruse.org.uk/understanding-grief/effects-of-grief/complicated-grief/

25 The At a Loss website: www.ataloss.org

can put in the type of bereavement they have suffered, their relationship with the deceased, and their postcode and the website will come up with support that is available locally and nationally.

The right support at the right time saves lives because for some bereaved people there is an increased risk of dying, for example, those bereaved by suicide.

Bereavement by suicide

A friend of mine, whose son died by suicide at the age of 21, said it took her two years for the numbness to subside and for her to start the grieving process. She says it was like the 'beast of grief' had caught up with her. She was offered one-to-one counselling shortly after her son's death. But two years after her son's death, when her numbness had started to wear off and everyone else had moved forward in their lives, she realised how lonely and isolated she felt in her grief. That is when she sought help. Sadly, at this point, due to the time between the death and the realisation that she needed help, it meant she had to finance this support herself.

My hope is that the medical profession, and some of the larger national support charities, extend the time frame in which they can offer support. At present, getting support at a later date can be prohibitively expensive for some.

It is not uncommon for people bereaved by suicide, and other unexpected or traumatic deaths, to be delayed in their grief. This can impact on their mental health and lead to depression and isolation. For some traumatically-bereaved people, the pain is so acute that they end their own life. Research from University College London found that those who are bereaved through suicide are 65% more likely to attempt suicide, than those bereaved through natural causes[26]. This shows that when we help and support those bereaved through suicide, we are helping to prevent more suicides.

Policy makers are often motivated by financial reasons to provide services. The cost to the UK government is huge for a death by suicide. It is an estimated 1.7 million pounds per person[27]. Prevention is key and the right support, at the right time, leads to better mental health, and more purposeful, happier lives. Therefore, it makes not just moral but economic sense to support people bereaved by suicide.

---

26 This research is available online: https://www.ucl.ac.uk/news/2016/jan/1-10-suicide-attempt-risk-among-friends-and-relatives-people-who-die-suicide

27 Source of cost of suicide death was estimated in a report into suicide prevention which is available online: https://publications.parliament.uk/pa/cm201617/cmselect/cmhealth/300/30005.htm

Every professional or organisation that encounters people bereaved by suicide or other unexpected or traumatic death (such as those associated with mental illness), needs to know how to support and guide bereaved people. *Help is at Hand*[28]is a booklet that can guide a family bereaved through suicide and similar deaths. It was produced by Public Health England and is available to all. This publication provides a lifeline to bereaved people and those in support roles. It is written with extracts from bereaved people who take readers through the whole process, from death to inquest. It answers questions such as: What does the coroner do? What is an interim death certificate? Who will be in touch and what is their role? So many questions are answered in one publication. It is available online but, in my opinion, it should be handed out by the police when they visit the family to impart the news of a death.

Support from funeral directors

Until you have been bereaved you just don't get it. You can read other people's accounts, even help support others with their grief, but you just don't get it until you have been bereaved yourself. When you are the one in the front row at the funeral, you suddenly understand the all-consuming power of grief. It is exhausting, overwhelming, and painful.

Working within the funeral industry you support people across the board, from the very young to the very old. All social classes, ethnicities, sexes, and belief systems. People affected by death and coping with bereavement do so in their own unique way. Some bereaved people have a lot of support from family and friends and others have no support at all. It is such a privileged role, to be supporting people at such a time of need and being able to be the 'rock' to support them. Guiding newly bereaved people through the difficult and often frightening path from the death to the funeral. Then after the funeral through bereavement support if they need it and seeing them process their grief and move forward with their lives in a positive way is very special.

My role in supporting families has been so varied. Sometimes, just being there and sitting with someone is all that is needed. I have found that often my presence is enough. Helping to answer the questions people never thought they would have to ask is important work too. Bereaved people might want to know: what does a coroner do? What is an inquest? The police took some of my loved one's processions, will I get them back? When will I be able to see my loved one? What do I have to do to organise

28 *Help is at Hand: Support After Someone May Have Died by Suicide* is available here: https://www.nhs.uk/Livewell/Suicide/Documents/Help%20is%20at%20Hand.pdf

the funeral that is fitting but within my budget? I need to be able to answer these kindly, competently, and calmly.

Organising a funeral for a loved one is difficult and, when you have never been through the process before, it can be daunting and overwhelming. My job is to be the steady force in the hurricane, to help navigate through the most difficult of seas, and to help to provide what is right and fitting for each family. That is always different.

Grief and mental health

Loneliness, isolation, and depression can lead on to severe mental health problems if not properly supported. Grieving is a natural process and in itself it is not a mental health problem. However, sadness, loneliness, and isolation are things many bereaved people will experience.

Often, I hear people saying to me, "I thought I had the early signs of dementia". Grieving often stops us from being able to retain information and to remember. A scary side effect to grieving can be the physical effects. The somatic symptoms of grief can be huge - from headaches, aches and pains across the shoulders and back, to stomach issues typically associated with Irritable Bowel Syndrome (diarrhoea, stomach cramps). It is not unusual for people to feel they might be having a heart-attack because the symptoms of stress can induce panic attacks which cause the heart to pump, and breathlessness.

Grieving allows us to process a death but for some people this is more difficult. When grief is complicated, prolonged, or especially difficult, some bereaved people might find processing and moving forward with their lives problematic. This is when mental health problems might arise, and depression or other issues such as Post Traumatic Stress Disorder can ensue.

I have always been passionate about supporting people and over the last decade I have seen people's mental health suffer more and more. I decided to train to be a Mental Health First Aid Trainer for Mental Health First Aid England[29]. I have delivered training to many people - from doctors' surgeries, publicans and councillors, to funeral directors. Those I train in mental health first aid will, in turn, support those suffering from poor mental health. They find that following the training makes them feel more able to offer initial support and signpost on to additional help when needed.

29 The Mental Health First Aid website is; https://www.mentalhealthfirstaid.org/

Offering hope

Grief is individual and no two people grieve in the same way, even when they are grieving for the same person. My role is always to offer hope and ensure those I support realise that although their lives will never be the same, they can still lead good and meaningful lives. Carrying the lessons they have learnt forward and having more empathy for others and realising how precious life is, enables that to happen. A poem that captures how important it is to make the most of our lives is *The Dash* by Linda Ellis[30]. A sense of hope often makes one better able to support others but also to live life, grab opportunities, and give back. Many of those who I have supported want to be busy to fill their time and to do something meaningful and to make a difference championing good causes and ensuring their loved one's memory lives on.

Living with the pain of a mental health illness is often invisible to the outside world. Keeping the memories alive of those who have lost their battle is vital to ensure better mental health provision is provided in the future, allowing those suffering now to have hope and those who have died, to have not done so in vain.

Life is precious. When someone dies waiting for help and support, ripples are created that extend into society. The ripple effect that occurs when a loved one dies lasts a lifetime.

---

30 *The Dash* by Linda Ells is available online: https://lindaellis.life/

Staying Angry
By Kate

Kate's heart was made by Zoë Eira's mother. It depicts how: *"Our precious daughter had a warm, warm and loving heart. Her warmth and kindness touched the lives of all who know her. She loved France and spent many happy summers there. She is forever in our hearts."* Zoë Eira's daughter added her initials.

About Kate

Kate qualified as a Social Worker in 1997. She has always worked in the fields of homelessness, substance use, or mental health. She currently works as an Approved Mental Health Professional (AMHP), for a local authority.

In this chapter, Kate reflects on the loss of people she cares about, who have died by suicide, and how this influences her work.

Staying Angry

I write from multiple perspectives. In 2012, my nephew, Ross aged 22, took his own life and in 2022, my friend, Zoë Eira, died by suicide. I work within the mental health system and I teach and practice educate social workers.

My role as an AMHP means that I spend time on hospital wards, in the community, and with mental health teams. It is a specific role within the 1983 Mental Health Act. It is the AMHP, not the doctors, who completes an application to bring someone compulsorily into hospital at a time of mental health crisis. AMHPs should try and understand the person within their social context and explore alternatives to compulsory detention. This means we can talk to families and friends, as well as interviewing the person, and look to identify alternative options. Our job is to declare we are satisfied that in 'all circumstances of the case' hospital admission under the Mental Health Act is the least restrictive option. The decisions, that I make on a daily basis, are shaped not only by the legislation and policies I work under but also by the resource context. As a practitioner, making decisions to remove people's liberty is not something I take lightly. Being able to demonstrate recognition of the power AMHPs hold is a key element of our training. The power to change things within the mental health system can feel more daunting.

Ross

In 2012, a year after I qualified as an AMHP, my nephew died by suicide. Ross was a brilliant and beautiful young man - funny, creative, sensitive, and bright. He seemingly had the future at his feet. One of our shared passions was music. I have very happy memories of going to gigs together. I watched Ross grow, from a somewhat awkward and unconfident teenager, into a young man who had seemingly found 'his tribe'. He was producing radio shows at university, had a girlfriend, and seemed to be enjoying life. He appeared to be doing everything someone of his age should. I have a lasting memory of trying to blag our way into a sold-out gig at a music festival. I watched Ross (unsuccessfully) negotiating with a ticket-tout to beat the price down. I felt so proud because the boy who had at times struggled to feel comfortable in his own skin, had somehow turned into this cool and confident young man.

Ross started studying in a different city but a devastating crash in his mental health led to him to attempting to end his life. The impact and shock on Ross' family at that time was beyond devastating. Ross had some mental health support before moving back home. Eventually, he felt well enough to make another start at a local university. It seemed he had managed to get through the period of acute rockiness. A return to the time when he had significantly harmed himself felt absolutely inconceivable. After a trip round Europe with his friends, Ross' mood plummeted on his return to the UK. When Ross died he was under the 'care' of mental health services. Following an urgent referral, Ross had been assessed the previous month by a nurse and prescribed medication by a doctor following a multi-disciplinary meeting. He was not seen by a doctor and no follow up was arranged.

The week Ross died, he had presented to his GP with clear thoughts of ending his life. An urgent out of hours referral, from his GP, was followed up by the assessment and treatment team at lunchtime the next day. They attempted to contact Ross by phone but did not manage to speak to him. It was decided that he needed to see a doctor but there was no doctor available. So, a referral was made to the home treatment team but not accepted until the following day

Ross' GP responded to his presenting crisis by staying on late after work and making a referral to the appropriate team. However, she did not ask him if she could share his thoughts of harming himself with anyone else. If she had, and he had consented, his mother would not have gone back to work on the day she did. She had taken seven weeks off to look after him. She thought he was brighter in mood. Sadly, his mood had probably lifted that week because he had made the decision to end his life. Ross died on the day professionals made telephone calls to each other. He died on the day his mother returned to work - because no information had been sought or shared with his family.

There are no words that can ever do justice to the maelstrom that losing someone to suicide brings. The shock; guilt; and the 'what if's?'. The blame, desperation, and the endless poring over what has happened – trying to work out how things could have been different. Those feelings are common to most families who lose a loved one to suicide.

It is easy for individuals to become dehumanised within the mental health system. I am bitter about Ross' inquest. The suited-and-booted senior managers from the mental health trust never once looked at his family or spoke to us. It was a strange situation to be sitting in the same row with people who were paid enormous salaries but who could not even acknowledge us as human beings. Instead, they preferred to 'look busy' on their phones whenever there was a pause. The coroner issued a Prevention of Future Deaths (PFD) report which highlighted a number of failures which had contributed to Ross slipping through nets when he most needed safety and care. His report, like most PFDs, makes bleak reading.

When you lose a loved one, people become frozen in time at the age at which they die. At an event to mark a celebration of his life, one of Ross' loving aunties made a cake with 'Forever 22' iced upon it. I think about Ross often, he would have been 32 now. His birthday or bereavement anniversary are particular triggers to wonder how his life might have been. Would he have settled down, had kids, travelled, or worked?

Zoë Eira

Ten years after Ross died, a friend of 30 years ended her life whilst under the 'care' of mental health services.

I will let her parents tell you who Zoë Eira was:

"Zoë Eira was a generous, kind, and caring human being, very witty and funny. Her enthusiasm, warmth, and friendly nature inspired everyone who met her. She was very creative, an artist, a poet, loved cooking, and gardening. But most of all she was a dedicated and very proud mother to her daughter.

Her passing has created an enormous hole and heartache in all of our lives, and it was a needless and untimely tragic death."

Zoë Eira's death plunged her parents' and her daughter's lives into shock, bewilderment, and chaos. It has left a legacy of unanswered questions about how an individual can be treated so badly by the system that is legally responsible to care for them. I feel ashamed that the service I work in can let people down in such a way.

Zoë Eira's had stopped taking the medication prescribed to her for schizophrenia and her mental health relapsed in November 2020. She was admitted to her local psychiatric hospital. After approximately six weeks, Zoë Eira was feeling much better. Her family were visiting daily and going for walks in the grounds of the hospital.

It seemed the most damaging experience was Zoë Eira's transfer to a Psychiatric Intensive Care Unit (PICU) on Christmas Eve. These units exist to manage patients who cannot be cared for on open wards. They can be extremely frightening places. Zoë Eira was desperate to be allowed home for a Christmas Day visit with her parents and daughter. Her mother had written to the ward pledging she would pick her up, drop her back, and take responsibility for Zoë Eira's safety. The ward was in chaos due to Covid, so the review to consider her leave request kept getting cancelled.

On Christmas Eve, Zoë Eira was told by a new ward doctor that she would not be granted leave. She was not given any reasons. Understandably, Zoë Eira was devastated and angry. She shouted and argued with nurses but she was not physically aggressive. Later that day, another patient threw a vase across the lounge. Zoë Eira believed this was wrongly attributed to her. The first she knew of her transfer to the PICU, which was 200 miles away, was when the secure ambulance crew arrived. It was only due to the kindness of the ambulance crew, who let her borrow their phone, that she was able to tell her mother she was being moved and where she was going.

Upon arrival, the staff at the PICU could not understand why Zoë Eira was there. She immediately caught Covid, which was rife in the unit. Once she tested negative, the PICU contacted Zoë Eira's local unit to say she should be discharged back to their ward. No one got back to them which meant Zoë Eira remained in a unit she should never have been in. Zoë Eira was hundreds of miles away from her family and, due to Covid, she was unable to have visitors. Six weeks later, she was discharged straight back to her own home.

Zoë Eira's experience under the 'care' of services left a lasting legacy of trauma, mistrust, and a deep fear of hospitalisation. There were a number of acute stressors that coincided in the weeks and months before Zoë Eira took her own life. One of these was a physical health issue that required surgery. After her experience in the PICU, Zoë Eira had been left with a fear of being hospitalised. She was acutely worried about going into hospital, albeit this time for physical reasons. Zoë Eira was worried that physical changes to her body might impact on the efficacy of her psychiatric medication and was terrified of a mental health relapse. There was no linking between the physical and psychiatric side of her healthcare. The general side were unaware of her psychiatric history until she told them. As a result, her request for a second opinion, regarding the need for an operation, was initially dismissed. The letter, finally agreeing a second opinion, arrived the day after she had died. If her care had been more seamless, this would not have happened.

Another significant stressor for Zoë Eira, was having her benefits stopped because she had been able to pick up a small amount of part-time work. With family support, she was able to appeal and was restarted on Housing Benefit, but her Personal Independence Payment (PIP) was stopped permanently, pending a separate appeal. Zoë Eira would have had to fill all the forms again and go through the process of appeal.

I wonder whether the doctor, who refused Zoë Eira one day's home leave in Christmas 2020, could ever begin to understand what a devastating set of consequences were initiated by that decision.

A tsunami of pressures

Resource pressures, including the Covid pandemic, have heaped additional burdens on an already creaking mental health system. An explosion of demand and new referrals coincided with a significant deterioration in the situations of people already under the care of services. Lockdown meant people were unable to physically access the services, such as day-centres or preventative services, that help keep them well. Lockdown also meant many teams stopped face-to-face work.

There is a recruitment crisis across mental health services. The resilience and morale of teams and wards have visibly suffered during the pandemic. This has been reflected by staff shortages and sicknesses, an over-reliance on agency workers, and team burnout. Years of underfunding by successive governments, the impact of Brexit, and the fact that mental health service-users are a stigmatised group (without a unified and well-resourced campaigning voice), means the provision of seamless, consistent, good quality mental health care often seems a fantasy, despite what the posters proclaim from the walls.

The thresholds for people to access services can be impossibly high due to the eligibility criteria. The pressures on teams to close cases can equally be as strong. This can result in service-users receiving a patchy or limited service; discharge too early from hospital or community teams; and a dearth of accessible, holistic, socially inclusive options for community-based support. It often seems people are treated like a football: passed between a set of disconnected services, who will place the responsibility solely on the person if there are any difficulties. We know that consistent, relationship-based care is effective in delivering positive outcomes. Yet, so often an individual's experience of the mental health system is chartered on a reactive and disjointed response from the very services set up to care for them. When the layers don't work people can reach (and act on) a crisis point much more quickly.

Having a Mental Health Act assessment should be the last resort for an individual. The layers before that should offer options for accessing community mental health support. Including support from primary care and, if needed, secondary mental health services. I have regularly encountered people referred into services but discharged for 'non-engagement' - when the engagement offered is a letter with an invitation to contact the service by telephone. I've even seen this when the referral states that the person is not managing their affairs (including not opening their post).

I know how tricky it is to get my own appointments with my GP. To book an appointment (weeks away) I need to ring an automated line and hold for 30 minutes or more. Alternatively, I have to ring on the dot of 8.30

am to try and bag one of the slots released each day. Imagine how hard it is to navigate that process for someone who is mentally unwell. They may not be able to voice clearly or succinctly what they are experiencing, and may not have the support of family or friends, or even any phone credit.

There are some brilliant and dedicated GPs. Likewise, there are practitioners and doctors within mental health services that consistently stand out as offering positive and cohesive care. However, I regularly come up against compassion-fatigue, where nurses or doctors in hospital or community teams have been socialised into delivering unquestioning responses. The system acts to dehumanise individuals and encourage defensive practice. Based on the high thresholds of their service, without any thought of the reality for the person or their family, they dismiss people. They can seem oblivious to how difficult re-accessing help can be. The priorities protect the system instead of the service-users.

What good practice means to me

I hope I never forget that for each assessment I undertake, that there is a person at the end of it, and that every single part of the intervention matters. I will gently draw the attention of colleagues how this is a person and someone else's son/daughter or partner. Entry to a psychiatric hospital can be bewildering, frightening, and traumatic. I do everything I can to communicate to the person, their family, and the ward about their needs. If I can, I ensure they are able to pack and take personal belongings with them to try and make their stay more dignified and comfortable. If someone is at risk of harming themselves, then compulsory admission to hospital may be indicated, but it is so important to try and prevent the experience of hospitalisation making the person's situation worse than it was.

I recognise, both as a practitioner and educator, that my impact on change remains on a micro-level. The systemic changes required remain out of my sphere of influence. However, if I can go to bed at night knowing that I have done my best, and I have never forgotten that the person at the heart of the process is a human being who deserves respect, care, good communication, and above all compassion, then I know it is not time yet to hang up my AMHP boots.

There are different ways I try and make a difference:

Explaining the process in an understandable way: It's important not to use jargon. Keeping people informed of timescales and/or likely outcomes, and making sure people have the means to contact me may sound like basics, but so often they are missed. I don't shy away from difficult conversations and am realistic about resource constraints, and facilitate people's right to complain.

Involvement of families: The inclusion of the voice of families is something that is often missing from mental health care. As an AMHP, I have a duty to consult the legally defined 'nearest relative' when making an application to admit someone to hospital. It is important for me to gather information from other family members, who may have knowledge or a role to play, with of course due sensitivity to the needs and rights of the person being assessed.

Too often, I see wards not being proactive or positive about involving families. Communication is seen as a perceived layer of extra work or difficulty. However, they can be quick to appoint families in the role of 'medication police' without ever providing helpful information or discussion about person's situation or treatment options.

Confidentiality: This notion is often used as a justification for the lack of a more systems-based approach and seeing the individual in their wider context. Often the consent is only asked at a person's entry point into services. Deficit-based, 'tick box' risk assessment forms, which take the format of simply noting risk type events and behaviour, need more free space to encourage practitioners to discuss with service-users what they might actually find helpful at crisis points. If risk of harm is identified, it would be useful if forms contained a prompt to revisit consent to share information in order help keep the person safe. If this had been done, Ross may well still be alive today.

Seeing beyond the presenting 'problem': At the point of admission to hospital, I always write detailed, holistic reports. In my experience, the AMHP report is often seen as something to be 'uploaded', whereas, the doctor's medical recommendations are viewed as containing the important information. My reports often contain a wealth of important information as well as up-to-date contact details for families. Sometimes, I need to be persistent in ensuring that the ward takes this on board. For me, discharging someone unsupported to a problematic environment is only going to increase the risk of harm occurring. A hospital admission should create the opportunity or catalyst for multi-professional conversations and referrals to take place. There should be planning from the beginning for a supported and cohesive discharge. Too often care is disjointed.

Resources: One of the questions I need to ask, before I set out to do an assessment, is whether there is a psychiatric 'bed' available should the person need to come into hospital. This generic term doesn't take account of what type of facility the bed might be in, where the bed is, let alone how it might feel for the person being transported and admitted to a unit that might be hundreds of miles away from their home or support networks. The pandemic has increasingly meant that every psychiatric bed including private (non-NHS beds) are full. Increasingly, as a practitioner, I use every available tool for escalation. If I think there is a resource potential missing, I flag up with my manager before I go out on an assessment. I make sure I know which manager of the relevant mental health trust will be on duty in and out of working hours.

Using my anger to motivate me: In addition to the 'biological' nature of mental illnesses such as clinical depression, social stressors have a huge impact to play on the shape of people's lives. Poverty, fuel poverty, poor housing, unemployment, domestic abuse, and cuts to education all impact on people's life chances and opportunities for recovery. The reality of so many people's lives is aeons away from that of politicians or policy-makers. I have just read headlines about benefit levels never having been as low as they are today compared with the cost of living. I find it outrageous that a portion of applicants for Personal Independence Allowance (PIP) will be on an accepted, in-built quota of being refused. Many who appeal will have their benefits re-instated. The impact of poverty and the actual process of appeal relies on having sufficient strength or opportunity to do this. People like Zoë Eira cannot navigate the system. For me, staying angry and taking part in political campaigns, by contributing or fundraising, is a key part of not feeling totally powerless in the face of the greater system change which is needed.

End notes

My car can get filled with the trappings of my AMHP work-life – papers, food, extra clothing, coffee cups, bottles of water etc. It often goes a long time between trips to the car wash. A few weeks ago, I took the rare step of giving it a total clean, including taking everything out of the seat pockets and door compartments. I was delighted to find a CD that Ross had burned for me. It was a total joy to rediscover it and see his handwriting again. He'd written comments by some of the tracks including detailing which ones were his favourites. For anyone listening to '*Nine Types of Light'* by *TV on the Radio*, please know that according to Ross, track 6, 'Will Do' is the best one on the album – and I, for one, agree.

Ross and Zoë Eira were casualties of a broken mental health system. I am staying angry about that. They died waiting for well resourced, cohesive, and compassionate mental health care - where people are treated as unique individuals and there is equal weight given to fund preventative accessible services as there is on funding acute care.

Ross and Zoë Eira inspire me to do my best every day.

Part Four - Agitating for Change

George Julian made this memorial heart. She says: #JusticeforLB is the foundation for my patch and my open justice work. The broken heart and the pieced together larger, fuller heart can be interpreted as the viewer wishes. One interpretation could be that the love continues to grow, and expand, after a preventable death. Initially I thought I would stitch words like answers, accountability, and candour but I realised that far too often those words are not the reality for many of the families that I walk alongside. Instead, I opted for the one golden thread that unites them all, love.

About George

George[31] is a freelance knowledge transfer consultant who has worked with researchers, policy makers, care providers and sector-led improvement organisations to support them to apply research into practice.

Following the avoidable death of Connor Sparrowhawk in a mental health Assessment and Treatment Unit, George supported the #JusticeforLB campaign[32]. She is described by Sara Ryan (Connor's mother) as having:

> *"…remarkable campaigning skills, tenacity and commitment to social justice, which involved countless hours of unpaid work, given cheerfully and with lots of laughs. You were the, too often unseen, brains behind the operation"*[33].

Since #JusticeforLB, George works alongside her other roles as a crowdfunded journalist, whose primary focus is live-tweeting coronial inquests into the deaths of learning disabled and autistic people. George does this in the hope that it will raise awareness, and provide scrutiny, into why so many people are dying from preventable causes such as drowning, constipation, unwitnessed seizures, malnutrition, and neglect.

Through this work, George brings into the public domain what happens at the inquests of people who have been failed by health and social care systems. George never takes her focus off the person who met the premature death and, through her compassionate 'story-telling', she conveys the uniqueness and beauty of people. She resists the dehumanizing constructs of learning disability and reminds us to see people's value. She also provides an insight into how families experience services and coronial processes by bringing into the public domain things that usually happen behind closed doors. She has worked as a family representative and advocate, supporting bereaved families with NHS death investigation processes and is a former special advisor to CQC.

George is a blogger, tweeter and online activist and she engages with people in accessible ways (such as bite-size videos) to share her work and agitate for change.

When not working or campaigning George is usually found sewing, knitting, or indulging in a spot of craftivism[34].

---

31 For more information about George and her work see her website: www.georgejulian.co.uk

32 For more information see the website: http://justiceforlb.org/who-is-lb/

33 *Justice for Laughing Boy: Connor Sparrowhawk – A Death by Indifference* (2018) by Sara Ryan page 272.

34 Craftivism refers to using craft (often textiles) as a gentle and thought-provoking form of protest. For more information see Sarah Corbett's (2019) book *How to be a Craftivist: The Gentle Art of Protest.*

Agitating for Change
By Caroline and Emma

Almost daily, we hear of increasing unmet need relating to people's mental health. Multiple pressures, coupled with embedded organisational structures and behaviours, created the crisis in mental health services. There is no single solution that can fix a system that has been starved of resources and, in many places poorly led, for so long. There are multiple ways of provoking and supporting change. The work that we do is underpinned by a desire to see improvements in mental health services but we come at this from different perspectives and skill sets.

An aim of this book is to be educative and inspirational. We want it to be used to prompt conversations about what needs to change and to support learning. In this section, we have grouped accounts by people who are all agitating for positive change but doing so in very different ways. When they are outspoken about perceived failings, none of the contributors are motivated by negativity. Their sometimes single-minded and forthright approaches reflect how attuned they are to the distress and pain of others. In *A Gladiator Spirit*, Geri provides a tribute to an outrageously vociferous and combative campaigner who operated from a position of love for those who might be stigmatised, invisible, hurting, or unloved by society. Not all agitators for change are outspoken banner wavers. In *Blinded*, Lisa gives her account of being a service-user and she presents a compelling case for trauma-sensitive practice. Lisa uses her gentleness and teaching skills to speak into peoples' hearts.

The media have an important part to play in influencing change. Responsible reporting has the power to illuminate examples of excellence or unjustifiable practice. 'The media' are not a homogenous group and there are wide differences in the way they work. We are pleased to include contributions from reputable journalists who have consistently reported on the quality of mental health services. When people are criticising the media for reporting on things like inquests, we wonder if they have ever considered why journalists do their jobs and the effect it has on them.

An area we feel change is needed, that we have only touched on in this book, is the way inquests are conducted. Several examples are cited by our contributors that touch on how difficult they find coronial processes. Some of them have been supported by the charity INQUEST, which does excellent campaigning about the deficiencies in the coronial system and also represents some bereaved families where injustice has occurred. We opened this section with a heart made by George Julian, whose important work reporting on inquests highlights what bereaved families can experience.

George was too busy to write a chapter for us but we wanted to include her work. We recommend taking a look at her tweets, blogs, and videos about the inquests she covers. Though you will need a strong stomach to read of the brutality, injustice, defensiveness, and disregard for people who receive the 'care' that she exposes.

We are both serious agitators in different ways. In our chapter, *The Accidental Activist and the Seasoned Campaigner* we explore this and demonstrate how we can challenge within the boundaries of our professional registrations as a social worker and nurse.

We need collective push-back in as many ways as possible. Even the tiniest challenges matter. We were discussing this and found the analogy of the Titanic helped us formulate how small amounts of power used together might divert disaster. A huge ship can be moved into position by small tug boats. One tug boat has no chance of pulling the ship off course. We feel mental health services are like the Titanic heading full steam ahead towards the iceberg. The arrogance of ship-builders and the captain means that they are not heeding warnings. It would take many voices in the ears of those in charge and many tiny tugs all pulling on their ropes to divert such a powerful vessel. But knowing what we know about the potential loss of life, we feel we have to try. We ask you to add your voices and put your weight behind those pulling on ropes, in the hope of changing course towards safer waters.

The Case for a Statutory Public Inquiry
By Melanie

Melanie's heart for Matthew shows her deep personal love and grief for her only son, alongside symbolism of the way she stands with others in campaigning for justice.

About Melanie

Melanie has undertaken a gruelling ten-year campaign for truth following the tragic death of her only child, Matthew. Her quest for answers and accountability has grown into a far wider campaign as other bereaved parents have stepped forward.

In this chapter, Melanie is sharing her view of what happened to Matthew, her thoughts and feelings about that, and her experiences following his death.

The Case for a <u>Statutory</u> Public Inquiry

Matthew died, aged just 20, in the 'care of the State' in November 2012. He died in hospital, in what ought to have been a 'place of safety'. Almost ten years on, I continue to fight for truth, accountability, and change to mental health services across our nation. Having once stood alone, I have been joined by: over 70 Essex families; eminent experts; the communities of SEND (Special Educational Needs and Disabilities); mental health, and addiction; and the public. Support for Matthew's Campaign widens nationally and it grows stronger with every passing day.

Matthew

I was thrust into a nightmare scenario without warning. The phone rang, and the doctor said, "It's Matthew, he's been found, it doesn't look good". I collapsed on the floor, my heart racing, I was unable to breathe. The next hours were horrendous. A travel sweet tin was passed across to me on our way to the hospital. It had an angel picture on the lid. In that instant, I knew he was gone.

On arrival at the psychiatric unit, my worst fears were confirmed. My sweet boy had become a corpse. I could see him, but that was all. I stood next to him lying dead on a trolley. In my mind, I was begging him to come back to me. I was threatened with removal by the police if I dare to touch my own son: "He's a crime scene, do not touch". I wanted to flee. I didn't want any of this to be happening. I wanted to wake up in my bed at home and realise it was all just a very bad dream. But this was far worse than any nightmare.

My young son had just died in, what I had understood to be, a top psychiatric hospital in Essex. The day he had been admitted to hospital I felt relief. I thought, "He will finally get the help he needs". I also felt grateful for the prospect of relaxation and sleep. Matthew was going to be kept safe. He was in a 'place of safety' and they would look after him. What a fool I was to believe that! On Thursday, my son was sick and by the following Friday, he was dead.

Matthew was a beautiful soul. He understood compassion and he cared for others. He was generous, he was kind, he was smart. He was funny and in his younger years, he wanted to be a comedian. He was quite shy in large groups and was a loyal friend. He was never one to encourage a fight but he would stand up for himself and the ones he loved.

Matthew loved the outdoors, anything water sports-related, and he was a fantastic skier. He had a natural talent for swimming. He actually saved two ladies from drowning and, when he was 18, he became a qualified lifeguard. Having left grammar school, where he excelled in mathematics and computer science, he set up his own computer business, travelling between clients on his motorbike and he was doing really well.

Aged 19, Matthew was having trouble sleeping and he was complaining of pains and cramps in his stomach. He was also hallucinating. When Matthew became poorly, we turned to professionals for help. Matthew's medical records show that the first psychiatrist involved in his care picked up a B12 and folate deficiency and possible ceoliac disease, combined with a thyroid issue. However, from the information provided to me, it looks like these discoveries were never addressed. Matthew was put on antipsychotic medication and any further physical checks appeared minimal.

I had been trying to get help for my son for over a year. He had five mental health assessments - but never a bed available. Finally, a bed became free. Later, the social worker would advise me not to visit for a week to allow Matthew to settle on the ward. I did speak to Matthew, he described the unit as being like 'hell'. He was distressed, frightened, alone, bleeding, and bruised. He told me he had been raped. I will forever feel guilty that I trusted the professionals and I left him in the 'care' of the state. I never saw my son alive again.

The aftermath

After Matthew died, I needed an infusion of truth and compassion. Death was a full stop for my son but it was only just a very terrible beginning for all of us who survived. The impact of this experience has been slow, painful, and toxic. This lack of transparency meant that as a survivor, I have been made to relive the experience over, and over, again. The parts that remain unclear have become voids. Without verifiable information, maybe I place blame where it doesn't belong. But without transparency what else can I do? To find *truth,* I need transparency. The Trust had the opportunity to learn from Matthew's death and be open but they didn't use it.

So much evidence went missing. The ligature and the defibrillator were destroyed. The door logs were not downloaded. The CCTV was hidden from me for over seven years and parts of it were either not retained, or they were deleted. It is hard for me to believe that these were not deliberate attempts to hide the truth. Without clarity about what happened, I am left questioning people's actions and motivations.

In my view, nurses on the ward failed to do their jobs. I try and imagine what they might have been thinking. I want other people to be curious and ask themselves what would they do in that terrible situation?

Just imagine if you had been one of those nurses and that a patient in crisis died. Would you go on, after that patient's death, to try to cover up your failings? What would you do if you realised vital documentation was missing, or that you hadn't written up a care plan, or hadn't observed your patient when you were meant to have done so? What if you had not been looking after your patient at all? Would you panic? Destroy paperwork and falsify documents? Try to cover up your failings? A mother's only child has just died. Do you just carry on and go about your business, all the while hoping and trusting that no one finds out? Or, would you tell the truth?

These are the kinds of questions that I think about. These are the questions I believe should have been asked in a police investigation. But, in my view, the police investigation was a shambles. It began by looking into 125 deaths by ligature, but the numbers were inaccurate because records were missing. So, it was whittled down to 25. Then closed. I joined with other families to fight this[35].

It is a crime to tamper with NHS paperwork. It came to light after Matthew died, that paperwork had been falsified, backdated, and slipped into his files. It took me four years to finally persuade the police to register this falsification of mental health documents as a crime. I thought, "At last they are listening to me". Then the bomb dropped – the police said they would not be prosecuting because it's not in the public interest! What I knew at the time, and what is blatantly clear from the numbers of mental health patient deaths in Essex, is that it was in the public interest. Had there been an investigation, *and consequences,* I feel many deaths might have been prevented.

I cannot know who might have failed in their duty of care to Matthew, or who might be trying to cover up what went on in that unit, because too much of the information that should be available is missing. I know that I'm not dishonest or heartless and if someone died in my care I would tell the truth.

The thing is, we all make mistakes. For most of us, the consequences are pretty small. We expect so much more from doctors and nurses. They are signed up to ethical codes of conduct and standards and registered with their professional bodies. We expect them to adhere to their obligations. We trust them with what we value the most - our lives and our loved ones' lives.

We waited over two years for Matthew's inquest where an 'open narrative' verdict was reached. The coroner concluded that my son:

---

35 You can read about this online: http://www.justiceformattandben.co.uk/

"...was subject to a series of multiple failings and missed opportunities over a prolonged period of time by those entrusted with his care. The jury found that relevant policies and procedures were not adhered to, impacting on Matthew's overall care and wellbeing leading up to his death."

The Trust investigated. They laid blame and promised change. After Matthew's death, it seemed easy for the hospital CEO to blame the Operations Manager. Fire him and assume the problem had been solved - because the bad apple was gone. Again, I believed. Again, I was wrong.

Unfortunately, the hospital in Matthew's case did not respond with openness and transparency. They reacted with a legal version of 'fight or flight'. Deny and defend. This means - keep your head down. Shut up. Cover up. Offer no information. Let the solicitors handle everything. This seems to be a standard NHS response, one that we should all be concerned about.

I started writing to the HSE (Health and Safety Executive) in 2014. I wrote numerous times, and can't express to you what a battle it was to get them to listen to me. I was initially ignored for weeks and months, despite sending repeat emails. Then I involved my MP and she started writing too. In the end, I was told, "It's nothing to do with us" because the CQC were now responsible for health and safety. My MP said that she had done all she could.

I wasn't giving up. Finally, a small crack in a door opened. A man from the HSE contacted me. He told me initially he looked in my son's file and it was empty. Empty? Then he came back to say, "Sorry Melanie, it's not empty, it doesn't even exist!". This led to a meeting with him. I took along four massive boxes containing my files of evidence. Years of investigation and procrastination followed. In 2020, the HSE brought a prosecution against the Trust[36] relating to how they "managed environmental risks from fixed potential ligature points in its inpatient wards between 25 October 2004 and 31 March 2015". Matthew died in 2012. In November 2020, the Trust pleaded guilty into failings of care over ligature points at its inpatient units[37].

I made a complaint and the Parliamentary Health Service Ombudsman investigated[38] Matthew's death. Multiple failings were revealed and he deemed the Trust's investigation flawed and not fit for purpose.

---

36 You can read a BBC report about the HSE prosecution online: https://www.bbc.co.uk/news/uk-england-essex-57496578

37 Report about the Trust pleading guilty is available online: https://www.bbc.co.uk/news/uk-england-essex-54917299

38 You can watch a video of Rob Behrens talking about this online: https://www.youtube.com/watch?v=6oaZQI9OCBg

All mental health trusts across the UK received a copy of *Matthew's Case*[39] so they could improve their own practice. This report maybe helped someone else, I will never know.

The coroner called for a public inquiry after the inquest in 2015. There have also been multiple calls from various MPs in the last few years. Years later, in 2019, the Parliamentary Health Service Ombudsman, Rob Behrens, published the *Missed Opportunities* report[40] into two deaths (including Matthew's) at the psychiatric unit where Matthew died. The reports said that the unit and the Trust had "...failed to manage environmental risks and carry out an adequate risk assessment". The report went on:

> *"We have established a timeline that demonstrates wider systemic issues at the Trust, including a failure over many years to develop the learning culture necessary to prevent similar mistakes from being repeated. It is important to understand why change took so long despite the feedback from patients' grieving families and the numerous investigations and inspections highlighting that it was so clearly needed".*

The Ombudsman went on national television, after the report was published, to say that, if he had had the power to, he would call a public inquiry.

'I' became 'we'

My response to what happened to Matthew is not unique. Like most people who have experienced failings in medical care, we want three things:

We want an honest, transparent explanation of what has happened.

We want a full and genuine apology.

We want to see that changes have been made, to ensure that was has happened to us, and our loved ones, never happens to anyone else.

Unlike what we can see nightly on television dramas, people don't immediately seek solicitors. We want answers, not money. Taking legal action is financially expensive - a last resort that none of us want to do.

I began to realise that what happened to Matthew, and what happened after his death, had happened to other people. Multiple patients had died in the unit Matthew had been detained in and they continued to die by the same means as he did. Changes had not happened. In my opinion, without being open and honest, the Trust had not been able to learn from their mistakes. How could they find the deadly system failures, and act

39 *Matthew's Case* is available online: https://www.ombudsman.org.uk/sites/default/files/page/Matthews_Case_PHSO.pdf

40 You can view the *Missed Opportunities Report* online: https://www.ombudsman.org.uk/sites/default/files/page/Missed_opportunities_What_lessons_can_be_learned_from_failings_at_the_North_Essex_Partnership_University_NHS_Foundation_1.pdf

to fix them, without being prepared to take a critical and honest look at themselves? It seems to me that they couldn't (or wouldn't). This lack of learning caused more deaths and more sorrow.

I feel that the Trust hid behind legal manoeuvres and dismissed me. I felt powerless and excluded. They also left me feeling humiliated and I feel that they denied Matthew his dignity. After ten years these wounds are far from healing.

I wish this story was rare, but it is not. Failings in our mental health system are common. The exact number of deaths poorly recorded, which is yet another side effect of deny and defend. Although it is almost impossible to quantify exact figures because of the way statistics are recorded, thousands will die in the UK this year due to poor mental health services. This means that, this year, there will be thousands of opportunities to learn. Thousands of lives we should honour. Thousands of opportunities to choose truth and compassion over deny and defend. Transparency after needless deaths will save money long term and make us all feel safer. Is this too much to ask?

Through social media, using #Matthewscampaign, I connected with people who were also asking questions. People started to share their harrowing stories with me. My quest to find answers and accountability for Matthew became a campaign. One by one, other bereaved people told me their stories. My fight became their fight. I became we. The similarities with what happened to Matthew made me believe that something was going very wrong in Essex. I became increasingly vocal in the media about Matthew's story and started looking for ways to bring about change. Our campaign has held protests and made ourselves as visible as possible. Other campaigns have backed us and share concerns about mental health services in their areas. We created a website with links to all the campaign's media reports and other activities[41]. Our campaigning has led to my engaging with the government.

During a Parliamentary and Constitutional Committee meeting in October 2019, to discuss the *Missed Opportunities Report*, the Mental Health Minister, Nadine Dorries, informed me that they didn't do public inquiries into individual deaths. This prompted me to unite with multiple bereaved families making a united call for transparency and a public inquiry. Each death was, in my opinion, preventable and arose from systemic failures in the provision of mental health care services in Essex.

41 Matthew's Campaign website: www.curementalhealth.co.uk

In November 2019, I completed a UK government petition calling for a public inquiry into my son's death. 105,580 people signed it.

A year later, during a debate in Westminster Hall[42] into deaths in mental health care, Nadine Dorries announced an intention to direct the establishment of an independent, *non*-statutory inquiry into deaths at the unit where Matthew died (covering the last 20 years and up to date). Our campaign wrote to her, urging her to urgently reconsider that decision and to direct the establishment of a Statutory Public Inquiry pursuant to the Inquiries Act 2005. She refused.

In April 2021, an independent inquiry into Essex mental health services commenced without the backing of myself or the bereaved families that I had united with. In our opinion, its terms of reference were not wide enough to uncover the scale of the deaths. Its limited scope did not even include the deaths that had occurred in the community. We were also concerned that this independent inquiry had no statutory powers to compel witnesses to give evidence and get the full answers the families deserve. Everyone involved, including hospital and community mental health services and their partners (the local authority, commissioners, police etc.), need to give evidence and help us to find out why we are losing such a high number of our most vulnerable day in and day out.

So, our boycott began. Grieving families stand side by side with me and refuse to engage with the limited inquiry offered by the government. Together, we are calling for a *statutory* public inquiry[43] into *all* of the thousands of needless deaths, *both inpatient and community*, that have happened in Essex. We are asking people to spread our message and help us find other families that have been failed too.

Too many of our children with special educational needs or disabilities are dying young because of the challenges they face with their mental health. Likewise, our older adults with mental illness and dementia patients too. We simply won't accept this anymore as an inevitable reality, because it is not. We want all those who are suffering to know that we hear them. We won't rest until Matthew's Campaign gets the *statutory* public inquiry, that we believe can change outcomes, and save lives that have not been valued highly enough.

42 You can watch a video of the debate online: https://www.youtube.com/watch?v=RIVDtyZHjw0

43 A BBC report about the campaign for a statutory public inquiry is online: https://www.youtube.com/watch?v=w_1v6SBFsMQ

In March 2022, it was announced that the independent inquiry was investigating 1500 inpatient deaths in Essex[44]. 1,500 people. Of those, the cause of death of 900 is still unknown. I was not surprised because the missing information relating to Matthew's 'care' and death in hospital has never come to light. The inquiry chair was on television calling for people to come forward. People came on social media congratulating me for uncovering these 1,500 deaths and getting the independent inquiry. I reminded people that the scope of the inquiry is restricted and that our campaign was boycotting this inquiry. People raised with us the usefulness of an inquiry that has failed to engage over 70 families who have horrendous stories to tell.

No one is even looking at mental health deaths in the community. These figures will be even higher. In all probability, thousands will have died in Essex. Our campaign will continue to boycott the inquiry because we feel we would be failing all the other bereaved people where the deaths are not even being considered. Nobody even wants to investigate why their loved ones died. In our view, the government continues to fail our most vulnerable regularly. We continue to read of new lives lost and tragedies that may have been prevented. We continue to read of death scandals at other NHS trusts where families have had to fight for truth and accountability. Successive government ministers have been made fully aware of these failings over and again. They promise 'lessons will be learnt' and 'never again' but the scandals continue to surface. Families will continue to fight because who else will stand up for those who have died?

Matthew died waiting for a place of safety to be safe. People are still dying waiting for truth to be uncovered, learning to occur, and actions to be taken so that mistakes are not repeated. We are still waiting for a Statutory Public Inquiry.

In memory of Matthew. 'Gift from God.' Full of life, uplifting, inspiring, and even charming. You were the life of the party with your lively, intelligent, and witty personality.

44 Matt Precey and Nikki Fox (BBC) offer their analysis here: https://www.bbc.co.uk/news/uk-england-essex-60865519

Dying Waiting: Waiting to Die
By John and Jane

Jane embroidered this heart with the Campaign logo. As she sewed, Jane thought about the people who have been part of the Campaign's journey and what difficulties people have faced. She also reflected on the lives that have been lost.

About John and Jane

John and Jane are both founder members of the Norfolk and Suffolk Campaign to Save Mental Health Services. Over the last nine years they have stood with service-users, carers, mental health practitioners, and bereaved people, who have raised concerns about mental health services.

In this chapter, John and Jane give an overview of the campaign and their view of the situation.

Dying Waiting: Waiting to Die

Our campaign was born following devastating cuts to mental health services in Norfolk and Suffolk. In February 2013, the toxic effects of austerity cuts, and a disastrous attempt to manage budget deficits, led to a 'radical redesign' which resulted in a dramatic drop in effective mental health services. The assertive outreach and homeless teams were closed, leaving a big hole in support. The crisis team was cut and had its priorities changed. In November, a meeting was called by staff who were concerned about the deterioration of mental health provision. They were frightened about how unsafe things had become and could foresee worse to come. People came from all corners of the two counties. The sense of anger and injustice was palpable as an estimated 330 ordinary citizens gathered to share their experiences of failing mental health services. The room was so crowded that we had to turn people away and some had to stand in the corridor.

Following this meeting, service-users, carers, and bereaved relatives, who were scared about the impact the radical redesign on their own or loved one's mental health, joined with staff. There was an increase in deaths of service-users who had been made extremely vulnerable by the closure of beds and cuts the community teams that they had relied on for support[45]. In our opinion, continuously changing, sometimes incompetent, managers meant that the existence and standards of services were now at an all-time low. Emma Corlett was interviewed on television about the concerns the campaign raised which the CQC had also flagged up[46].

Nine years later, the service reductions, which led to that evening when the public gathered to express their collective disgust, seem like 'the good old days'. Beds and services have continued to be cut to a level that was previously unthinkable. Since our inception, to the best of our knowledge, over 1,000 people have been recorded in the Trust's 'unexpected deaths' statistics. We don't have figures for every year and the official statistics only capture some of the deaths. The Trust has now been in 'special measures' for the best part of the last seven years. Every attempt by the NHS to turn the situation round has failed. We are committed to continuing our campaign until we see improvements.

---

45 In May 2016, Verita published a report into the deaths: https://www.verita.net/wp-content/uploads/2016/05/Norfolk-and-Suffolk-NHS-Fundation-Trust-independent-review-Verita-25-May-2016.pdf

46 Emma Corlett on BBC Look East can be viewed here: https://www.youtube.com/watch?v=E1grfE3Qew8

A grass roots campaign

Our members are volunteers who are up against an organization with vast legal and financial resources. We have zero budget, no IT support, and no communications team. Yet, through the power of collaboration and determination, we have consistently and effectively challenged the trust. We are indebted to the media and have been supported by both local and national television, radio, and newspapers. Our campaign website[47] and social media presence have exposed injustice and poor practice at the trust. Over and again, the trust has criticized us and said we are sharing untruths. Every time, we have been proved right.

Campaigners have continued to meet regularly. Zoom replaced face-to-face meetings during Covid. This has enabled us to reach out to people in rural areas who might have limited access to public transport, or those with social anxiety who could not travel to Norwich to meet with others. Meetings increasingly involve supporting each other through dark times. As the years go by, we have less and less staff who are brave enough to speak out. They tell us that raising concerns does not feel safe. However, some anonymous whistle-blowers consistently feed us nuggets of information.

We have had two marches, where over 1,000 people took to the streets to demand better services, and a group of us walked from Norwich to Ipswich delivering letters to MPs along the way. We have held numerous public meetings and protested outside the Trust's premises and NHS headquarters. The campaign has lobbied MPs in Parliament and given evidence to professional bodies.

Since the campaign began, there have been eight CEOs and three Chairs of the Trust. We now hold the history of the organization. As we watch them try to work out what has gone wrong and how to fix it, we think 'here we go again'. We have criticized the Trust for, in our opinion, too often recruiting from within which results in a perpetuation of mediocrity, an inadequate culture, and people holding jobs above their level of competence. An example of this is the promotion of someone with false qualifications to CEO.[48]

Dying waiting

Watching the slow decline and avoidable deaths of patients and service-users, through what we consider institutional neglect, drives the campaign on.

---

47 Campaign website: https://norfolksuffolkmentalhealthcrisis.org.uk

48 A BBC report about this can be found here: https://www.bbc.co.uk/news/uk-england-norfolk-57748553

Bereaved parents and family members make up a proportion of our members. They tend to join for a while, often in a distressed and confused state, and we walk alongside them as they go through the brutal processes that follow an unexpected death.

Initially, we were able to hold the Trust to account on the increasing numbers of unexpected deaths. However, these figures are no longer published and the only way we hear of tragedies is from families, media reports, and published information about inquests. We can no longer keep up.

In a 2014 Community Care article, where Emma talked of 'some lives being worth more than others', she cited messages from frontline staff who were desperately trying to keep people safe.[49] She describes how in an attempt to prevent suicides, hoardings were erected at the site of two deaths (instead of addressing the unmet mental health needs). What was shocking to us then, has become normalized now. Many people have, and are continuing to, pay the ultimate price for the failing in services.

Waiting to Die

Another core group of our campaign are family members and carers. They often express fears that their loved ones will die through lack of services. The trauma of waiting for loved ones to die is unbearable. Carer members say:

"I know he will die and I feel powerless to stop that."

"When my partner asked for help from the Trust, she had some hope that they could help her condition. She was waiting for a peer support worker but then discharged without anything. Now she feels there is no hope and nothing can help her. She feels worse. I am so worried about her."

"We are in despair and losing hope. I have been meeting carers in the same position as me for years. Sometimes the inevitable happens and the person they care for dies."

"I fear for my child. I am trying to keep them safe 24/7. They need to be in hospital. No one will listen. I am exhausted and frightened."

49 The article is available here: https://www.communitycare.co.uk/2014/05/22/feels-like-lives-worth-others-working-mental-health-frontline/

Trying to stay alive

We regularly have people attend our meetings who are at risk of dying by suicide. Many people feel they have been abandoned when discharged from mental health care. Sick people, often living in poverty, feel cast adrift by an uncaring bureaucratic system. When a person suffers from a physical illness, we expect care from the NHS. If the illness is chronic or incurable, they are usually monitored regularly, with treatment adjusted accordingly, to maintain the best possible quality of life for the longest period. Many people are diagnosed with a severe mental illness which are incurable, life-long, and life-limiting. Their quality of life could be improved by tailored support. In the real world of mental health services, little support is available or tailored to the person's needs. We repeatedly hear similar things from service-users. For example:

"I waited months for an appointment. I was told I would go on a waiting list for treatment. Nothing happened. Then months later I got a letter saying I had been discharged."

"After an attempt to end my life, I was discharged from hospital with no follow-up or care set up in the community. I still feel suicidal. I think they just don't care if I die."

"I used to have a care-coordinator and a support worker. They left and were not replaced. Now I have no-one and my mental health has deteriorated. They keep making promises and breaking them."

Power and accountability

CEOs of foundation trusts are paid more than the Prime Minister. Executives, senior managers, and very senior managers, are also well rewarded. It doesn't seem to matter whether they succeed or not[50]. We see a dichotomy between extremes, between those with power and those who feel powerlessness. Them and us.

The powerful make lots of noise about engaging with families, often following the death of a service-user. Powerless families and friends, who may have information that could save future lives, seem almost routinely dismissed. Nowhere is the dichotomy of power starker than in the Coroners' Courts.

The trusts use NHS resources to employ expensive barristers to defend

50 Tom Kark QC, reported on the way senior leads in the NHS are recycled: https://assets.publishing.service.gov.uk/government/uploads/system/uploads/attachment_data/file/787955/kark-review-on-the-fit-and-proper-persons-test.pdf

their (often in our view indefensible) actions. This power is used to diminish bereaved families and convince coroners that working practices have changed and similar tragedies will never occur again. We hear from bereaved relatives who feel deprived of their last shred of dignity. Their last, and only, hope for them to obtain justice for their loved one feels deleted. They feel destroyed by tax payer funded, very expensive, power.

Since the radical redesign there have been 37[51] Prevention of Future Deaths reports issued against the Trust by coroners here. They represent the tip of the iceberg. The same issues arise over and over. Themes of poor communication, risk not being assessed adequately or acted upon, families and carers being excluded, and warnings ignored.

A continuous journey of failure and lack of improvement, that has gone on for years, should not be acceptable. This leads to the question: does this cycle benefit the powerful? By continuously denying a section of the population decent health care, are the powerful cementing their position as the people who dictate the life chances, indeed the life expectancy, of the powerless? Our campaign can protest but we still remain relatively powerless. The powerful may be embarrassed, dented, by our protestation but they rally together to ensure they retain control. They make hollow promises that will not be kept. As campaigners, we often feel othered, powerless, even hopeless, but we have not given up our 'David and Goliath' of a fight.

Political

Our campaign is apolitical in the party sense. We recognize that service-users and carers come from across the political spectrum. However, our campaign is political because government policies and funding directly contribute to the state of mental health services. Indirectly, politics influence mental health via poverty, housing, education, employment, and racism. The UN disability committee said there were 'grave and systematic' violations of disabled people's human rights occurring and the chair said what was going on in the UK was a 'human tragedy'. Within the disabled persons' group, those suffering from severe mental distress and illness were amongst some of the worst off.

---

51 We got these figures from the Trust as a result of two Freedom of Information requests.

Spin doctors

To ensure the balance of power remains firmly with the powerful bureaucrats, it is important the public is ignorant of the gulf between the mentally unwell and (generally) healthy people. So, trusts employ 'spin doctors' (rather than investing in real doctors). They spend vast amounts of money on communication (comms) teams who use social media to circulate happy videos of satisfied, possibly cured, service users. People are told it is easy to access a service – simply phone up or log-in and ask for one! These messages are, in our opinion, gaslighting. There's no mention of interminable waiting lists, gatekeepers, staff shortages, or commissioning gaps. Service-users and carers tell us that it's often a fight to get *any* mental health service. The reality they face is: people discharged without care; families at the end of their tether trying to care for a sick person who should be in hospital; and people left feeling alone and abandoned.

We would prefer the trust to get rid of the comms smoke screen and tell the truth about services and stop creating false expectations. If their funding and resources mean they can only provide for emergencies, or for those with serious mental illness, then they need to say so.

Whose truth?

It would be fair to say that the trust and our campaign do not share the same truth about the situation. We call them out on things and they protest we are 'shroud waving'. They have on a number of occasions sent letters from their legal team but we have been scrupulous in only saying things we can verify. Over the years, some issues pop up on a regular basis:

Finances - With resources so tight, something our campaign has consistently raised is how wisely the trust spends money. For example, the trust are spending £44.4 million on 15 new beds[52]. We have observed an exponential rise in highly paid executives and non-executive directors, managers, and what we call 'non-jobs' (communications, project leaders and people whose roles only seem to involve attending meetings). Does this represent value for money, when the trust is desperate for psychiatrists and nurses?

Out of Area (OOA) beds: From 2013, the trust began closing beds. In mental health, beds can be places of safety. So, for each bed that was closed, one person was deprived of a place of safety each and every day, 365 days a year. It quickly, and unsurprisingly, became apparent that this was a disastrous move.

---

52 This article details these plans: https://www.edp24.co.uk/news/health/step-forward-for-new-hellesdon-hospital-wards-8682130

Coupled with cuts to community services and austerity, people continued to become unwell. This meant patients had to be sent out of area, often to private 'hospitals' hundreds of miles from home. This involved expensive transport as well as the high costs of the stay. Soon it was challenging to get a mental health bed anywhere in the country. The CQC have found many private hospitals, motivated by profit, to be inadequate. Within our counties there are examples of these unsafe settings[53]. Additionally, private ambulance firms saw transporting patients across the country as a business opportunity. There appears to be poor regulation of these firms. Our campaign had already been challenging the transportation of people to inappropriate OOA beds when Peggy Copeman died[54]. It took the CQC two years to de-register the 'ambulance' provider.

Failed by the whole NHS system: We feel that the trust's inadequacies reflect the failure of the NHS bureaucracy in NHS East of England and NHS England and Improvement. The continuous journeys through special measures after CQC inspections, and the appointment of improvement directors, has led to no improvement. Indeed, many people feel things have got worse. We have observed how many of those tasked to help seem to be quickly caught up in the spin that protects the status quo, thus rendering the person or organization 'parachuted in' seemingly ineffective. No improvement occurs and the cycle begins again, with different faces in charge but the same results. However, the service-users and carers cannot move on. They see their hopes repeatedly extinguished and feel stuck in a hamster wheel, never to break free.

What do we want?

Co-production: Genuine co-production is one small way where the power differential between the powerless service-user and the powerful managers could be reduced. We feel that lip-service has been paid to co-production at the trust. New initiatives have been planned and, as an afterthought, service-users are asked to give their views. They are not involved from the beginning, which would be true co-production. Also, a wide range of service-users and carers need to be involved (not just the same people who are asked every time because they will nod through the trust's plans). The trust seems to disengage from good service-user involvement systems. For example, a disabled people's organization in the voluntary sector was replaced with an expensive professionalized service inside the Trust. In our view, this meets their 'command and control'

53 Two reports can be found here: https://www.bbc.co.uk/news/uk-england-norfolk-58466839 https://www.bbc.co.uk/news/uk-england-norfolk-41707256

54 See Nick and Maxine's chapter, *Peggy: Not 'Acting Up' But Dying.*

management style but abandons any pretense of being user-led. The trust has consistently resisted engaging with our campaign. We believe this reflects their unwillingness to hear criticism or to engage with service-users and carers who are not 'on message'.

Disbanding: In 2015, the Trust was the first in the country to be placed in 'special measures'. In April 2022, the CQC rated the trust as 'inadequate' for the fourth time. Surely a trust that has been failing patients across two counties, for nine years, without sustained improvement, must be disbanded. Special Administration is the means to achieve this although it has only happened twice in the history of the NHS. Under Special Administration, would things improve? Would the balance of power tilt towards the powerless? And if so, for how long?

Urgent action: In December 2021, our campaign wrote to the CQC demanding urgent action. We set out points that we believed needed addressing for safety[55]. We believe that the lack of urgency in addressing the Trust's problems is responsible for unnecessary deaths.

Individually we are powerless: Together we can create change

All campaigners set out to get justice and make a difference. Regardless of outcome, they cause the powerful some degree of anxiety or annoyance. By shining a light and speaking out, you encourage others, you help others process their experiences, channel hurt and anger into a positive force for change, and encourage others to speak out. By joining together in groups and campaigns you become more formidable and can really make a difference.

We will continue to endeavour to hold the powerful to account, however much we feel demeaned. We take courage from those who have gone before: our friend and co-founder, the late Terry O'Shea[56]; those, like Julie Bailey, who exposed the wrong doings at North Staffs which resulted in the Francis report; as well as many other successful campaigners, such as Melanie Leahy[57], who fight tirelessly for safer mental health services.

We still hope to forge good working relationships with those in power at the trust. There are new senior leads. We will give them a chance. But they have to be prepared to hear what our members have to say. They need to accept and work with the anger, despair and frustration of people who have been so badly let down.

---

55 You can view our open letter here: https://norfolksuffolkmentalhealthcrisis.org.uk/a-call-for-urgent-action-open-letter-to-cqc-and-nhse-i-about-nsft/

56 See *A Gladiator Spirit* by Geri Scott

57 See Melanie's chapter, *The Case for a Statutory Public Inquiry.*

A timeline of shame

In 2022, the Eastern Daily Press ran an article about the out of area bed situation. They created a 'timeline of turmoil' from a few of the key stories they had covered regarding the trust[58]. We think it is a timeline of shame.

On the day the CQC report came out we held a memorial event where hearts were laid at Trust sites in memory of those who had died. Some of the hearts were beautifully made and they were heartbreaking. Like the little stitched one that simply said 'Mummy'. We had hoped the Trust would respond sensitively to this gentle protest. They did not. Not even a standard comms statement. Then we heard they were disputing the death figures. We were appalled. Through conversations with journalists we came to suspect that either they have lost count of those who have lost their lives because they could not, or would not, come up with the data.

Our response to the 2022 CQC report[59] is - 'So What?'. We want to know what difference the report, and any plans arising from it, will make. We want to see decisive and swift action from NHS England, the Department for Health and Social Care, and Clinical Commissioning Groups, who have all allowed this dire situation to continue. We want to know when the people of Norfolk and Suffolk will get a mental health service that's fit for purpose. To this end, we are calling for a fully independent Statutory Public Inquiry that has two main aims: to establish how many people have died, and why; to investigate how this situation has been allowed to go on for so long and to identify a way to rectify it. We are lobbying our MPs in the hope of spurring them into action.

Holding on to hope

Our campaigners are weary and we grow older. However, we are encouraged by the feedback and support we receive from those who feel unable to speak out themselves. We hear heartbreaking stories too regularly to let those who suffer down. Together, we must speak truth to power and hold power to account.

Too many people in Norfolk and Suffolk have died waiting for services to improve. Many more live with the fear that they or their loved ones will die. We will not forget those who have lost their lives or leave behind those who mourn.

---

58 Dave Hannant's EDP article, with the timeline of turmoil, can be viewed here: https://www.edp24.co.uk/news/health/nsft-mental-health-out-of-area-patient-woes-8711416

59 Link to 2022 CQC report can be viewed here: https://www.cqc.org.uk/provider/RMY

The Accidental Activist and the Seasoned Campaigner
By Caroline and Emma

Caroline uses textiles, images, and creative writing as a form of protest. Emma takes a more direct approach as an active union member and co-founder of the Campaign to Save Mental Health Services in Norfolk and Suffolk. Caroline sews and Emma marches – both ways can be powerful and effective. The images on this are from a memorial hearts event where our different forms of protest converged.

The Accidental Activist and the Seasoned Campaigner
By Caroline and Emma

As a nurse and a social worker, we are both bound by codes of conduct. These extend into our personal lives because we have a duty to uphold the reputation of our professions. There is no requirement to agitate for change in the NMC code but a key part of the International Federation of Social Workers' social work definition is about promoting social justice. This is ironic because Emma, the nurse, is a seasoned campaigner whereas, Caroline, the social worker, describes herself as an 'accidental activist'.

Caroline writes and talks about the need to challenge the 'system' and poor practice. She tempers this with reminders to do this within organisational policies and professional codes. It can be difficult, even frightening, for professionals to speak out about poor practice. There is no doubt that we both feel freer to speak out about injustice, or expose unsafe or unethical situations, since we went freelance. Nevertheless, neither of us wants to be de-registered (or sued). Additionally, we want to model the kind and fair behaviours that we wish to see and we stand with those who have the least power.

In this chapter, we are going to share how we campaign for change whilst remaining within our professional boundaries. This can be tricky and there is a delicate balance to be struck. We shall begin with Emma's reflections because she is the seasoned campaigner who has encouraged Caroline to find her inner activist.

Emma reflects on her campaigning activities:

I became a union representative in 2006. Unions rely on the solidarity of collective, political action to ensure employees have fair, safe, and equitable working conditions and pay. Through my union activities, I have organised and attended marches, rallies, and demonstrations.

The result of the 2010 General Election was a wake-up call for me. I believe that Tory governments create social conditions that are very bad for mental health. I literally joined the Labour Party while watching BBC Newsnight footage of Nick Clegg and David Cameron signing the coalition agreement in the Rose Garden at Downing Street. I knew that we were in for a battering in the NHS and I wanted to get more involved in trying to stop the impending inevitable harm.

It didn't take long for the first round of cuts to bite in my local trust. Out went evidence-based teams that mitigated the greatest harm and focussed on supporting people to live good quality lives. Assertive outreach teams and the homeless outreach team were axed. Skilled, experienced staff were down-banded. Avoidable harm to patients started to emerge and staff morale started to plummet. As a staff member and union representative, I (and others) became increasingly worried about the safety of patients and what seemed a failure to properly assess and monitor the impact of the cuts. Further cuts included cutting both beds and community services at the same time, along with the redundancy of almost one hundred of the most experienced nurses, occupational therapists, psychologists, and social workers. Staff became increasingly worried about the failure to pilot and properly evaluate these massive service 'redesigns' and the lack of a 'Plan B'.

Concerns were initially raised internally through the trade union representatives but as I and my colleagues saw real harm emerge, these concerns were escalated externally for the first time. In January 2013, Approved Mental Health Practitioners (who are responsible for co-ordinating assessments under the Mental Health Act and admission to hospital) wrote, via their union, to every Norfolk MP, every Norfolk County Councillor, NHS and Social Care Commissioners, and the regulator the Care Quality Commission, to raise concerns about the lack of mental health beds and the impact of not being able to maintain patient safety and dignity. Not a single MP acknowledged or replied to the letter, despite the Minister for Mental Health role being held by one of those Norfolk MPs. The Care Quality Commission and local commissioners did not respond or act.

Things deteriorated and harm continued to occur. There was a palpable feeling from staff that deaths were happening as a direct result of the cuts and changes to services and thus wholly avoidable. Staff told us that they shared the same concerns and anger as patients and their families. A couple of high-profile inquests had confirmed staff fears that they would be scapegoated instead of a proper focus and accountability of Trust leadership and the wider system that had caused the terrible circumstances that staff were struggling to provide care in. We realised that we needed to work together with our wider community and speak out collectively.

As union representatives, we met with the then CEO, a couple of directors, and the head of communications, to let them know about our plans to call a public meeting[60]. We made it clear that we appreciated that there are some things that it is politically impossible for them to say publicly.

60 This inaugural meeting of the Campaign to Save Mental Health Services in Norfolk and Suffolk (the Campaign) is described in John and Jane's chapter, *Dying Waiting: Waiting to Die*. Emma is a founder member.

We suggested that if we worked together we could formulate arguments for more resources. For this to happen, we needed them to acknowledge that cuts were having an impact and to start having a more honest conversation with the public. We made it clear we wanted to work constructively together and the sole aim was to get more resources for services and maintain patient safety. Part way through this meeting we noticed that the head of communications had fallen asleep.

At the first, packed, public meeting, we heard passionate accounts from staff, patients, and families concerned about their loved ones. The interim CEO of the Trust, who had listened from the corridor, sent a supportive email the next day. He thanked the staff members who called the meeting for the way that we conducted ourselves in a measured and professional way. He said he wanted to continue to work with us but he didn't get the permanent CEO job and eventually moved on. Any genuine engagement with the very real safety concerns evaporated with his departure.

Through my political allies, I have developed an understanding of how government works and the importance of legislation. With this in mind, I have made several visits to Parliament to meet with MPs and lobby for change. This included taking the youth participation group to London so they could have their say and accompanying service-users, carers, and bereaved relatives involved in the Campaign. An important element of getting politicians support, is bringing the debate into the public eye. I have lost count of how many times I have been interviewed by the media. The issues I raise, remain stubbornly the same. In various campaigning roles, I have given almost the same speech for nearly ten years. It is exhausting and disheartening. I want to give up but I can't yet.

Caroline reflects on her reluctant activism:

I have always been outspoken about injustice but in my formative years, it was impressed upon me that this was not necessarily a good thing because it often led to me struggling with the consequences. I have a lifetime habit of putting my head over the parapet and standing with others, only to discover they have all retreated to safety.

A thread that runs through *He Died Waiting* is how I was constrained and whispering when I should have been shouting. I outline in the book my very loose engagement with local mental health campaigners who, if I am honest, were a bit too outspoken for me. After my son died, I remember sending an email to my bosses almost begging them to work with me because I had no intentions of campaigning against the Trust. I genuinely did not want to but I guess I had a feeling that I might feel provoked into it at some point.

I have lost count of the number of marches, vigils, protests, or demonstrations I have been asked to participate in over the decades. I'm happy to sign a petition or get involved with gentle protests but, until very recently, had only 'banner-waved' once (30 years ago as part of a campaign to win back a free school bus).

Conversely, Emma has been described by some as militant. She's always up for a protest against injustice. Give her a megaphone and a placard and she's in her element (even if she feels nervous). Over the years, I think she has whittled away at my resistance. We don't always agree on how to protest but I admire her courage and persistence. She is someone who stands up for what she believes is right and she gets things done.

Through Emma, I gradually got to know some Campaign members. I came to understand their militancy comes from fear or frustration and that they are kind and supportive of others. They are decent people who have been treated appallingly. Their anger is justified.

Publishing *He Died Waiting* meant exposure. I had to overcome my reluctance to talk to the media about my experiences. As my main motivation for writing the book was to prompt positive change, it seems I accidentally became a campaigner. Even so, I remained only loosely affiliated with the Campaign.

Sometimes, there's a tipping point that means I cannot keep quiet any longer. A series of events occurred over one week at my local trust. First, a Prevention of Future Deaths report was published. This contained concerns about the way the internal serious incident report was conducted, including staff reports of conditions on the ward being removed from the document. Next, the CQC rated the Trust, which has been on and off in 'Special Measures' since 2015, as 'inadequate' for the fourth time. Both of these things were triggering for me. On the day the CQC report was released, the Campaign members placed handmade memorial hearts at the trust head-quarters. This was a gentle protest that I fully supported. When I was asked to speak to the media, I was more outspoken than I usually am. As if things were not bad enough, the Trust started disputing the death figures. My tipping point had been reached. I decided to become more actively involved with campaigning and to use my knowledge and experience to support the Campaign's efforts.

My professional values moderate me. However tempting, I avoid getting involved in personal attacks. I do openly challenge individuals who hold a lot of power because people in positions of responsibility, who are being paid to uphold a public duty, should be held accountable. I hope I always do this respectfully. I try to balance calling out the things that are not good enough, with being affirming and positive. This is an uncomfortable position and it requires a reflexive stance.

I have got to a point in my life where my need to challenge is greater than my need for a career. My #PledgeForTim is to speak out. But this is a relatively new freedom that's based on the worst already happening to me. Earlier in my career, I was not so bold.

Challenging professionally:

In our different roles, we (Caroline and Emma) grapple with similar issues. We are freelance but we still need to uphold our professional codes. We are open about our positions and any conflicts of interest. We hold strong boundaries. For example, we would not disclose to campaigners things we are told confidentially by trust staff and leaders or other interested parties. Neither, would we disclose Campaign information to the trust or anyone else without permission to share.

When staff raise concerns with us we suggest they use their legitimate channels. For example, those in healthcare settings should Datix[61] things they feel are unsafe or use their Freedom to Speak Up Guardian[62], report to the CQC, or union. In social care, there are safeguarding procedures, the LADO[63], and local authority councillors who can be asked to intervene. Anyone can ask their MP for support. However, we have heard countless examples of these safeguards not working as they should. So, we would urge people to think carefully before acting. In principle, we would say always report things but we would urge practitioners to think through possible negative consequences before they do. We regularly have concerns shared with us by people who are too fearful to speak out. We understand these are legitimate fears, particularly if someone is working in a toxic culture. We would never want someone to put themselves in a position where their career or registration would be at stake. However, sometimes the actions staff are expected to take, or the inactions they are expected to ignore, could cause them to breach their registration requirements.

There is strength in numbers. Healthy teams can support each other to make collective challenges to managers. Likewise, there are grass-roots campaigns or groups that health and social care practitioners can legitimately join. We have found our professional social media networks to be a way of having conversations about the things that matter to us and forming connections with like-minded people. In many small ways, we can encourage and support people who are spearheading change.

---

61 Datix is the national NHS safety incidents reporting system.

62 The Freedom to Speak Up Guardians were created following the Francis Report.

63 The LADO is the Local Authority Designated Officer who is responsible for safeguarding.

Our different campaigning styles converged in July 2022. We were part of a group who went to London to lobby our region's MPs. We asked them to support a call for a statutory public inquiry to establish how many people receiving services from the Trust have died, and why, to reduce further deaths. Emma wrote a template letter that people could adapt, to ask their MP to attend the meeting and intervene. She liaised with Clive Lewis MP (who was hosting the meeting) and sorted out all the practicalities. She made banners. Caroline wrote a heartfelt speech on behalf of bereaved relatives which she delivered to MPs, the Minister for Mental Health, and campaigners. We were both interviewed by the media. We both were mindful of the emotional impact on the bereaved relatives who came with us to bravely tell their stories and we extended our genuine love and support to them. In Parliament Square, ITV News asked for the group to hold our banners and chant. Much to her surprise, it was Caroline who suggested, and led, a chant of - "Too many deaths. Public Inquiry now!".

So, there we were, the reluctant accidental activist and the seasoned campaigner, standing shoulder to shoulder. We urge you to be activists and support positive change in whatever way feels right and safe for you.

Inconvenient Truths
By Nikki

This heart is not whom *I* have lost, but the sheer number of strangers who have opened their hearts to share their loss with me. Poor mental health surrounds us all. It's in the lives of my own family, and friends who've broken down and ended up in A&E. It's in the life of a work colleague, who held the wrists of a girl while trying to talk them off the railings of a multi-storey car park and simultaneously messaging me to get help. It's in an old Radio Norfolk jacket that I took out to a man shaking in the cold, sitting in a wheelchair, outside Norwich's main police station. Journalists need to be independent but we have a heart that reflects a need to document the truth, to try and make a difference.

About Nikki

Nikki[64] is an award-winning BBC Health Correspondent. For the last 8 years, she has been covering stories relating to health, including mental health, across the counties in the eastern region and nationally. Nikki is passionate about her work. She is diligent and meticulous when researching stories to ensure the veracity of the content and has been commended by the British Journalism Awards. Nikki has proved herself to be trustworthy among those who have been bereaved. Several of the contributors to this book refer to reports that Nikki has produced.

In this chapter, Nikki offers her perspective of being a journalist reporting on the crisis in mental health services.

64 Nikki Fox is the BBC Look East Health Correspondent https://muckrack.com/nikki-fox-2

Lunch?

The waiting room of the brand-new coroner's court smelt like a furniture warehouse. Plastic and MDF, after the wrappers had just been peeled back. The inquest was examining the death of a hospital healthcare assistant from Covid-19. Vulnerable and in her 60s, she refused to stay at home, choosing instead to keep working through the pandemic. She didn't want to let her colleagues down.

Uncharacteristically early, I perched on a chair and waited for the coroner. I wanted to log on to my laptop and get ahead, but the premium bulk-buy tables were stupidly lower than the chairs. It meant no one could work on them unless they sat on the floor. Realising how undignified that would look to bereaved relatives, I instead made eye contact with another journalist...

"I nearly phoned you the other day", he said, looking well-informed.

"Oh, why's that?" I replied, failing to guess why.

"Did you listen to the last board of governors meeting at the mental health trust?"

"No", I replied. (I often don't get the time because I'm either researching, filming, editing, or 'on air' but I catch up on minutes of meetings when I can.)

"You got a mention."

"Did I?" I said, sounding slightly awkward and puzzled.

I had covered stories relating to the trust in question for 8 years, with three reports in the past six months: one story regarding refugee mental health nurses recruited to help with staffing; another about a hugely valuable counselling service set up to help NHS staff affected by the pandemic; and a third, more recent, about the now massive numbers of children and young people needing mental health help, post-pandemic.

With 8,000 children and young people waiting for treatment or assessment across two counties of England, I thought it was a valid issue. For so long, children haven't received the right support. Now the burgeoning demand means crisis teams are making even more difficult decisions about which seriously ill child is the more likely to take their lives. The number of children and young people waiting was almost double the number that this trust could deal with. My report reflected the massive demands it was facing, which is why the ensuing exchange left me slightly bemused...

"He suggested that they might want to take you out for lunch", said the other journalist.

"Who did?", I replied.

"One of the governors."

"Why?", I said. Even though I was, by now, deducing the answer.

"He seemed to view you as a journalist who had a bit of a negative view of the trust. I think he thought taking you out for some lunch, would help." His words were uttered with a tinge of disbelief, to tease out a reaction.

I was disappointed for two reasons. Firstly, local journalists don't operate like that. I get a salary, I don't get paid per story. I work on what I think is important, what viewers get in touch with me about most (mental healthcare comes second only to dental care – which people are more comfortable shouting about). I work on the subjects that, if raised, give a voice to those who don't usually have one. The things that can educate or inform people or could result in improvement. Journalism tries to reflect what is going on in the real world. The truth, even if for some, it's an inconvenient truth. Like 8,000 children and young people, waiting for help.

I was perturbed that a governor would think journalists are 'bought' with a sandwich. That they would think that with a mug of earl grey, or a cappuccino at Costa, I might be more inclined to run a story that puts a positive spin on things, rather than showing how difficult things are for mental health trusts. When there's no chance of staff meeting demand, even if they're working at maximum capacity, it's my job to raise that point. "A governor would understand that wouldn't they?" I thought. Their job is to help improve services and hold trusts accountable. However, reporting the truth is sometimes misinterpreted as being the cause of the problem. Of course, the governor in question may have thought developing a relationship with me would help highlight the positive things being done in mental health. In fairness, the trust did put the governor right and say the coverage in recent weeks, "had been more balanced" (I'm not aware it was unbalanced before). However, it is impossible for me to ignore the many people getting in touch who are suffering. Even when there are changes for the better, I cannot document a narrative where desperation and indeterminately long waits have disappeared.

Inside the room

When I attend inquests, the harsh reality of the pressures in mental health services are often exposed. The desks for the media are usually at the back of a small room and because they're more intimate proceedings, it rarely feels like a courtroom. Sometimes the sense of grief from the family is so strong, it can seem like you're trespassing. You can feel some relatives viscerally shutting everybody else out so they can deal with the detail that's to come.

I remember hearing about the death of a 15-year-old with anorexia and how the trust tasked with keeping her safe was so stretched that six people were trying to do the work of 20. I also remember the death of a man with paranoid schizophrenia who ran out of medication. His mental health worker had been made redundant. In the same year, another man with schizophrenia died of pneumonia living in squalor with no hot water. The local authority had stopped paying for his homecare. In that particular case, an inquest was only held after the BBC raised the circumstances around his death, followed by a sustained campaign by his family.

For some relatives, it's a shock to see journalists sitting behind them to hear such personal details. To share such a close interrogation of their relative's last moments with an outside observer. But we don't do it to 'get a story'. In fact, if it's not in the public interest, we will choose to leave. Occasionally, it's important to draw attention to the circumstances, in the hope it will prevent other such deaths in the future.

Similar issues come up in different trusts. Sometimes, when I sit passively listening at the back of that courtroom, what is revealed inside the room is horrific. Ligature points which trusts have been warned about for years, resulting in deaths and still nothing is done, safety observations not being carried out on patients for hours, staff falsifying paperwork, and suicidal patients begging for help and not getting it.

"Onwards, exhausted"

When I first met Melanie Leahy[65] she had already lost her son days after he became an inpatient in a mental health unit. Six years on, she's also lost her husband, but her search for the truth is indefatigable. "You'll probably still be visiting me in ten years time", she said during our most recent meeting. Relatives cope in different ways, but some develop quite a dark sense of humour to cope with the long search for unanswered questions.

Melanie's son, Matthew, was 20 when he was taken to a secure unit with a diagnosis of delusional disorder. Three days later he reported he'd been drugged and raped. Four days later, he was found dead. The post-mortem examination found traces of a 'date rape' drug in his blood and four or five needle marks on his groin and there was bruising above both his ankles. A police inquiry was recommended by the coroner, then later dropped. An inquest recorded a narrative verdict. That's why it's important to her, that the media doesn't definitively say he took his life.

---

65 You can read more about this in *The Case For a Statutory Inquiry* by Melanie

I didn't cover the inquest into the death of Melanie's son but I recall my colleague reporting on how the then CEO of the trust had disappeared out of the back door of the Coroner's Court, presumably to avoid questions from journalists (unless it was closer to where he'd parked). Later, there was a health and safety investigation after which the trust was fined £1.5m.

I remember Melanie calling for an independent public inquiry to be discussed in parliament. Her online petition gathered traction, but 17 days before it was due to close, parliament decided to freeze petitions after a general election was called. If Melanie didn't reach the number of signatures needed, she would have to start a new petition from scratch. She had 40,000 signatures and a week until the deadline. I remember thinking, "That's tough, she'll have to start again", and, "100,000 is pretty impossible anyway". How very wrong I was.

This was a woman who looked me in the eyes and assured me that her son had told her after his passing, that the truth would come out in a proper courtroom. She believed that courtroom was a full public inquiry. With four days to go, and only 60,000 signatures, she went to Downing Street, and stayed in London to lobby. With 12 hours left, she still needed a few thousand signatures. I think, that the death of Melanie's son represented the strength of feeling about mental health services up and down the country because 100,000 people signed. It was astonishing. I sent her a message about this. "Onwards. Exhausted", said the reply.

Because of the sheer number of investigations, I've been to Melanie's house several times. Each time she tells me about a new piece of the jigsaw and another catalyst for grief: police releasing the 999 phone call her son made just before he died; a letter from an old friend of her son; or a former staff member making contact. For her, it is all-consuming until she gets a full explanation.

Got away with it

It is, of course true, that there's only so much mental health trusts can do with so few doctors and nurses, at a time of massive rising demand. But some do have a history of prioritising reputational management over being solely focussed on confronting the problems head on.

In 2020, a communications manager at a mental health trust, mistakenly, copied the local paper into an email to his bosses. It said the service had 'got away' with its failings being highlighted after the death of two people with dementia. This is what it said:

'We seem to have got away (again) with the Adult Safeguarding Review story. I used iPlayer to check Radio Norfolk between 4 pm and 7 pm last night, and it was not on there at all. I think we may have been saved by the death of Terry Jones [Monty Python star]. However, it was the lead story (Nikki Fox) on BBC Look East last night at 6.30 pm and again at 10.30 pm (Leigh Milner!), but not on the lunchtime bulletin at all. Yet again, though, we emerged virtually unscathed. We weren't named but our Nikki said something along the lines of, "No agency involved in Doreen Livermore's care emerged without criticism".

'Our Nikki'? The above quotation made it into many national newspapers. The uneducated observer might be forgiven for thinking I was 'in on it' when it comes to helping to protect this trust's reputation. Indeed, some of my national colleagues took it to mean that I might be too close to them. It is, perhaps more likely, it was a sarcastic remark referring to the fact I may have been a bit critical. I'll never know. When I tried to address it, in a subsequent phone call to the then communication team, I was told they didn't know *what* the author of the email meant.

These are the failings in Mrs Livermore's care that the trust's *former* communications manager was less than keen to see widely publicised: Mrs Livermore died on her 89th birthday after being knocked to the floor by another patient in a care home. She was vulnerable and frightened. The man had attacked her four times and other residents too. He had been discharged too early by the mental health team and the care home couldn't cope. Mrs Livermore's death resulted in multiple lessons for all agencies, including the mental health trust and a care home[66].

I still get occasional contact from Doreen Livermore's son. He, like many bereaved relatives I speak to, is polite, educated, and living in a state of disbelief. He can't understand how warning signs were missed and he wants to believe the same failures won't be repeated. I see his views as a part of a more detailed picture. I'm always in awe of the focus and strength of bereaved relatives who want to improve services for others. Some I've met, worked in NHS in mental health services themselves.

Managing the emotions

It is disturbing to have spoken to so many struggling or bereaved families. Depressing to a point that, occasionally, I've felt like I need a change of job. Sometimes, I do find it overwhelming to listen to so much pain but then I sleep on it.

66 https://www.bbc.co.uk/news/uk-england-norfolk-51210654 and https://www.bbc.co.uk/news/uk-england-norfolk-51224339

I am grateful that I do sleep and that I have a supportive husband and beautiful child, who I can lie with on a swing in a park. Becoming a parent changed my perspective and there have been occasions when I've shed a tear during an interview. It's often when parents tell me how they feel about not being able to see their child walk down the aisle, have a family, or their guilt about something that was beyond their control. Or it's their testimony of being turned away; photos of bruises; accounts of sleeping or abusive staff; and diaries documenting lives that suddenly stop - leaving three-quarters of the year with empty pages.

The acute distress, that I sometimes witness, has an impact on me. For example: facing a man in his 90s, who had lost his wife and childhood sweetheart, was one of the most uncomfortable and saddening moments. Neville Copeman stood before me, smartly dressed, leaning reliantly on a walking stick. He'd already overcome the part where he got in the car to travel to his son's house to speak to me. But he stood in front of me, and just said, "I can't do it". His eyes were filling with tears. His wife, Peggy, died after being transported across England and back again, in the space of a few days, due to bed shortages[67]. Neville, never had the chance to say goodbye to Peggy before she was transferred to Somerset. Neither Neville, nor his wife, had ever left Norfolk. To them, Somerset could have been, the other side of the world. He couldn't picture a distance he'd never travelled, so how could he process that he'd lost the love of his life, when she was finally on her way back? His family says that he often wakes in his sleep dreaming that he'd seen his wife at the end of his bed, then feeling panicked about not being able to help her. So, when people talk about 'out of area placements', it's the (often unheard) impact on the families, rather than the numbers on a sheet, that are at the forefront of my mind.

What people don't see is everything that happens off-camera. At one point, I had around seven or eight desperate people a week get in touch about not being able to get mental health support. I even wrote the Samaritans number down, carrying it with me, so that I could try and give them something. Regularly I'd have 45-minute conversations while sitting in the car parked down the road from my house (so my young daughter didn't see me and get excited). Many were with people who'd got in touch but had no intention of going on television. They were just desperate for someone to talk to.

Some I can't help because they can't give consent or there are other things I also need to report on. That can weigh heavy on my mind. I know they must be in a bad place if the only option for them is to contact a journalist, and I wonder what will happen to them.

---

67 You can read the family's account of this in Nick and Maxine's chapter: *Peggy: Not 'Acting Up' But Dying*. This includes a link to one of Nikki's reports.

Earlier this year, the worst thing possible occurred. Someone contacted me for help about their relative but the person died before I could return their call. I froze on the spot when I found that out. I was left with a tremendous sense of guilt. I try and tell myself that I'm doing the best job I can, I also know I may not have changed anything, but it still eats at me.

I've had people diagnosed with schizophrenia call me at 2 am (my fault for not protecting my number better) and people emailing from inside mental health units. I talked to one girl with anorexia who was placed 380 miles away from her parents. I needed to make sure she was strong enough to go on television. So, with her permission, I spoke to her parents to assess both her welfare and their support. It took time before I could promise to get the story 'on air'. By that point, she'd changed her mind. I have to respect that. These continuing conversations are all part of my job.

Integrity

I will not run a story unless I can verify the information. Additionally, the public need to see the evidence. It is not unusual for me to be told about something that I believe, but I cannot report it because the person sharing (even whistle-blowing) is not prepared to go on camera. Most people in that position are scared of losing their jobs, scared of upsetting people if they tell the truth, or worried that they might be breaching patient confidentiality by recounting unsafe events. On one occasion, I met a staff whistle-blower in a cemetery to try and protect them while they passed me documents vital to the investigation. If it wasn't for the bravery of these people, many failures would not be highlighted.

I have a lot of respect for the NHS, so the responsibility of making sure I'm fair and balanced is a priority. I once got a tip-off from someone saying that the CV of an incoming mental health Chief Executive Officer (CEO) needed looking at. There were unaccounted for gaps, after degrees taken abroad, and some quite significant changes in career direction. They were about to become responsible for a budget of over £300m of public money. So, during a spare moment, I wrote two emails to two universities checking the qualifications listed.

A few days later I got a response and couldn't quite believe it. Confirmation that the person concerned did not have the postgraduate law degree, as stated on official documents. I checked twice, with the US university in question. The woman on the other end of the phone was friendly. I remember having a surreal conversation with her, where she asked me to pronounce American words in English so she could hear my accent.

"I love the English accent … say Georgia", she said.

"Georgia", I replied. She then attempted to teach me to say it the "proper American" way.

I was slightly embarrassed by the exchange but knew she was just trying to find a moment of light during a potentially mundane shift. After a bit of banter, she said she'd put the evidence in writing. I put the phone down and sat in my car, parked again, around the corner from my home. I worked on a television report but it didn't go out for three weeks. It took more than a dozen calls to lawyers and an editorial policy department. I knew that the person concerned could lose their job. The public interest had to be weighed against the reputational damage it could cause. Confidentially, I rang three respected people outside of the area, to seek an independent opinion. One of them said, "Nikki, now you know this, if you don't publish you'll be complicit yourself". In a way, they were right. My job is to report the truth. An investigation followed and the person concerned was sacked. At the time of writing, they are working in another senior position in governance. In their biography, they describe how they developed the NHS 'Well Led Framework'.

Exposing inconvenient truths

When the inconvenient truth emerges, relationships can get frosty. A few years ago, I was invited by a trust to tour a new mental health facility. The CEO was there, as were some people from local charities. Unbeknown to me, one of the charity representatives wasn't particularly pleased with a TV report produced by one of my colleagues. Because they were tight for air-time, my colleague had cut the interview with the charity in favour of comment from a former health secretary. The charity had a right to be slightly aggrieved. But I remember how, having introduced me to the unhappy charity representative, the CEO walked off laughing to himself. I missed the tour, while trying to field the complaint. The same former CEO followed this action with a complaint on the phone, to my News Editor. I was accused of producing a report that wasn't true. My article was about the planned reduction of 90 posts in the mental health trust because of cost pressures. It was confirmed to me, in an email by the trust's communications team, that 90 posts were indeed planned to go. My News Editor came off the call pretty stunned at the unbending criticism that ensued.

Various trusts' staff report to me, the strict control by the NHS over what they can, and can't say. So, sensitivity over any failure, shortage of funding, or closures, is no surprise. Some NHS staff report that they're put on the 'naughty step' if a negative report unnecessarily finds its way into the media. This runs contrary to the NHS policies on whistle-blowing and Duty of Candour[68].

---

68 https://www.england.nhs.uk/ourwork/whistleblowing/ and https://www.gov.uk/government/publications/nhs-screening-programmes-duty-of-candour/duty-of-candour

A broken system

After compiling stories about mental health services for so many years, it is depressing to hear some staff, patients, and bereaved relatives continue to talk about a 'broken system'. Often behind this are large numbers of people needing help to live a life worth living. In many of my reports, staff shortages, particularly a lack of specialist workers, feature. Occasionally, I run a story on staff who have done the wrong thing: the psychiatrist with fake qualifications; the staff in inpatient units who sleep when they should be observing; or the practitioners who have dismissed risks and someone has died.

I hear about, and report on, good practice too: the fantastic perinatal units that help keep mothers overwhelmed by psychosis together with their newborn babies; the work to provide a listening ear to children in schools; and the optimism and energy of Syrian and Lebanese refugees leaving their children and families to come here and work as mental health professionals. Seeing the refugees was particularly poignant, their witness to war has seen them mature beyond their ages. Despite their nursing qualifications, they start here as healthcare assistants. This country doesn't make it easy - many landlords in the seaside town where they now reside, won't make agreements with under 25's, making even finding somewhere to stay, a hurdle. Nevertheless, they have big ambitions of working their way up in the NHS. Convincing them not to move to bigger, more attractive cities like Liverpool or Birmingham will be a challenge.

As far as leaders go, one staff member told me that, if their management led a football team, they would have been relegated by now. But no one can deny it's a challenge. The pressures of working in over-stretched services means that some staff need counselling and others leave altogether. Each time someone with their skills and experience is lost, the crisis is exacerbated. Instead, agency staff who don't know the patients as well, plug the gaps. Strong leaders are needed if the system is to function well enough to attract and keep good people. Staffing the service may be a challenge, but we can't be without them.

How a society treats its most vulnerable is a credible measure of humanity. When mental healthcare is seen as important as cancer care, wards don't shut because staffing numbers are so unsafe, and teenagers are no longer placed in intensive care because it's the only safe place for them - I hope people will talk about how this country provides a world-class mental health service, protecting the most vulnerable.

Among the names that I'll remember are Thomas and Katherine Kemp, a young couple who were deeply in love. Katherine had begged for help for Thomas' mental health. Police took the couple to A&E but they were turned away. Hours later, Thomas killed his partner before taking his life. The coroner said that he loved Katherine and wouldn't have knowingly hurt her. Like Thomas and Katherine's best friend, I think of them.

Sometimes transparency can be a friend; it helps people learn the reasons why things go wrong, and, after all, looking after people's mental health means looking after their lives. Over eight years, across several counties, I have reported on a vast number of people, who have died waiting for the right help. They were aged 15 to 89. They were waiting for help that listens, that has time to provide individualised care, and that is available in the right place, at the right time. Zero suicide pledges and promises to end the practice of placing people miles away from their loved ones for mental healthcare, still seem far in the future. Life is hard for many.

I will remember all of those who've opened their hearts to try and make a difference, as well as the most vulnerable who have no one to speak for them.

It Shouldn't be Down to Luck
By Rachel

This heart represents how Rachel felt when her daughter was sent hundreds of miles from home for mental health treatment. She felt like her heart had been ripped out and the thread connecting them could easily be undone. The vibrant background reflects the strength of Rachel's family.

About Rachel

Rachel works part-time as a primary school teacher. She has lived experience of mental illness in addition to being a parent and carer. Rachel is co-founder and chair of the charity Mental Health - Time for Action Foundation (MHTFA)[69]. She also works in various lived experience roles at the Royal College of Psychiatrists (RCPsych).

Rachel has for many years spoken out about mental health services and she is a passionate campaigner. She has met with many MPs and spoken at conferences and events, including the 2019 RCPsych International Congress. Rachel feels that people like herself, who have survived dreadful ordeals, have a responsibility to speak out and act on behalf of those who cannot. For those who are no longer here, or who don't have the support and resources that she has been lucky enough to possess.

69 For more information see MHTFA'a website: https://mentalhealthtimeforaction.org/

It Shouldn't be Down to Luck

In the past, I may have been described as quiet and unassuming. Not someone who often spoke out, and certainly not someone who'd ever contemplate standing up in public or writing about my family's experiences. But life events change us. What has happened to our family over the past few years is truly extraordinary. None of us, not least my daughters, are who we were back then. Somebody recently described me as 'too outspoken' and 'too political'. I am a campaigner and a survivor. I believe myself lucky to be both. I also believe in the possibility that the world, and indeed our corner of the world, can be a better place for all of us. For this to happen, ordinary people like myself need to speak out and challenge the status quo. To put our head above the parapet and say things that may make others feel uncomfortable.

This is our story.
Nine years ago, we were just an ordinary family. I'd had a diagnosis of anxiety and depression, but this was managed successfully with medication and the continuity of care that my long-standing GP was able to offer.

I knew very little about other mental health conditions. I'm sure I felt that we were somehow immune to serious mental illness. After all, we were a robust and happy family. Both of us were in work and with an extensive support network of family and friends. We were strong, resourceful, and ultimately enjoying life without the insecurities and instability that so many of us endure. So, when we first began to have concerns about my eldest daughter, I felt confident that her difficulties would pass. I believed that, with perhaps a little extra support, we'd overcome these challenges together as a tight family unit.

How wrong I was. Firstly, and significantly, our GP took early retirement because he was unhappy about the direction that the NHS was heading following the introduction of the 2012 Health and Social Care Act. This left a GP practice in chaos because several other experienced doctors followed suit. Our new GP was a man of kindness and compassion. He was experienced enough to recognise that our daughter needed a referral to CAMHS (Child and Adolescent Mental Health Services) but not long after that, he too moved on.

We found ourselves thrown into a secondary health care system that I, naively, thought would have all the staff and resources required to ensure my daughter would make a quick and full recovery. I believed that she would at the very least, have a similar continuity of care to that she'd received for her first 13 years.

My daughter clearly had issues around eating and nutrition but for the following 18 months, she did not receive any dietetic input. Instead, she had a series of erratic appointments with a number of clinicians. Almost two years on, our daughter was still at the same dangerously low BMI that she had been since the referral to CAMHS was made. Then a new and highly experienced clinician joined and she was finally given a diagnosis. A diagnosis that had not been mentioned to us before. One that our under-resourced outpatient team did not have the staffing, expertise, or resources to deal with in the community. We found ourselves suddenly, not only facing a diagnosis of anorexia nervosa, but also faced with the certainty that our young, vulnerable, and clearly very poorly, daughter would need to be hospitalised.

As if the situation we faced was not bad enough, we learnt that not only was there not a bed available locally, there wasn't a bed available anywhere in the entire country that could manage our daughter's specialist needs. Disbelief piled on disbelief, which turned to blame. Not towards services, or the professionals in which we'd placed 100% of our trust and belief, but on myself. My instinctive and strongest feeling was self-blame. How had I let this happen? Why had I not insisted she saw a dietician? Why had I not raised my concerns earlier, and with the right people?

As I lay awake soon after we received this terrible news, I could not see how our family could survive this. Our beautiful, once happy, carefree, and always loving and affectionate, daughter was being taken away from us and going many, many miles from home.

On a summer's day in August 2014, after weeks of uncertainty and what seemed like an eternity, our daughter was finally admitted to a specialist inpatient unit more than 50 miles from our home in Nottingham. I'll never forget the warm welcome we received at this hospital. The staff were clearly highly experienced, compassionate and they did everything within their power to make admission as easy as it could be. But nothing could take away from me the guilt, the intolerable sadness, and feelings of utter impotence as a mother. When the time came to say our goodbyes, I was overcome with acute anxiety. How could I be sure that she was now going to get the right care, especially so far from us her family? The unspeakable possibility loomed large in my mind that my beautiful girl might not make it.

I don't think in the weeks and months that followed, I once considered that this admission would last so long, or that it would be a situation that would be repeated over and over. I never imagined that for years our whole family would be utterly consumed, not only by this illness but by a fragile and fragmented system, that would lead to me becoming so ill that I too would end up needing acute care. My middle daughter would become so fraught with worry and sadness, caused by the long-distance separations, that she would develop Post Traumatic Stress Disorder and be unable to attend school. The extent to which a whole family's mental health is entwined is too often ignored or underestimated.

A seriously mentally ill person has a much better chance of long-term recovery if they are surrounded by those that they love and are loved by. Yet, in our mental health system, the level of care and resources available continues to be a 'postcode lottery'. Very few young people are offered any continuity of care within their home community. Instead, they continue to be sent the length and breadth of the country, away from friends and family at a time of great vulnerability. Small wonder then, that so many end up relapsing and the cycle of admission and discharge is perpetuated.

When I look back now, I can see how lucky we were that the initial inpatient treatment my daughter received was so good. It was a structured and evidence-based approach. The ethos of the hospital was positive and there was never any question that the young people there wouldn't recover and return to a full life back home. The young people were cared for by staff who treated them with the kindness and love they'd offer their own children. Self-harming and other maladaptive behaviours happened. However, the level of supervision and the structured daytime activities meant that it was very much rarer than the hospitals that we have since experienced.

As my daughter approached discharge from this first hospital there was much discussion about the type of care, she would require from her outpatient team. It was described as the 'discharge package'. I naively assumed that this so-called 'package' would have everything she needed. My daughter had responded well to the boundaries set in hospital, and was eating the most varied and nutritious diet she ever had, but we worried that she could quickly relapse without a dietician's support. She had also benefited from the input of an occupational therapist and had begun to explore new interests and make plans for the future. To me, it made complete sense that two such professionals should form the basis of her care package.

However, this promise of a planned and resourced discharge package was little more than a pipe dream. It belonged to a fantasy world where a CAMH team have a fully resourced 'mental health toolbox' at their disposal with the security of an intensive 'step up' service if needed.

During my daughter's hospital stay, she'd developed some excellent therapeutic relationships with the nurses and the psychologist. The importance of such relationships can never be underestimated in mental health. It can take many weeks or months to reach the point where a relationship is strong and trusting enough to begin therapeutic work. As we planned for my daughter's discharge, I was desperate to find a solution that would enable some continuity, at least regarding this all-important therapeutic work. Over the years, I have come to realise the dreadful reality that a major obstacle to my daughter's recovery was an absence of this all-important continuity of care.

The inevitable relapse happened over a very short period and although it became evident very quickly that she required intensive support, the speed at which she was able to access help was dangerously slow. Unable to get a hospital bed, because there were other people who were assessed as having higher priority, what followed was a common-place scenario for many eating disorder patients. They fall deeper into the depths of this terrible illness until essentially, they become a higher priority. My daughter went from managing to keep herself stable to requiring an emergency admission through our A&E department. She then spent four weeks languishing on a general paediatric ward until a bed was eventually located at a unit 100 miles away from our home.

We had been lucky with my daughter's first hospital admission. The contrast in treatment in her next admission could not have been starker. Four weeks into this admission my daughter had made no progress. She was fed entirely through a nasal gastric tube which she chose to have running throughout the day. We would arrive for a visit, after a two-hour journey, to find her wandering aimlessly around the hospital carrying her pump, or lying listlessly on her bed. It became clear that she was not being enabled to move towards recovery. She was getting more ill and showing signs of severe depression and suicidal ideation. We were horrified to discover, despite how ill she was, that there would be no attempt to transfer her to a hospital nearer home. Instead, it was decided that as she was relatively 'weight restored' she could 'continue her 'recovery' in the community. She was swiftly discharged without a plan in place. Our family found ourselves in the most horrific situation imaginable. At home without support, managing a complex and daunting nasal gastric feeding regime ourselves.

Then, following her third relapse, as if the pain and suffering we'd experienced as a family wasn't enough, my daughter and I found ourselves boarding a plane and flying over 300 miles to a hospital in Scotland. The grief and pain as I handed her over to yet another team of clinicians, although mitigated by the warmth and compassion of the staff, overwhelmed me. Our whole family had been pushed to the limits by the challenges of previous out-of-area placements and lack of consistent treatment. Facing what lay ahead, filled me with fear and utter hopelessness.

This fear has been constant. The brutal day-to-day reality that my daughter could lose her life. The utter powerlessness as her mother. My inability to find for her the holistic, compassionate, and trauma-informed care she needed to recover, to thrive. My once strong family had become critically fragile.

"All separation causes a wound. A rupture of the mind" (Roma Tearne). There is no better way to describe the pain and despair that resulted from my daughter being ripped out of the heart of our family and placed so many miles away.

The resulting sleeplessness and anguish quickly led me to overuse prescription sleeping medication. As the weeks became months, and my daughter still no nearer to returning home, this reliance soon became a dependency - or perhaps more accurately a dangerous and life-threatening addiction.

Decades-old unresolved traumatic experiences were compounded by a psychological wound caused by separation from my daughter. This led to a catastrophic 'rupture' which became 'infected' and was only manageable through the pain-numbing benzodiazepine drugs.

By the time any help (therapeutic intervention and management of my prescriptions) was offered, I was deemed too unstable and, eventually, a danger to myself. I remember very little about my admission to hospital. Another layer of trauma for which I will undoubtedly at some point need to explore and resolve. I do remember the final meeting before my discharge. I was described in ways I did not recognise or, I believe, deserve. Never have I felt so disempowered, stigmatised, and so utterly misunderstood and alone.

Without a chance conversation with one of my daughter's health professionals (another magical, curious stroke of luck), I have no doubt I wouldn't have survived my discharge from hospital and my daughter's subsequent readmission. This conversation led me to explore, Parks Inner Child Therapy (PICT)[70], which I found gentle yet so powerful. This therapy enabled me to heal the deep dark 'hole in my soul'. It would stitch my deep and painful 'wound' and allow me to move forwards towards recovery by rediscovering who I really was. Fortunately, I was able to fund this privately. It is my hope, that 'trauma resolution' therapies like this, including EMDR (Eye Movement Desensitisation and Reprocessing) and innovative approaches such as Dr Gabor Maté's psychotherapeutic Compassionate Inquiry[71], will one day be accessible to all, as part of early intervention within statutory NHS mental health services.

---

70 More information about this is on their website: https://parks-inner-child-therapy.com/

71 See website: https://compassionateinquiry.com/the-approach/

As I regained my strength, and gradually healed from years of underlying trauma, I realised that merely hoping, or asking politely, for what my daughter and myself so desperately needed, was no longer enough. Something had to change, not just for us but for all those other young people and their families who were facing similar challenges. So, I took the difficult decision, borne of sheer desperation, to go public with our situation. Since then, I have taken part in various radio and television news items as well as a documentary for Channel 4 Dispatches. I am driven to do this because, aside from chronic underfunding and lack of investment, the voices of patients and survivors are missing. People need to hear the all-important voice of lived experience in mental health services.

There is much to be proud of in our NHS and mental health services. So many hardworking, talented, and compassionate individuals face the daily challenges of underfunding and underinvestment. They do this, not for money or status, but through a desire to provide help and hope to those of us whose life's challenges have led to mental ill-health.

I feel strongly that the key to ensuring we all have good mental health is to firstly ensure that we support a society where equality is the priority. We must also cease to lay the blame of mental illness solely on the individual.

The keys to ensuring that the care and treatment offered within services is effective and life-saving are compassion and empathy. A fundamental component must be the development of trauma-informed care and services. For this to become a reality we need properly funded services that have safe staffing numbers.

Early intervention is, of course, fundamental to this. But this needs to be community-driven with coproduction and lived experience at its heart. Properly resourced and staffed outpatient teams can, and should, work to ensure that admission to hospital is a last resort and not an inevitable outcome. Programmes like the Open Dialogue Approach[72], a truly patient-centred and holistic approach, currently being piloted across NHS England will hopefully become the 'gold standard' of care. In eating disorders, the Royal Free CAMHS[73]offers an intensive community based approach that has dramatically reduced the need for inpatient care and consistently achieves excellent clinical outcomes.

Without approaches such as these, too many will fall victim to the 'revolving door' of inpatient admission. Repeated admissions can add layers of trauma. Some of the young people, who were in hospital with my daughter, remain in hospital many years on. Institutionalised, traumatised,

---

72 http://apopendialogue.org/

73 https://www.royalfree.nhs.uk/services/services-a-z/child-and-adolescent-mental-health-services/eating-disorder-service/

and devoid of hope. Years of living a half-life waiting for recovery. Sadly, others have not survived.

Over the last few years, I have joined various organisations as a representative of people with lived experience. I want to help clinicians to understand that many of their practices are not working for people. Too many are wedded to a medical model that pathologises an individual as having something 'wrong with them' rather than understanding what 'happened to them'. We can no longer ignore the wider societal issues, including systemic racism, health inequalities, and poverty.

Fundamental in the drive to improve better mental health services is continuity of care. The time and space for individuals to build strong therapeutic relationships that enable clinicians to understand individual stories, truly empathise, and work collaboratively towards authentic and lasting healing.

In my view, services should provide therapeutic interventions, including the trauma resolution approaches mentioned earlier, alongside art, drama, and somatic work. These delve deep into our unconscious, and/or use movement and self-expression, to gently, yet effectively, enable healing from, and reprocessing of adverse and traumatic events that shape our lives. Without this, we risk leaving too many behind. Too many are, too often, dismissed as 'treatment resistant', or 'complex', or not 'engaged enough'. There are too many lost lives.

In 2018, I co-founded a campaigning group, and now a charity, Mental Health Time For Action (MHTFA). We set an ambitious agenda of trying to engage people with power and influence to change their policies and increase funding. We don't want to see more explorations into what is needed. There is plenty of evidence about what needs to change. What we want is for people to start working on solutions. The time for action is now. We also aim to raise enough money to be able to fund trauma therapies for those unable to access them. In 2019, we held a joint conference with Keep Our NHS Public (KONP) which was well-attended. It enabled people who are involved in various initiatives to connect with each other. I have discovered one of my strengths is to get people in influential positions to listen to me. Once I get them in my sights I am persistent and tenacious.
I have written articles about my daughter's experiences, my battle with addiction, and my views on mental health services[74].

When Covid struck, our fledgling charity found it hard to progress without being able to hold conferences or gather with others face-to-face. However, we have been able to support other people in their work. I was

74 https://blogs.bmj.com/bmj/2020/07/24/rachel-bannister-on-struggling-with-addiction-you-just-need-a-hand-to-hold-to-see-you-through-this/

proud to be able to support Melanie Leahy with her campaign[75]. In early 2021, our charity hosted the launch of Caroline's book, *He Died Waiting*. In my speech, I referred to the way I feel lucky my daughter has survived, whereas Caroline's son Tim did not. It shouldn't be down to luck whether people can receive a mental health service or a particular therapy. It shouldn't be down to luck whether a hospital bed is available, or if it is, whether it is near enough for families to be able to support their children.

Covid heightened my fears and sense of life's fragility. My world has shrunk and I desperately miss mixing with people. Psychologically I do not feel fully myself. A great many other people's mental health has been similarly impacted. I feel like an emotional snow-blower has shaken up the whole world and it hasn't settled yet. Although MHTFA activities have been limited as a result of the pandemic, we are in the planning stages for our next conference. This will focus on innovative treatment approaches, including those that have proved to be transformational for myself and my family. Behind the scenes, I am also supporting and encouraging people who are making a difference. I can connect with like-minded people and support others with their campaigns and projects. When funding allows us, MHTFA hopes to offer places on a trauma resolution programme via our sister charity Imara[76].

Reflecting on my own treatment for mental illness, I wish I'd been offered some hopeful words and preferably with a hand upon mine. I needed to hear, "Rachel this suffering is not of your own making. This illness does not and will never define you. It is where you are not who you are and there is hope for recovery and a future".

I have realised that keeping myself and my children alive is an achievement. I feel lucky. I also feel angry because others have died waiting for the treatment and support they need. Professor Dame Elizabeth Nneka Anionwu says, "Anger creates energy. The right kind of anger, directed well, fuels the desire and willingness to challenge injustice." I will use my anger at the injustice faced by so many and continue speaking out about mental health services, in memory of all those whose lives have been lost to mental illness.

---

75 See Melanie's chapter, *The Case for a Statutory Public Inquiry*.

76 https://www.imara.org.uk/

Blinded
By Lisa

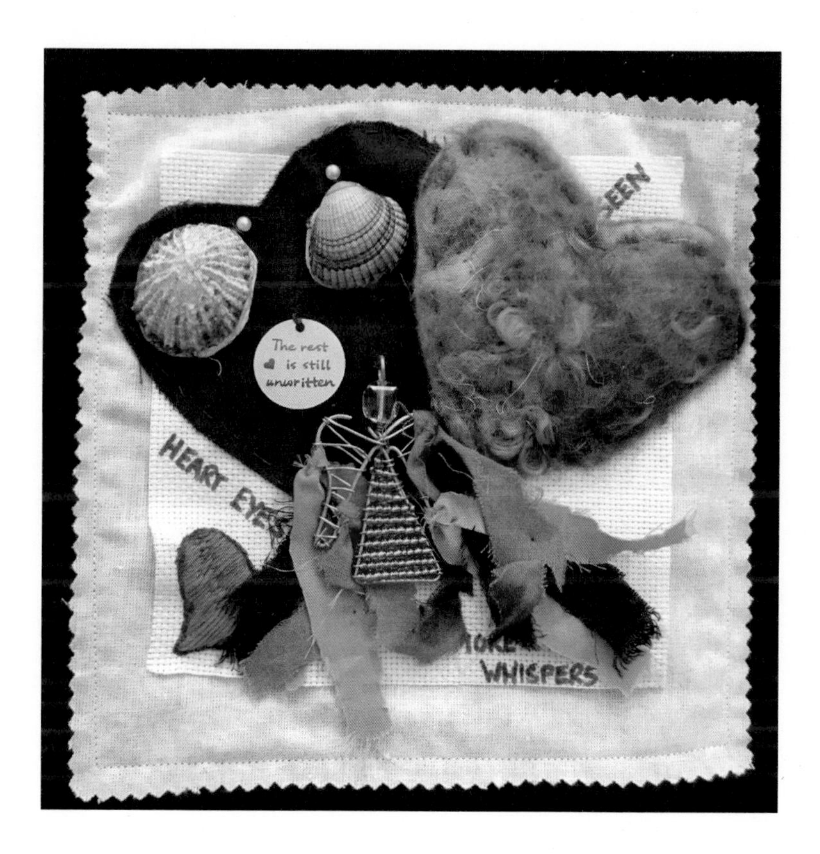

Lisa explains her heart: It is busier and brighter than I would usually choose because I wanted to honour people who are invisible and judged, and to represent the colours, textures, and depths of each person. The 'felt' heart is a reminder to move from head to heart because this is where real change begins. The beaded angel is from Durban (South Africa) my homeland and the shells are from Donegal. The natural world helps guide, touch, and encourage me. 'The rest is still unwritten' is from a bracelet I bought about surviving suicide attempts. Even though they are not physically here, those we have lost, continue to help write our story.

About Lisa

Lisa's first career was as an early years educator and lecturer. She worked as a family support worker with SureStart. Following a long period of being unable to work due to mental illness, Lisa began working for her local mental health trust as a peer trainer. She contributed to many local and regional mental health initiatives, including the *Towards Zero Suicide Programme*[77]. Having become passionate, and knowledgeable, about trauma-informed practice, Lisa felt she needed more choices and autonomy. After much deliberation, Lisa started her own training and consultancy business[78] so she could fully utilise all her skills and experiences. She wants to honour her own healing journey, whilst finding new ways to give back from the abundance she has received, through her work.

77 www.zerosuicide.edc.org

78 For more information about Lisa and her work, see her website: www.lisamorrison.co.uk

Blinded

I will never forget reading the words in Caroline's first book where she spoke about Tim and others leading 'whispered lives'. I felt seen and immensely sad. My throat filled with unfallen tears and the countless words I had never been able to speak. My body told the story with desperate acts of self-harm and suicide attempts. Visions and voices no-one else could see or hear. It's a very lonely place. Caroline's words also brought renewed hope and determination in my own work. I was reminded that others, that I've met on my journey, do understand the heart of the matter. Because only the heart can brave the darkness and unknown and see with kindness. This is a part of who I am. Someone who went into mental health services at the age of 14 and has yet to leave.

But it's different now. I've had multiple diagnoses and spent too many years 'contained' in inpatient psychiatric units where scant resources and inadequate knowledge, coupled with over-medication and electroconvulsive therapy, compounded my trauma. I was slowly dying. Things have changed. I will share some of my journey and highlight the relevance of trauma-informed and responsive services at an individual, and organisational, level.

I am so much more than any label, judgement, assumption, or 'thing' that has happened to me. It's important to reflect on how, sometimes unintentionally, services can dehumanise people. Strip us of our personhood. We become risk assessments and caseloads. Problems to be fixed through service provision, that's narrowly defined by the service, rather than relationships being nurtured in conditions where the inherent worth and potential of each person can flourish. Curiosity about the language familiar to us is needed because words can take on different meanings depending on people's experiences. Who is writing our story? What is the language of our organisations and the language we use to define ourselves?

My story

As a parent of two small children, I completed my honours degree in Education and did many odd jobs in between. Then, once again, I became too unwell to work. This time for a number of years. Untreated trauma had caught up with me. In 2017, I spent five months in a treatment centre in South Africa. I returned ready to rejoin life. Working as the Lead Peer Trainer at my local Recovery College, I came to understand more about the system from the other side of the locked door. Imagine - I was given a key and fob for the very building I'd attended as a patient for ten years. I felt there was power in that key. During this time, I saw the best, and the worst, of 'co-production' and how staff can also feel voiceless and powerless, in systems deeply entrenched in structural inequalities. The 'doing to and for' not 'being alongside and with'. Siloed cultures of suspicion and blame, breathing inside stark, lifeless walls and corridors, that would dysregulate anyone. Wholesome values splashed across logos can cause cynicism when processes, and protocols trump compassion, knowledge, and integrity. It's not all gloom and doom. I know many good people who compassionately do brave work despite the challenges.

Co-production is just one way of describing those who need services, and those who work in them, doing things together. When real co-production happens, it feels like a light going on. There is something magical and quite profound about people being brave enough to work through the messy, sometimes challenging process of building trust, listening, hearing, respecting, and valuing every person's views. Inevitably, the outcome is a meeting of our common humanity. That deeper place, beyond roles, walls, judgements, and the assumptions we hold.

But I found myself struggling in a lived experience role where, despite throwing my heart and soul into all I did, I was still unable to affect sustainable change. With no decision-making power, too few of us represented, I ticked many boxes but changed very little. It was exhausting trying to manage, and stay true to my values, in a hierarchical system that retraumatised me. It didn't matter that I now had a key to the door because it was tokenistic. I had 'progressed', from the very unwell 'service user', to the picture of 'recovery', and I felt suffocated by binary labels.

Psychiatry finally labelled my lifetime in services as Complex Post Traumatic Stress and Dissociative Disorder. I don't use the word disorder to explain what has happened to me. As Viktor Frankl says, "An abnormal reaction to an abnormal situation is normal behaviour". There is too much focus on mental illness and addiction being 'failings' of an individual or their family. If only service-users took more personal responsibility, did what they were told, and practiced better self-care, all would be well. This is a convenient way to avoid the harsh realities that many people face in the context of social injustices and inequalities.

Looking at the world right now, pressures on services, the impact of Covid (and the inequalities this has highlighted), it's easy to get overwhelmed. That's when I quieten and find ways back to my heart space. I remember the years when I woke every day wanting to die and believing I was a hopeless case. I am now able to hold both my children close and feel their hearts beating next to mine and their breath on my skin. I laugh. Often. I am finding my way back to me. In all my imperfection and human frailty, knowing hopelessness allows to me to hold hope. There are others who journey alongside me, and I am so grateful for each one of them. We all need this.

Educating about trauma, and the power of human connection, forms the basis of my work. How we are with people. Why we are the way we are. And, why a trauma-informed approach benefits everybody. I believe an understanding of the theory of trauma, that Caroline and I outline in our introductory chapter, can help us understand what is happening in our minds and bodies. Working with an EMDR therapist who is very skilled, and very human, has been life-changing for me. Finding a language to make sense of what has happened to me is so healing. I am learning to listen to my body and have discovered a wise, untouched core. My special friend bravely walks this journey with me. Feelings of shame are lessening as I've allowed a little space for self-compassion to soften some harsh and unhelpful judgements. Against myself and, at times, others. There is no 'one size fits all' for processing trauma. Understanding of, and access to, different trauma therapies and ways of healing are limited. This needs to change.

Professionals are taught that they are the experts. If we truly allow ourselves to really hear another's pain, it would be arrogant to assume we should have all the answers. Compassionately being *with*, bearing witness, being able to say, 'I'm so sorry you are in so much pain', is, in my opinion, highly underrated. To facilitate this, practitioners need to be working in the right conditions. Staff are people - with lives representative of all the issues we as a society face and experience. These issues cannot be ignored.

I believe the things which are often sacrificed because of 'pressures in the system', are the same things that lead to workforce issues that have long been identified as problematic. Staff absence, burnout, high turnover, and a traumatised workforce. There is the added issue of what we measure is what is funded and prioritised. Values, meaningful impact, and quality of life are notoriously difficult to measure because they are difficult to quantify. Who decides how the money is best spent? One four-month stay for me, during an eight-year period of many inpatient admissions, cost approximately £50,000. That could have funded so much specialised trauma therapy.

In my fourth year, cycling in and out of the local inpatient unit, having lost my job, my marriage, and any last semblance of self-respect or hope, I found myself huddled on the floor in a stark corridor crying. I was in my dressing gown bandaged from self-harm wounds. A young male patient, whom I'd come to know over the years, bent down and gave me a religious pendant. I don't recall what he said but I felt seen at a time when I'd become invisible. His kindness will never leave me. He is still cycling in and out of hospital all these years later. We forget that every person represents a family and possibly children and friends and a community. We are not 'beds' to be vacated for the next person, or 'complex cases' to be solved. We could be your son or daughter. Parent, brother, friend. My fellow patient instinctively understood 'co-regulation'. His humanity, that place deep within each of us that can be lost under layers of armour, ego, disconnection from self, others, and our planet, knew what was needed in that moment.

Although there are many reasons for self-harm, eating disorders, and different forms of addiction, what they have in common is helping to regulate a dysregulated nervous system. People who present with self-harm or suicide attempts can face harsh judgements. Being called 'time wasters', 'attention-seeking', 'repeat-offenders'. From my own experience, I know how little dignity I was afforded when being stitched and stapled. There were times when anaesthetic was withheld. Attitudes pervade about people not deserving help because they've done this to themselves. The shame was awful.

Finding a way forward

My work involves educating people about trauma and why 'how we are with people' matters so much. I use that phrase when delivering reflective training on the power of being *with* people, based on trauma-informed values and principles. I bring together my learned and lived experience in the hope that I can bring to life the theory, and in so doing, remind us of our common humanity.

I am a *4 Mental Health Connecting with People*[79] trainer and part of their Expert Reference Group. As all 4 Mental Health training material is developed using evidence-based principles, I can deliver informed community suicide awareness training which also resonates with my personal values. Compassion is at the heart of this training. I particularly like the inclusion of free and accessible safety planning[2] that supports anyone in distress. Safety planning is for everyone; staff and service users alike should have a safety plan. I would be keen to bring this training to the police and ambulance services.

I have concerns about safety planning for people, like myself, who have been in services long term and face repeated crises. I have found a more detailed plan taking learning from what has and has not worked well in the past, has been very helpful. It also offers an opportunity for people to work collaboratively with key workers on different aspects of their plan. This should be a dynamic document. Distinguishing between safety and crisis planning has worked well for me and my mental health team[80].

---

79 https://www.4mentalhealth.com/

80 Lisa shares her wisdom on safety planning in an excellent video: https://youtu.be/UB86CiOmqBI

I want to develop training about this and hope there will be a willingness from those leading on suicide prevention work to listen and learn. Involving those with lived experience in this kind of training really needs to be increased.

I have collaborated with a Human Rights organisation, Participation and the Practice of Rights (PPR)[81], in Northern Ireland. They are independent of government funding and therefore able to highlight broader social issues and challenge the dominant narrative around mental health. One of the projects I've been part of is called 'The Rest of the Story'. This brings together people with a common social cause to write their own and share stories in a trauma-informed space. This has been a powerful way for people, from all different backgrounds, to listen, share, connect, and learn together which has inspired hope and possibilities that together anything is possible.

I believe there is too much focus on including the voices of those with lived experience around tables for meetings in environments that are retraumatising for many people. Here, roles and titles divide, and the power remains with the system. There is a place for this but arts, crafts, writing, poetry, music, movement, sports, dance, drama, yoga, creating ... these are non-threatening ways to break down barriers and help people learn about each other. We know that trauma is held in the body so all of this can help the healing process too.

When we feel safe and connected, we are open to being curious, listening, learning, and problem-solving. Good facilitation in co-creating safe spaces, where people feel welcomed and accepted, changes lives. A shift from the focus on individuals to inter-connection and community building in every sense of the word. Small community projects powerfully respond to needs but they are often unable to access ongoing, sustainable, funding because there are too many barriers and legalities.

I have also been involved in a research project led by Dr Paula Houton, Queen's University, Belfast, exploring the use and development of an interdisciplinary, forum theatre-based training approach for professionals involved in mental health crisis assessments in the community. This training was interactive, and the creative format encouraged participants to move beyond theory to exploring the complexity of human interactions and the decision-making processes. They were keen to ensure a wide range of service-user and carer views and experiences were heard through a variety of different mediums and plan to publish a paper on this work later this year. I believe this training approach has the potential to be truly inclusive and models the values of trauma-sensitive and collaborative practice.

---

81 You can find out more about PPR online at www.nib.ie

We need to be thinking beyond just firefighting and taking steps now to realise a different future. Because 'doing the same thing over and over and expecting different results is insanity' (Einstein).

Staff across the board need training on trauma and what helps regulate themselves and patients. They need to be able to sit with people's distress. Embracing a trauma-informed approach can deescalate situations which can lead to restrictive and coercive practice for people highly distressed. This is not rocket science. It requires a commitment and openness to learning other ways of being with people in distress.

I've had the privilege of meeting with the forensic doctor who dealt with my rape in 2014. Seven years later, I heard that she had seen *me* behind my illness. Extraordinary and so healing. I will explore ways of educating about and changing the way victims of crime are discriminated against and blamed. I believe too many women are labelled and retraumatised in a mental health system born in the patriarchy. We need to do better.

The challenges for me are balancing my own healing journey with the emotional toil that this work requires. Systems which can be quite insular and defensive, where lived experience is not afforded the value it deserves. I think with all the current challenges it is easy to become overwhelmed, and lose hope and belief that each one of us can affect change, however small. We forget that every life matters, that every interaction is an opportunity to do something, and that people are suffering and unnecessarily dying. Families and communities are torn apart.

People are lonely, isolated, and disconnected. Traumatised individuals and trauma-saturated organisations. Against this backdrop, I believe we need to encourage each other to reconnect with our heart and souls. Our humanity. It takes courage and a collective intention. We cannot do this alone. If our desire is to bring compassion and light into the dark, forgotten places, then humility and honesty are needed. My hope is that we can hear a symphony of soulful sounds from those whose lives are 'whispers' lost in the wind. Together we can all weave a beautiful tapestry as we walk alongside each other on this extraordinary journey of life.

I could easily have died waiting for someone to really see me and to provide the trauma-specific therapy I needed. Too many people like me, have died waiting.

Memoriam: In each grain of sand and oceans wide, in stars above and trees of every size, you are guiding us back, to seeing with heart eyes.
This poem captures the essence of my experience and what I endeavour to bring to my work:

Blinded by Lisa Morrison

What did you see when you looked at me?
Bandaged, broken, breaking down.
Symptoms smothering, suffocating sound.
Risk assessed, year on year
Those boxes ticked,
The plans you made
The same each time
Which I then went and disobeyed.
Repeat offender, that was me,
Revolving door, we all could see
Or not!!

Textbooks teach many truths,
They have their place.
But I am me and you are you
Did you not see?
A hundred stories carved upon my skin
Speak a truth I needed heard,
But I'd been labelled to be understood
And a heavy cost was incurred.

Not all is as it seems you know
For me or you.
Behind the walls and masks we wear
We're all just human, we all know despair.
Before you judge or label me
Please make some space and truly see!

'Angry of Bury'
By Rebecca

Rebecca's heart reflects the way CAMHS services are failing families. She says: *"Whilst I paid over £5k for legal representation at my daughter's inquest, CAMHS had a large legal team paid for by public money. We hear constantly that 'lessons have been learnt' - they haven't. The system is still inadequate and while families face an unequal playing field, and mistakes are covered up, this is unlikely to change."*

About Rebecca

Rebecca's daughter, Elspeth, died by suicide in 2014. Rebecca, who is a textile artist, found crafting helped her cope with her grief. In recent years, Rebecca has reached out to others and been involved with, or instigated, projects to support bereaved people and suicide prevention initiatives. Rebecca is director of The Big Fandango[82]. This is a social enterprise in Bury that uses creative ways to provide a community-centred, wrap-around suicide prevention and postvention service.

In this chapter, Rebecca shares some of her story. This includes: insight into the impact of suicide; her successes and frustrations in effecting change; and her opinions of mental health services.

82 The Big Fandango can be contacted via e-mail: info@thebigfandango.com

'Angry of Bury'

The aftermath

When Elspeth died ... Why does every sentence I begin start with those three words? An event that was so catastrophic that it blew my very existence into two. My life was torn apart into the before and the aftermath. I find myself here, eight years on, living in the debris - still trying to process and make sense of what is still unfathomable.

When Elspeth died, I not only lost my daughter but my identity as a mother, and as a woman. I lost my confidence, my career, my friends, members of my family, and probably my mind. Of course, there is only so much time you can spend howling on the floor. I think this is something the non-bereaved don't understand when they tell you how brave you are. Bravery implies choice but there is no choice involved here. You have to get up at some point and you have to carry on living. And we suicide-bereaved people do that, carrying with us all the trauma. Usually, we are unsupported because a broken health system does not adequately look after the families left behind.

I spent five years trying to seek help. I had another child, who was going through his own trauma - in and out of a psychiatric inpatient setting. I was very much left to flounder. One child was dead and my other seemed to be floating further out to sea, leaving me watching powerlessly on the shore. Mental health services would neither engage with, or support, me. I remember one afternoon going to see a member of the crisis team who assured me I was not going mad. They told me that I was not mentally ill. They suggested a self-help book on anxiety and advised taking up yoga. They showed no empathy, just offered ill-thought out 'quick fixes', as if my distress would vanish with a bit of effort from me. I became more and more isolated as friends, now resigned to the fact I was not going to buck-up and return to my usual outgoing self, left me to get on with their lives. I gave up my work as an accounts manager and took to the back bedroom, where I became immersed in crafting whilst listening to old episodes of Hancock's Half Hour on Radio 4 Extra.

Periodically, I would emerge and have another go at accessing support via my GP. Every time, I was referred back to the Healthy Minds IAPT system. My experience of this was a circus of referrals and assessments, with a catalogue of disinterested counsellors who had no experience of suicide bereavement. The final straw, was trying to book in on their phone line and trying to explain I did not need another assessment because my GP had arranged I could go straight to the CBT service.

Apparently, the 'computer said No!' I was broken. I sobbed down the phone that my daughter had taken her own life and I was not going to tell my story *again* to another assessment person, in order to be seen by another counsellor. I was properly full-on sobbing, snottery, and unable to reason with the unreasonable.

I wailed, "this system is shit."

I was told, "I don't have to take this abuse from you", and the phone was slammed down on me.

My subsequent complaint to PALS (which took nine months) found that I was at fault for using the word 'shit'. And there my engagement with mental health services ended.

My interactions with a shit system left me feeling even worse. I had been gaslighted, my hope broken, and I felt emotionally abused - by the very services that should have helped. Just as my daughter had been seven years before.

I believe it's important to detail this experience because it isn't unusual. So many bereaved parents, that I've since spoken to, come up against these barriers in the aftermath of a suicide. It highlights the lack of understanding about suicide and the stigma that still exists within the health service. Our type of bereavement is unlike any other, it is grief with the volume turned up. Six weeks of counselling and anti-depressants are rarely the solution but it seems it's all primary care have to offer. Rather than invest time in changing that, they would rather sweep it under the carpet and leave people unsupported. This might be considered an unfair judgement by some but it is my experience.

The road to the Big Fandango

When all seems dark, there are chinks of light that give you hope: an unexpected friendship with someone who holds you up; finding something that gives you pleasure; and random acts of kindness. One of the things that drew me out from under the duvet, was connecting with other mothers on Twitter who had also been bereaved by suicide. We began to help each other through our grief, giving one another support through anniversaries, holidays, and the day-to-day struggles. We 'warrior mothers' have become firm friends. Out of the storm comes unexpected rainbows.

Our type of bereavement is unique, it's a very different grief and it's not something people like to talk about. It's shrouded in stigma, it's lonely, and it's bloody hard. Support is a lottery and you have to fight for it. I survived through knitting and sewing; it kept the anxiety at bay and gave me a focus.

Those who have lost a loved one to suicide are at increased risk of dying themselves. So, it is essential there is effective support for families – not just immediately afterwards but ongoing help. It isn't rocket science that robust bereavement support equals prevention.

However, nationally, this type of bereavement support service lies very thin on the ground and, where it does exist, it's often provided by charities and third sector organisations. As my experience shows, in Bury we had no specific (fit for purpose) support. Yet, about 250 people die by suicide each year across the Greater Manchester area. Each of these leaves an estimated 136 people who are impacted in some way. Elspeth left behind parents, grandparents, her brother, schoolfriends, teachers, and a whole network of people whose lives she touched.

I could not change what had happened to me but I could do my utmost to prevent other people go through what I had endured. I decided that if there was no help available, I should set something up myself. A local councillor helped me secure the use of a local library so I could hold a weekly suicide survivors support group. A Facebook post about the plans was shared and I was inundated with messages from people who had lost family members to suicide and had been looking for support. The group's ethos was to offer a positive message that enabled us to celebrate our loved ones and go forward together, trying to lead our best lives. At the same time, we acknowledged how hard this can be, so we aimed to help each other through the tough times.

Through contact with other bereaved people, it became clear that the support that mental health services had to offer, to those struggling to manage their grief, was limited to medication or six sessions of counselling. This seemed too narrow a view. Support groups based on talking have their limitations. For centuries people have used sewing and crafting to manage their grief. In the absence of any effective mental health support in the aftermath of Elspeth's death, it was textile arts that enabled me to have respite from the grief and manage my feelings.

I realised that if other people could be taught crafting skills, this might help them following a bereavement. In 2020, Adele Owen, the suicide prevention programme manager from the Greater Manchester Health and Social Care Partnership, commissioned me to run a creative peer support group that would culminate in a collaborative memorial quilt[83].

This was an opportunity for people to develop skills and discover healing through a gentle and creative process. The pandemic scuppered

---

83 The National Suicide Prevention Alliance have produced a case study that you can view online: https://nspa.org.uk/wp-content/uploads/2021/03/NSPA_Case_Study_Speak_Their_Name_Feb21-1.pdf

our plans for face-to-face workshops but we set up a 'closed' Facebook group and moved the project online. This actually benefitted some people, like the newly bereaved, because they could join in when they felt ready.

Through lockdown, my postman delivered exquisitely crafted squares to me. I felt that I was opening envelopes of grief. Each square was made with complete and unconditional, love. Connections were made between the bereaved members of the group who found peer support. People also expressed how making their squares helped connect them to the person they lost, loved, and missed. Likewise, the bereaved felt they connected with the people their peers had lost. The finished, and absolutely stunning, *Speak Their Name* quilt was displayed at the Manchester City Art Gallery and a beautiful video was made[84]. Three of my warrior mother friends, Anna Scott, Karen Sykes, and Pat Sowa,[85] are picking up the baton and producing their own *Speak Their Name* quilt project in Yorkshire.

When the quilt project ended, I wanted to create a space where everyone could come along and have a go at art or craft activities. This would be a way of learning new skills that people could keep in their emotional tool boxes to help them when life got overwhelming. That's the road that brought me to The Big Fandango in July of 2021.

The idea was that this space should be easily accessible for everyone and would help prevent people reaching crisis point. We particularly wanted to create a space for bereaved people to find the support they needed. At the Big Fandango, anyone can take part in crafting activities to combat isolation, enhance skill sets, and strengthen their mental wellbeing. In addition, the intention of the Big Fandango is to help foster a culture that allows everyone to thrive, find emotional support, and hope.

We hear so much talk about getting people to reach out but if there is nowhere to reach out to, then it's pointless. Suicide prevention and improving mental wellbeing isn't just about helping people in crisis, it's about preventing people getting to crisis point in the first place. We know crafting is meditative, soothing, and builds confidence but sometimes it can be expensive and you need a bit of guidance. At the Big Fandango we create an inclusive space where everyone can have a go at doing fun stuff with workshops and drop-in sessions. So, the crafting revolution that is the Big Fandango sits on my local high street. It is run by volunteers. We run a wide variety of crafting workshops, suicide prevention sessions,

---

84 We highly recommend watching this inspirational video on the Shining A Light On Suicide website (which has some excellent resources): https://shiningalightonsuicide.org.uk/speak-their-name/

85 Pat Sowa has co-written a book about losing her son to suicide: *Take My Hand* by Kerry Fisher and Pat Sowa (2020).

and bereavement support groups, in this welcoming space. The planning, fund-raising, and administration of this community resource is a story of triumph out of tragedy. That's another story!

It's important to understand that many of those who take their own life have not been engaged with mental health services in the 12 months preceding their death. These are not necessarily people who are mentally ill but rather people for whom life has just become overwhelming due to a variety of factors, that could be different for each individual. In the first few months of our project, this was something that services struggled to understand. We opened an arts centre to support mental wellbeing but we were inundated with people who were suffering from enduring mental illness or in a state of extreme crisis. It seemed that, from across the area, people in mental distress were being signposted to us. I found 'Angry of Bury' surfaced when I tried to explain to a social worker why the Big Fandango was not an appropriate substitute for day-care services.

Our mental health system is in absolute crisis at present but there must be spaces for all. From a safeguarding perspective, our arts centre was not the venue for people in crisis. Plus, the volunteers that work there are not qualified to support people with enduring or severe mental health conditions. It's a tough call and, although I hate to turn anyone away, difficult decisions had to be made.

Part of my role involves raising awareness of the Big Fandango's work and raising funding. This means I attend things like multi-agency health groups. I sit on the Local Authority Suicide Prevention Panel for Bury and regularly present to multi-disciplinary health groups that include GPs, pharmacists, social prescribing teams, etc.

Funding can also be a bit of a nightmare as often funders insist on limiting funding to short-term, project-related work. As a craft centre we are project-led, and therefore funding opportunities can create more work without providing income to cover our core costs (such as the rent). We try to be relatively self-sustaining but that in itself causes issues - our activities are reasonably priced but not free. It sometimes seems that the more you offer, the more people want you to do (with no concept of cost implications). The whole process involves constant re-evaluation and fine-tuning. I think it also needs to involve some proper understanding and appreciation of value from those that provide these funding streams. However, the plight of the third sector, who appear to be holding up services, is possibly another subject for another book!

GPs might be the only professionals that someone bereaved by suicide has contact with. Too often, I hear from bereaved people that they have not had any contact with their GP following their bereavement. Worse,

I might hear that having disclosed their loss, bereaved people are prescribed medication over the phone. Given what is known about the elevated risk of suicide in suicide-bereaved people, this is not safe.

Therefore, educating health professionals about how to support suicide-bereaved people and ensuring that they know what support is available for the bereaved is important. One resource that is freely available for bereaved people, and should be given to those in this situation by NHS professionals, is the *Help is at Hand* booklet[86] which offers guidance and links to sources of support for people who have experienced this kind of traumatic or unexpected death. I was really disappointed to find out that many GPs have not heard of this resource and that they were not routinely handing them out. 'Angry of Bury' surfaced briefly but the more positive me decided to take a supply of booklets to where they are needed.

Isolation, stigma, and shame are issues that many of us bereaved by suicide contend with. It is not unusual for people to arrive at the Big Fandago following months, or even years, of being unsupported with their raw grief. Often, we hear that we are the first person who has been able to talk to them about their loss. Or, we are the first that understands because it is very difficult for people who have not had this experience to 'get it'. We also see people, who are concerned about someone who has been bereaved by suicide, bringing along the person they are worried about to a crafting workshop. They might be unsure how to help or are feeling desperate to find support for their friend or relative. Through crafting activities, we can gently explore what is going on for them and offer companionship and support. This makes the Big Fandango unique in its approach.

To tackle some of the myths surrounding suicide, and to empower our community, we decided to embark on a very proactive campaign to help build a suicide-safer community. We were already providing a peer support group for families left behind but, ultimately, we had to get people talking about suicide, understanding risk factors, and knowing how to open up a conversation that could keep people safe.

In December of 2021, just five months after opening, we were awarded funding from our local authority to deliver suicide prevention training. Working with Andrea Newton from Confident Conversations[87], we were able to offer two sessions a month, for a year to anyone in the community. The emphasis would be 'this is everyone's business'. By the time of writing in April 2022, we have trained over 80 people ranging from third sector volunteers, solicitors, local councillors, retail staff, and public sector employees.

86 https://supportaftersuicide.org.uk/resource/help-is-at-hand/

87 You can read about Andrea Newton's confident conversations here: https://confidentconversations.co.uk/time-to-talk-day/

What I found alarming in this process is the number of professionals working in social care and mental health who have never taken suicide prevention training and who are relying on a third sector funded organisation to get it. But the fact that they have rocked up is brilliant and credit where it is due. What is disappointing is the number who are aware this training is freely available, who still have not come forward to take advantage of this offer. The very people, who are always keen to rally the troops to 'reach out' and 'be kind' on social media, are loudly silent when asked to learn how to make a real difference by reaching in themselves. So, here we have it, we keep coming around in a great circle of stigma. There is a place for 'Angry of Bury' because this keeps me motivated to keep challenging those who prefer to keep the subject firmly under the carpet in the belief that it will not affect them.

We know that suicide is the biggest killer of middle-aged men. What isn't as widely shared is the growing number of young women under the age of 25 who take their own life. In fact, it is the biggest killer of young people in this age group. These deaths are largely preventable if only we know how to spot the signs and know how to signpost. By signposting, I don't necessarily mean the traditional routes of IAPT services, anti-depressants, and long waits in A&E departments. We should be looking at other solutions - spaces like the Big Fandango where people can learn self-care skills and activities, find peer support, and be understood.

The road to the Big Fandango has involved a steep learning curve for me. There have been many pitfalls and barriers but it is a story of hope. I always remember that working with bereaved people, and hearing their stories, is a gifted and privileged position. There is no place for egos and humility is needed. The purpose of all my work is to help people develop peer support. The bonus that comes from doing this through creative activities relates to the skills people learn that they can use to keep emotionally regulated. My daughter may have been a statistic from a local authority data collection perspective. Those bereaved by suicide might be figures and numbers for research papers. But to me, my daughter was a 16-year old geeky teenager, who wore stripey tights and battered Doc Marten boots with yellow laces. No one fills those boots.

Elspeth died waiting, let down by the very services we reached out to for help. I carry her in my heart. Through the quilt and the Big Fandango, I will be her voice for change. I am very honoured to be part of these projects and do so in memory of my beautiful girl.

A Gladiator Spirit
By Geri

This memorial heart is based on an image from the film, *Spartacus,* with a gap where the central character should stand. However, those surrounding him around have taken up arms and they stand together. The shield represents truth and love.

About Geri

Geri[88] is an award-winning journalist. She is a political journalist for The Times who started her career at the Eastern Daily Press (EDP) in Norfolk, where she was a health correspondent. When she became a health correspondent for the EDP in 2017, Terry O'Shea was one of the first contacts she met but he became much more than that and was a close friend right up until his death. Geri spent many hours speaking with Terry about the campaign and about her own family's struggles with getting support for her brother, who suffers from paranoid schizophrenia. Terry always offered not just a sympathetic ear, but solutions. Geri feels that he was one of the only people to truly understand what it is like to be a relative of someone with serious mental health problems in Norfolk.

Geri has based this tribute to Terry on the obituary she wrote when he died in April 2021, which was published in the EDP. It includes quotes from the people who knew him well.

88 You can read more about Geri and her work here: www.geraldinescott.co.uk

A Gladiator Spirit

For nearly a decade, there was one consistent voice speaking out against failing mental health care in Norfolk and Suffolk, an unstoppable force in standing up for the vulnerable and holding those with the power to make changes - but not always the will to do so - to account. And since his death, aged 53, the true extent of the colossal impact Terry O'Shea made to the lives of those lucky enough to know him has become clear.

Terry was known by many as the power behind the Campaign to Save Mental Health Services in Norfolk and Suffolk - although you wouldn't know it by a mere glance, he often kept himself out of the limelight. It was staggering that despite the number of protests that he had organised which I had covered over the years, finding a photograph with him in for his obituary was a struggle.

Terry was a sympathetic ear, a tireless activist, and above all a father, husband, and friend. Terry moved to Norwich with his wife in 1999, where psychiatry, the field in which she worked, had taken a turn for the worst. Unbeknown to the couple at the time, this foreshadowed what would become Terry's most passionate fight in Norfolk and Suffolk. Terry's wife - who he once described to me as "the anchor of my life" - later told me:

"I remember him going to that first campaign meeting in 2013[89]. But I remember him saying 'you do know if I go, there might be some trouble' - and there was some trouble!"

From that point, there was no looking back. Although he hadn't really intended to, Terry became the propeller behind the campaign - organising rallies, protests, and making sure he knew everything there was to know about Norfolk and Suffolk Foundation Trust (NSFT) and its workings.

One of the campaign's founders told me:

"The campaign has continued for almost ten years and has great support and involvement from many people mostly, I believe, down to the energy, empathy, and intelligence of Terry O'Shea. The lack of any improvement has demotivated some members but not Terry who had always kept up the fight and encouraged the rest of us. He'll be badly missed but the fight will go on."

89 This refers to the meeting described by John and Jane in *Dying Waiting: Waiting to Die.*

When the campaign began, the trust was proposing drastic cuts to staffing numbers, which has since become known as the 'radical redesign'. Terry's wife said:

> *"That was the driving force behind what was causing the issue at the time, and then it became everything. It became a real passion for him, and for the last seven years, that was what he did. It became really important to him to try and sort it out and do something to make things better for people."*

Terry's wife described how campaigning became all-encompassing with Terry taking calls at all hours from fellow campaigners, families in distress, bereaved parents, and often journalists like me. Terry cared about the people who contacted the campaign for help. He met a lot of bereaved parents and once you get involved with the bereaved parents, it becomes very personal. More than once I sat across from Terry in a cafe, in later years with the family's springer spaniel puppy in tow, as he told me about a new person who had reached out at their wit's end over how to get their loved one the help they needed.

More than that, Terry knew how to work with the media, especially locally, to make an impact and make sure those who were not affected by the failures were aware. Whether it was being a trusted link between a parent and me so they knew I would be compassionate in telling their story; the willingness to explain in layman's terms the complex board papers; or not taking it personally when I said, "No, not this time, this isn't one we can do".

It can be tricky to maintain a professional relationship with a friend, but it was never difficult with Terry. He respected that I had a job to do and that while I'd do everything for a story worth telling, there were times when we'd disagree. I didn't always think his interpretations were right, I remember him accusing me of running a 'puff piece' when I interviewed one of the many chief executives I saw during my time. But Terry knew he could trust me, and I'd tell him if I thought there was nothing in a piece.

One of the most powerful things I've written in my career is when the trust was once again judged as inadequate, and we used the front page to show to photographs of all those who had died under trust care. I was often struck by the contrast between some, but by no means all, NHS communications staff who would not treat journalists with anywhere near as much consideration despite being the paid professionals.

One bereaved mother, whose son died, described Terry as "her rock".

She said he was:

"A precious friend who was the cleverest, most caring, kind, and humorous person I have ever met. He helped me survive the tragic death of my son and phoned me at least once a week to help and advise me on anything from buying a new washing machine to IT problems. His priority in life was his family, always planning their future. I shared Terry's passion for improving the lives of those with mental health conditions. He analysed the failing system of healthcare, speaking up for those less articulate and confident than himself. Terry's spirit will live on, inspiring those whose lives he touched and enriched to continue in his memory to care for others in the unselfish, determined way that he exemplified."

Terry's outspokenness drew ire from the trust, some senior members of staff painted him as someone who was unnecessarily critical or who exaggerated the problem. Neither of these was ever true. Instead, as another bereaved parent described him, he was:

"A fearless champion who spoke out in the media against unsafe, ineffective, or unkind mental health services. Over the years we became friends and I came to understand just how many bereaved relatives Terry quietly supported. It has been my absolute privilege to know Terry. He had a huge capacity to love. It was love for his fellow human that kept him speaking up about mental health services. He loved life and his family and he had so much more he wanted to do for others."

Another campaigner added:

"Incurring the 'wrath of Terry' you did at your peril if you were one of the 'bad guys'. In this increasingly grey and cynical world, Terry brought colour, humour, friendship and passion. He was a one-off and has left an indelible mark on so many people and lives on a positive and extraordinary way."

The only thing more important to Terry than the campaign, were his wife and three children. He once gave me the sage advice to:

"Marry someone cleverer and kinder than you are - that's what I did, worked well! I managed better looking too, that was pushing my luck…"

But even they sometimes took a backseat … Terry's wife joked that at some point their children had an anti-campaign campaign going on. When they were little they made banners that said: 'save our father from the mental health campaign'. However, Terry's family knew why he was so

involved.
His wife said:

"It was about standing up for people who he felt didn't have a voice. It was about defending people who couldn't defend themselves or felt they couldn't at the time."

Terry's methods often attracted criticism from those at the top - which he secretly saw as a badge of honour - and even after he had been diagnosed with colon cancer which had spread to his liver, and knew he would not survive, he received a letter threatening legal action by the trust over the use of information leaked to the campaign. His wife said:

"Terry was never against the people who were delivering the services, it was about changing the system. It was about funding and also just the organisation and the way it was run, the focus and the values of the organisation. The campaign was set up by staff. I think he wanted to be remembered as somebody who tried to make a difference to vulnerable people. I think that's what was important to him, and obviously us [the family], but the work he did for the campaign to genuinely try and stand up for people who couldn't stand up for themselves."

Even after he knew he was ill, he was looking out for others. I know I wasn't alone in receiving encouraging text messages from him in his final weeks. But those messages also went to those he knew would need to continue his legacy - even in his final days, he was handing over information on how to keep the pressure on.

Every life lost mattered to Terry. Since he died, many have stepped up to the plate to carry on the campaign. Although none may fill Terry's shoes, the fight continues, with one campaigner likening it to the 'I am Spartacus' scene in the famous film *Spartacus*. It is that gladiator spirit that they harness every day to channel their 'inner Terry'.

Terry died waiting for the improvements in mental health services that he fought so hard for. May he rest in peace.

Part Five - What Does This Mean?

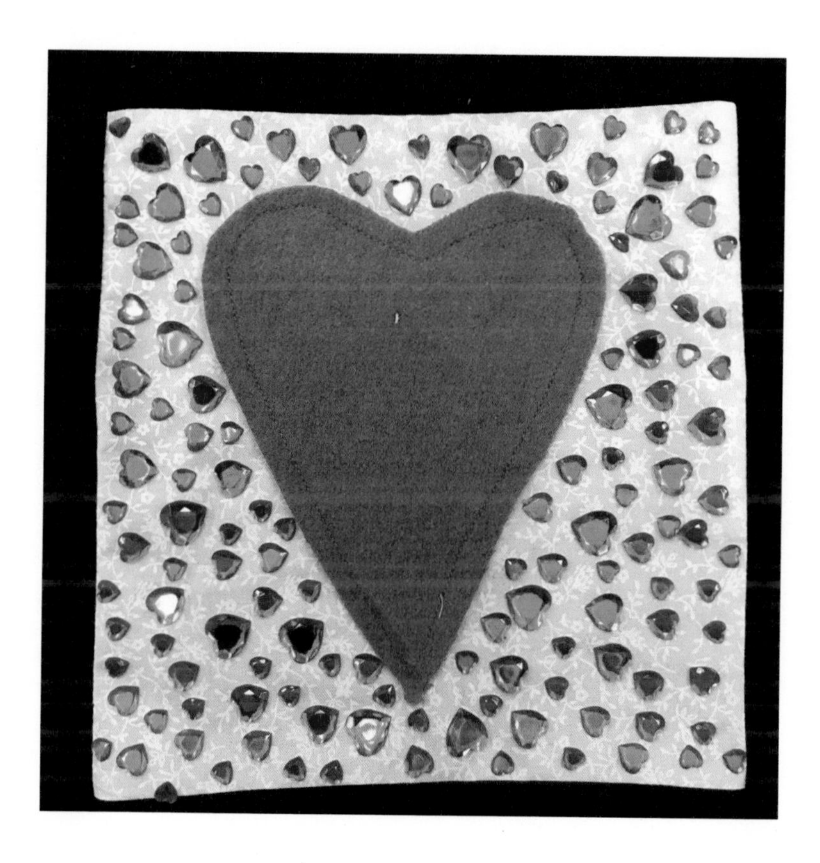

For every life lost, the impact can be huge and a network of people mourn. This image reflects how sparkly jewels of love and happy memories will continue because bonds of love endure through time and space.

What Does This Mean?
By Caroline and Emma

Having gathered all these stories of love, loss, and hope, together, we asked: what does this mean? In these concluding chapters, we do not have space for deep analysis of all the key points. So, we decided to focus on a few things that come up repeatedly.

What you have read might have been shocking or surprising but for us, sadly, we are familiar with the thoughtless, and often brutal, way that people in mental distress, bereaved families, or caring staff are treated. We find it disheartening that those responsible for providing, commissioning, and monitoring services, will have heard similar stories to those presented in this book frequently over many years. At every level of governance, from Health Ministers through to boards of Governors, they already know that people slip through the gaps, too many die, and that the system does not learn the lessons. Do not be fooled by their expressions of surprise … they will most likely have heard it all before.

The areas we have chosen to highlight are:

As if by magic: We look at themes of magical or distorted thinking and consider the way the same things, such as patient deaths, are viewed so very differently by people and organisations

Not the right kind of bereaved: Those who die due to the crisis in mental health services show up failings in services. Those that are left behind are expected to be polite and compliant. People like Nick and Maxine, Rebecca, or Melanie are 'not the right kind of bereaved' from organisations perspectives.

Prevention of future deaths: Many of the chapters contain references to inquests. There should be accountability via the coronial service when people die due to failings in mental health services.

The pit of inaction: Caroline created a model that helps make sense of the way good intentions of health and social care organisations do not always transpose into actions. She argues for those with the power to change organisational behaviours to resist being drawn into a 'pit of inaction'.

Heart work: There are many examples in this book of poor practice where the 'care' has been missing from care. Kind and compassionate practice, steeped in with integrity, dedication, and love for others, comes at an emotional cost.

A terrible kindness: Heart work, in the form of authentic involvement with people who have been traumatically bereaved, can be likened to performing 'terrible kindnesses' because it means getting alongside people in times of personal and familial disaster.

We have to stop: We consider why it is left to volunteers to challenge unsafe and unethical practice and question the morality of those who are bereaved needing to spearhead change in organisations that have highly paid leaders. We conclude by arguing that something needs to change.

As If By Magic
By Caroline

Reflecting on the chapters of *They Died Waiting*, I felt there is something almost magical, in different senses of the term, within the narratives. From the magic of being transported into the stories presented and feeling the emotions, through to the sense of corporate 'make believe' that pops up in many of the chapters, alternative realities are presented. I was fascinated to read Dr Chloe Beale's 2021 open-access paper, *Magical Thinking and Moral Injury: Exclusion Culture in Psychiatry,* which I shall quote from because it articulates themes within our book.

Magical thinking: Young children have active imaginations and they can use make-believe and fantasy to make sense of the world. Jean Piaget's Cognitive Development Theory suggests that, typically between the ages of two and seven, children can believe they are capable of making events happen, or reversing things that have happened, by thinking it. He called this 'magical thinking'. For example, a child might create a reason in their mind that leaves them feeling responsible if they experience something that they cannot understand, such as a bereavement. In psychiatry, when people hold false beliefs, about the way their thoughts, actions, or words could cause or prevent something in a way that defies the causality believed by society, magical thinking is seen as a disorder or symptom.

Children often resort to magical thinking when there are tragic events or things that they cannot make any sense of. It seems to us that professionals can behave in the same way. They might be triggered to do this when they are tasked with making the impossible possible or defending the indefensible. Somehow, they have to make sense of their working world and find ways of feeling okay:

> *"Clinicians learn the art of self-delusion, convincing ourselves we are not letting patients down but, instead, doing the clinically appropriate thing."*

I expect that most of the clinicians that failed the people discussed in this book believed they were doing the right thing. They will be operating within magical thinking cultures that believe if they think it, that makes it true. Thankfully, we see counter-narratives in the accounts by practitioners who describe their horror at the way poor practice has become normalised. They are not buying into the magical thinking but that is an uncomfortable position for them.

Corporate 'make-believe': With services stretched to breaking point, corporate magical thinking takes place. It distorts reality and creates in a 'make-believe' world of services. This is where we see cuts dressed up as improvements, neglect billed as autonomy or empowerment, staff shortages re-framed as staff not working hard enough, and so on. Mental health services will advertise themselves as inclusive, welcoming, supportive, accessible, meeting needs, and able to deliver high-quality services, when the reality is:

> *"We exclude based on postcode, diagnosis, complexity, co-morbity. Too much need, not enough need. Risk, lack of motivation, readiness for change, any possible reason to keep people out."*

The stories in this book bear testimony to the way that those who will not indulge in the corporate make-believe can find themselves on the wrong end of a power imbalance. We applaud the campaigners and journalists who refuse to buy into the corporate magical thinking. They bring people's attention back to reality.

Conjuring tricks: Magicians perform tricks. They aim to deceive using distraction, smoke, and mirrors. In *They Died Waiting* we have exposed some of the unpleasant tricks played on bereaved people. In Melanie's account, we read about the extremes that trusts can descend into when trying to cover their actions. The NHS conjures with death data. Precious loved ones become statistics that nobody wants to own. I shall explore this further in the *Prevention of Future Deaths* chapter.

Language: Within the accounts you have read, you will have seen how language has been used to distort and demean. Whether it is the judgemental vocabulary that is used to explain people's mental illness, or the words used to shift blame from organisations onto the bereaved, a shameful lexicon has been normalised. That needs to change and it starts with each of us thinking about the language we use.

> *"We have developed an entire lexicon of weasel words and magical thinking that we pass between generations and disciplines ... patients are of course aware of this absurdity ... perhaps the most widespread example is the language of suicide risk."*

'Capacity' is a weasel word that crops up in several of our chapters. Professionals have a core duty to preserve life. Somehow a distorted concept of mental capacity has crept in and is often used as a rationale for not exercising a duty of care or for legitimising neglect. The language of 'gatekeeping', 'thresholds', 'placements', and 'eligibility' all reinforce exclusion and create barriers to services. One word, that epitomises this, is 'beds'. As the crisis in mental health services grows, we see services that are focussed on protecting beds instead of patients. The system has become heavily defended and seems to be working towards keeping people out.

> *"An excessively risk-averse and under-resourced system may drain its clinicians of compassion, losing sight of the human being behind each 'protected' bed and rejected referral."*

Invisibility: Magicians can make things disappear. Some can even make people invisible. Likewise, mental health services can render people invisible. Those on waiting lists can disappear at the click of an administrative button. People in distress can disappear via referral to partner agencies where their unmet needs are no longer visible. Those who have died and their bereaved relatives are out of sight and therefore out of mind.

Those made invisible by the system are brought into sharp focus in this book. We want you to see them and consider they represent a tiny minority of the people who are quietly suffering. Many people struggle privately with mental illness. There is a silent army of bereaved people who are expected to remain hidden. We need to remove the smoke and mirrors that prevents the public from seeing them. Because if they remain invisible they are too easy for society to ignore.

Emotional magic: I have felt an emotional magic reading some of the stories or receiving the memorial hearts. Heart flutterings or whooshes of feelings as I opened envelopes or emails. The aim of writers and artists is to transport you from words and images into the minds of others. To see and feel the world as the characters do. Through the chapters and the textile art, I have been able to imagine the experiences of the contributors to this book. When we allow our imaginations to stand us in other people's shoes, we can empathise and learn.

Love ethic: One of the magical elements of this book is love. Love abounds in the narratives and it underpins the hope that is being held by our contributors. One of the last hearts that came in was George Julian's. She had no idea of what the other contributors to the book had written about. Her memorial heart had love emblazoned on it. I was with Emma when it arrived in the post. It was a magical moment. It confirmed to us that our message, of the importance of operating with love, is shared. Bell Hooks[90] describes a 'love ethic' - love as a transformative and political process that

90 Hooks, B. (2000). *All About Love: New Visions.* London. The Women's Press.

challenges injustice and oppression. In a journal article[91], Naomi Godden suggests that love has become marginalised in social work but it could be harnessed to support radical practice. A love ethic underpins this book. Emma and I have collated the stories and edited them from a position of love for others and with a view to challenging the injustices inherent in mental health services that are particularly apparent when a patient dies.

Making the unimaginable happen: Sometimes we cannot imagine what lies ahead of us. Often that is a good thing. When Tim died, the worst kind of unimaginable happened and I was thrust into a different life pathway. Being someone who likes to plan, it has been difficult for me to follow an unimaginable path but that is precisely where I am career-wise. I have no idea where my path leads and at times I get tempted to retreat to well-worn tracks. A wise friend urged me to go with the flow and reminded me that I could never have imagined the things that I am doing with my life now. This is the best kind of unimaginable.

Within the chapters of this book there are magical examples of people making the unimaginable happen. People, like Lisa and Rebecca, who have been in absolute despair and unable to contemplate a future, who are now inspiring others and making a difference. I would like to entice readers to be part of making the unimaginable happen in a good way.

Our magical thinking: Emma and I want to be positive magical thinkers. Despite some serious knocks in life, and being surrounded by people who are distressed and despairing, we hold on to hope that things can get better. We strongly believe that this book, much of which is based on our personal thoughts, can have a direct effect on society, in particular on mental health services. Some might argue we are holding delusional beliefs but we are hanging on tight to our magical thinking.

---

91 Godden, N. (2017). 'The love ethic: A radical theory for social work practice'. Australian Social work **70** (4).

Not the Right Kind of Bereaved
By Caroline and Emma

A key theme running through the chapters, is the discrepancy between what bereaved families need and how they are treated by professionals and organisations. This often starts pre-bereavement with carers being excluded or vilified for raising concerns about the services (or lack of services) their loved one received.

It is as if some families are 'not the right kind' of bereaved. Organisations seem to want bereaved people who will remain silent. People who will stay quiet because of stigma and a sense of shame. Bereaved relatives are too often expected to be satisfied with a 'cut and paste' condolence letter that offers nothing personal. These are all the same apart from a change of name. "We are sorry for your loss" doesn't suffice when it is followed up with nothing (because why bother to keep families informed?), misinformation (because transparency is in short supply), or evasive tactics (because why take responsibility?). Bereaved families should not have to fight for basic courtesy or answers to their questions. However, as many of our contributors testify, this is the case.

We were having a writing retreat when a series of messages were received by Caroline from Lydia (author of *Precious Boy, You Were Loved and Loved*). Lydia's distress dripped from her messages which included screenshots of paperwork she had just received. Caroline felt a physical reaction and recoiled in horror at what she read in those 'professional' records. The derogatory, mother-blaming, and oppressive language being used by practitioners who were 'caring' for her son was offensive and unjustified. They clearly found Lydia's requests to be listened to, about her son's history and behaviours, threatened their greater knowledge. The evidence that they were wrong is that Lydia's son died in their 'care'. Did they send a condolence letter that said, 'We are sorry we did not listen to you and include you in your son's care?'. Of course not. What they did is heap further trauma and shame on Lydia for being the wrong kind of bereaved. Because she is not quietly accepting of things. She has in her words, a 'crack legal team' and plans to 'raise hell'. We wish her luck.

It would be reasonable to question whether our contributors had unusually bad experiences. From the sheer number of bereaved relatives that we have encountered over the years, we think that it is quite common for people who ask questions to have negative experiences. Some bereaved people are welcomed in with obsequious thanks for highlighting some failings but they might be dropped if they are not grateful or compliant enough.

Some of the stories in *They Died Waiting* are about people who, from the system's perspective, *are* the 'right kind of bereaved'. Billy, Laura, and Bridget complied and did not make a fuss. There is much to learn from their narratives but their voices would remain unheard if they had not contributed to this book.

We suspect that many bereaved relatives are unaware of what should happen, so they do not challenge. We have come across people who have been bereaved by failings in mental health services but they don't seem realise that. For example, a young woman whose older sister was discharged from mental health services and died of a drug overdose a few weeks later. The young woman did not receive a condolence letter and neither was she informed about any serious incident report. We are left wondering how many other bereaved people are like her. She is the 'perfect kind of bereaved' because she will never question or complain.

We know from the many reports into deaths in mental health services that families are not treated with the respect and dignity they deserve. An example is a report by Verita into unexpected deaths at one trust[92]. They found that only 60% of bereaved families received a condolence letter and only 36% had any input into serious incident reports after their loved one died. The report stated:

> *"[The coroner] said it was a common theme at inquests that families did not feel they had been engaged by the trust, either when their relative was under the care of the trust or after their death."* (page 33).

The trust in question has changed some of their processes and we do not have up-to-date figures. However, anecdotal evidence provided to us suggests that the inclusion of families is still not good enough. The arrogance of not valuing information from relatives or carers and believing that professionals hold all the knowledge is breath-taking. If any investigation is going to be worth the paper it is written on, then the information it is based on needs to be triangulated. By that, we mean different perspectives are called for if an unbiased and holistic view is to be formed.

In our opinion, there needs to be a massive shift in attitudes towards bereaved people by those responsible for providing mental health services. It has become normalised to lose service-users. People have become collateral damage and dealing with the aftermath seems to be viewed as a series of administrative chores.

---

92 https://www.verita.net/wp-content/uploads/2016/05/Norfolk-and-Suffolk-NHS-Fundation-Trust-independent-review-Verita-25-May-2016.pdf

Condolence letter – tick.
Get advice from in-house lawyer – tick.
Serious incident review – if we must.
Talk to families – if we must.
Managing the messages to media – tick.
Send paperwork to coroner – only the bare minimum, at the last minute.
Report death to NHS systems – only the ones we cannot disown.
And so on.

We firmly believe that unless there is a measure of emotional literacy shown when responding to bereaved relatives, and this is done in a fully transparent and humble way, then more damage is done. From the narratives in this book it is clear that that relatives and carers experienced peri-mortem trauma which was often compounded by the insensitive, and sometimes brutal, behaviours of organisations and professionals afterwards. There are examples of bereaved relatives being repeatedly retraumatised by the events that happened after their loved on died. For example, Nick and Maxine have to live with the final images of Peggy being bundled into the back of a glorified van and the knowledge that she died in horrible circumstances among people who barely noticed her as a human being. Following Peggy's death, they have endured a series of re-traumatising events as they have sought answers and service improvements. They are not always reasonable but grief is not reasonable and neither is what happened.

Across health systems there are:

> *"...significant difficulties in listening to and involving families in the organisational responses to safety incidents and for healthcare staff a blame culture often persists. These in turn, lead to a sense of sustained unfairness, unresponsiveness and secondary harm"* (Cribb, O'Hara and Waring, 2022)[93].

Our views are consistent with the calls for a restorative approach to investigating deaths because the prevailing approaches are responsible for 'compounded harm' not healing[94]. Cribb et al describe the need for organisations to develop 'just cultures' which takes a systemic approach that focusses on learning and risk reduction rather than fault-finding and blame.

---

93 Open access journal article: Cribb, A., O'Hara. J.K. and Waring, J. 'Improving responses to safety incidents: we need to talk about justice'. (2022). *British Medical Journal* Vol **31** (4).

94 The Harmed Patient Alliance have been working on restorative models and approaches. An open access journal article explains this: Wailling, J., L | Kooijman, A., Hughes, J. and O'Hara, J.K. 'Humanizing harm: Using a restorative approach to heal and learn from adverse events'. (2022). *Health Expectations.*

We would argue that organisations are not always the 'not the right kind of sympathetic'. What is needed are people who behave humanely and kindly to those they have failed. Organisations and professionals need to find ways of engaging with, and responding to, bereaved families that centre around each unique bereaved person's needs. Whether they are outraged and shouty, questioning and engaging, silent and withdrawn, they are all the 'right kind of bereaved'. Everyone would benefit from healing and learning so that future harm is minimised.

Prevention of Future Deaths
By Caroline

Ask any of the contributors to this book, who were bereaved in circumstances they feel were preventable, and they will tell you how important it is to them that other families do not lose their loved ones. This motivates them to get involved in different ways of advocating for change. This is why our chapter-writers, who live in disparate parts of the country, do what they do. They want to spare others from going through the agony of traumatic loss. This is why I do what I do. The phenomenon of wanting to see learning and action following a death can be observed if you listen to bereaved relatives talking about any failing of care. Pleas for prevention of deaths can also be heard by those who, quietly or not so quietly, complain or ask for answers.

In *He Died Waiting*, I discussed my experiences and opinions on the empty 'lessons will be learnt' rhetoric. It is trotted out with ridiculous regularity against a backdrop of evidence that suggests mistakes and failings are repeated. Since then, I have examined some of the systems and processes that surround deaths of people with mental illness. I have become convinced that the national systems and structures for recording and using the data for learning are fundamentally flawed. I am not alone. The Verita investigation, into the numbers of people who had died at my local mental health trust, found:

> *"In considering the data on unexpected deaths we noted the lack of national data on which to base analysis. This is outside the trust's control and is a national issue. National data about unexpected deaths in mental health trusts offers limited means for making meaningful comparisons between mental health trusts …"* (page 13).

I would not presume knowledge of all the ins and outs of the way data is gathered and used regarding patient safety and mortality in mental health services. However, as a concerned member of the public, with some practice and academic knowledge to draw on, I am certain that much of the data relating to mental health deaths is confusing, contradictory, and (often) of poor quality. Having spent many hours trying to understand how many people have died, I have concluded that the statistics feel impregnable. No surprise then, that there are examples where trusts seem unsure about their death statistics. Melanie[95] raises questions about the numbers that have died in her locality and the futility of investigations. Aside from the issue of

95 *The Case For a Statutory Inquiry* by Melanie

what this means for learning lessons and preventing deaths, this reflects the way organisations seem to lack an appropriate level of concern over service-user deaths. The chapters in this book highlight how painful it is for bereaved families to realise that the death their loved one is of little consequence to those responsible for providing mental health services. When met with responses that lack empathy, or convey a sense of every life not being valued, bereaved people can be further traumatised.

The systems for gathering mortality data are all over the place. Maybe expert statisticians can make sense of things but I find it very difficult to pin the numbers down. All deaths of someone with a serious mental illness (inpatient, outpatient, or in the community) should have a serious incident review which is reported to NHS England but there does not seem to be an agreed definition of serious mental illness[96]. The Office for National Statistics (ONS) usually provides reliable death data, however, they gather deaths under different categories, such as suicide, drug, or alcohol-related, rather than generic mental illness, and by locality rather than by trust catchment areas. The National Reporting and Learning System (NRLS) gathered data with very strict criteria which means these figures are lower than reported elsewhere. The criteria these systems use changes periodically which further complicates the picture. Every trust lodges their 'death' figures in the Annual Reports with NHS England. These figures differ from NRLS statistics and from figures of 'unexpected deaths' that might be presented to trust boards. The terminology used is one reason why it is impossible to compare like with like data. 'Avoidable', 'preventable', 'unexplained', 'unexpected' and 'deaths' seem to be used interchangeably or with differing criteria.

The majority of 'independent investigations' within the NHS involve trusts essentially 'marking their own homework'. I suspect there is an element of deliberate obscuration that goes on. Trusts present data in ways that arguably skews things. For example, at a board meeting, my local trust presented slides that were open to interpretation. One graph suggested a lowish number of suicides but it was based on an average since 2001. In recent years, the suicide numbers in my county have risen faster than the national picture[97], so this seemed to me an attempt to make things look 'not so bad'. I could be wrong. The person drawing up these graphs might not be great at maths.

---

96 https://www.england.nhs.uk/patient-safety/learning-from-deaths-in-the-nhs/#National-guidance-on-learning-from-deaths

97 https://www.edp24.co.uk/news/health/figures-show-norfolk-suicide-increase-1468166

To be fair, trusts that are short staffed and under multiple pressures should concentrate their energies on those still alive. Maybe this is one reason looking at the deaths might drop down an organisation's agenda. However, learning from errors is key to prevention[98]. We know from the scandals at Mid-Staffordshire, Southern Health, Telford and Shrewsbury, and elsewhere, that death statistics are important in highlighting problems and identifying learning points. The national statistics should act as indicators of quality or warning systems that something is going wrong. Indeed, the reports lodged with NHS England include 'learning from deaths' information. Given how many times in recent years high numbers of deaths at different trusts have not been flagged up, it seems remarkable that statistics continue to be gathered in such an unhelpful way.

There are other formal processes whereby preventable deaths should lead to learning such as the Prevention of Future Deaths (PFD) reports issued by coroners to organisations. This system has been criticised as a learning tool because PFDs are not easy to analyse and draw themes from[99]. Coroners have a lot of autonomy and some issue more PFDs than others[100]. PFD statistics were gathered for the first time in 2021; 440 were recorded (these will cover all kinds of deaths not just those from mental health). The North West reported 86 (the highest), but Wales only 16. Some coroner areas issued none. Coroners will not usually issue a PFD to an organisation if they have recently issued one about similar concerns, or they have been reassured by an organisation saying that changes have already been made and they have actions in hand. This means that where there are clusters of similar deaths, only one PFD might be issued. Nobody seems to be picking up on this.

Another critical thing that makes learning the lessons from PFDs limited is that there is not a clear system to monitor whether organisations have implemented, and sustained, their promised changes[101]. All PFDs and organisation responses should be available on the Ministry of Justice website. I examined the 36 PFDs and the responses that had been issued to my local trust since 2014. The most recent ones were repeats of failings reported in the media of other inquests (but not necessarily PFDs).

---

98 Two books that provide good overviews of learning from errors are: Russell Kelsey's, 2017, book, *Patient Safety: Investigating and Reporting Serious Clinical Incidents* and Alessandro Sicora's (2017) *Reflective Practice and Learning from Mistakes in Social Work*.

99 www.patientsafetylearning.org

100 https://www.gov.uk/government/statistics/coroners-statistics-2021/coroners-statistics-2021-england-and-wales

101 www.patientsafetylearning.org

This reinforces the importance of local journalism. Without media reports the wider public, including campaigners, would remain ignorant. However, research as found that the scrutiny of coroner's courts provided by local journalists is shrinking, leaving some inquests unreported and investigations of some deaths happening 'behind closed doors'[102].

If there is to be learning from deaths, something has to change. Organisations need to be willing to be honest with themselves and others about the people who have died because of the crisis in mental health. Throughout the country, trusts are 'lawyered up' and put a lot of energy in to deny, defend, distract, dismiss. They go through a process of working out which deaths they do not need to own. I can almost imagine their corporate 'phew' when someone can be categorised as dying of 'natural causes' even if underlying mental illness means they were self-neglecting or unable to access physical health care. My local newspapers are littered with reports of people who had 'long-standing mental health problems' who have died by suicide or other means but will not be in the trust's statistics because they were not receiving a service (or had not within six months). This is not isolated to my area because the criteria that exclude so many from the 'unexpected deaths' are set nationally. It would not be right to blame individual trusts for this.

I am not a fan of inquiries because too frequently they tell us what we already know and don't lead to any learning or action. However, I do feel that without knowing the scale of loss it is hard to get the policy changes and resources needed to make mental health services safer. Therefore, I support the calls by campaigners for public inquiries.

We need those responsible nationally, to stop being 'shocked', 'outraged', or 'surprised' by failings within mental health services because this is all happening in plain sight *and they already know*. We need health ministers, and all the layers under them, to shift gear into valuing people like Danny, Sam, and Lisbeth and commit to learning (and taking action) to prevent future deaths. To achieve this, we all need to push back in whatever way we can. We can start by noticing and querying the deaths of people due to their mental illness.

---

102 Binns, A. and Arnold, S. (2021) 'Death of a watchdog: reduced coverage of coroners' inquests by local media.' *Journalism Practice* 15:10.

The Pit of Inaction
By Caroline

A theme that comes up repeatedly in the chapters is the way no lessons seem to be learnt and how despite a lot of effort things remain the same. Many of the contributors to this book describe how powerless they feel and how frustrated they are by inaction. I explored in *He Died Waiting* how 'the system' has become a self-perpetuating morass of non-improvement. I have pondered on it since because, like many, I am frustrated by the way large organisations seem to get stuck. In this chapter, I will consider why is it that over decades similar deaths occur, reviews and investigations lead to similar findings, but mistakes are repeated? When reflecting on the different stories in this book, the pit of inaction model (see Appendix 1) offers one possible explanation.

The pit of inaction model is based on my observations, reflections, and experiences, so it reflects my perspective. It is not based on any particular organisation, individuals, or research. I am not an expert in organisations, systems, or management theories. It is not an area I am particularly interested in. I am a voracious reader/researcher and probably have more underpinning theoretical knowledge than I give myself credit for. I am interested in organisation cultures, how we learn and change, values-based practice, building strengths and healthy relationships, and finding creative ways to make sense of the world. Additionally, I have worked for different kinds of health, social care, and education organisations and I have lived experience as a carer.

One day, I created a 'messy map' to make sense of my observations about this pit of inaction that seems to stymie organisations. Even though people at every level are working really hard, somehow things do not change. On impulse, I posted it on Twitter with a 'laugh or cry?' comment. People started commenting and messaging me:

"You have captured the NHS."

"This is my local authority."

Even (this one made me smile), "Diagram of how the Church of England works, with the special ecclesiastical terms left out"

So, I refined my scribbles into a neat graphic of my model which has been shared many times. This model applies to large organisations in the statutory and private, voluntary, and independent sector. It seems to fit government and their quangos too. I can get pretty steamed up about initiatives that cost millions, where most of the money is spent talking about what to do and reporting to the commissioners. Just imagine if the money was spent on doing something useful.

People at the very top are very busy and they are reliant on delegating tasks to others (upper-middle management and a plethora of boards, subgroups, workstreams, working parties, core groups etc.). They also have a habit of commissioning audits, reviews, and investigations. Too often meetings are fruitless because without senior management present nobody has the power to action anything. Personally, I find these meetings tedious and unproductive, frustrating and stressful, or just plain pointless. But some seem to thrive on them. The upper-middle management seem to spend all their time in meetings (with the senior leads or in all those working groups), running the audits and reviews, and delegating down. Often there is conflict because the middle management knows just how frustrated and concerned their front-line staff are. They are the jam in the proverbial sandwich. All of the activity above the management line generates multiple reports or meeting minutes (sometimes hundreds of pages long and full of cut and paste from previous documents) that no one has time to read properly, let alone action. Boards and senior leads just get given the edited highlights in briefings. Those below the line rarely get interaction with the above the line folk. So, they just carry on as best they can and manage the flip-flop directives by digging in and continuing as they are.

And what about the front-line staff, service-users and carers? Well, they sit firmly below the line. A chosen few are recruited to be part of co-production innovations. In too many organisations this means they need to join the endless meetings that produce endless reports (which effectively excludes anyone who cannot manage that). I have even seen adverts for service-users or carers that explicitly state they need to behave 'professionally' in meetings. As if the professionals always do!

What is missing from my graphic is where the power sits. An easy mistake to make is that the power is held by those at the very top. But often these people do not stay long. They are reliant on their team to brief them. They shuffle between similar posts as their careers progress. In my opinion, the real power is held by a few hardy souls in the upper-middle or middle management. They hold the history of the organisation, have formed relationships, and know whose ear to whisper in. They might even be organised enough to have all those blessed reports and minutes stored where they can refer to. Like a rabbit out of a hat, they pull out their 'good idea' (which might be based on someone else's work) and reinforce their power base. These people tend to see off threats and block change. They somehow withstand, or benefit from, restructures (don't forget they have the ear of whoever is designing the redesign). If anyone comes along who might have the knowledge, skills, and courage to implement change they see them off. Forgive my cynicism but I have seen this happen too often.

My advice is to work out who really holds the power. It might be the one who sits quietly behind their laptop in meetings.

Something that goes hand-in-hand with the pit of inaction is a lack of urgency. Any progress is glacially slow because all the activity - report writing, checking back, and meetings where the only outcome is to set up another meeting, compound the situation and act as effective brakes. Too often, I have observed nothing starts to get going until a deadline looms or there is an external threat (such as removal of funding or a contract, or an enforcement notice from above). Then there is a flurry of activity but even this might not be progressed or implemented because key people go on annual leave or go off sick. Where actions are taken, despite months of pit of inaction activity, a rushed or ill-conceived plan or decision that is not acceptable to all stakeholders, often occurs. Too late now to co-produce or even consult with service-users, carers, or staff – there's a deadline to meet.

I would argue that leadership is vital in creating a healthy and effective culture where intentions become actions. Those at the top need to model the behaviours they want to see. If they want a learning culture they need to immerse themselves in learning with and from their staff and service-users. If they want values to underpin services they need to display those values. If they expect their staff to work extra hours or cancel leave to cover staffing deficits, they need to be the first to arrive and the last to leave (and not go on holiday in times of crisis). If they want change, they need to be the change. And so on.

It is not very helpful for me to have a rant about what's wrong without offering any suggestions about what might lead to shrinking the pit of inaction. Here are some ideas about how you might use this model to support positive change:

- Use the model as a reflective tool. Ask yourselves questions about: what you recognise; who holds the power; what you might be able to do differently; what this means for recruitment and retention of staff; and (most importantly) what this means for service-users and carers … and whatever you do … do not set up a working party to look at it and report back.
- Rectifying the pit of inaction should be centred around relationships, values, compassion, emotional intelligence, and co-production. Consider what might you do to increase those things in your organisation. Kindness, emotional containment, and empathy are important in healthy values-based organisations.

- Take a look at Julia Unwin's (Carnegie UK) *Kindness, Emotions and Human Relationships: The Blind Spot in Public Policy* (2018)[103]. This describes the 'rational' and 'relational' lexicons - how 'native speakers' of these languages (lexicons) communicate with each other really well but struggle with each other because their priorities and approaches are different. Healthy organisations need a balance of both.
- If you are an organisation leader, why not consider getting all the people above the line to spend part of their working week working alongside, or engaging with, people who are below the line? Resist the temptation to recruit more leaders set up another working group, or write endless reports nobody reads. Be brave and push back on whoever needs these things. Show them the pit of inaction and ask them to think differently.

The corporate and bureaucratic behaviours, that occur at every level of the health and social care system, are responsible for a lack of actions to prevent deaths. Too many people have lost their lives due to the failings in mental health services. They are mourned by those who loved them. The pit of inaction that seems to have become habitual in many organisations must be eliminated or precious lives will be swallowed into the pit.

103 This is available online https://www.carnegieuktrust.org.uk/publications/kindness-emotions-and-human-relationships-the-blind-spot-in-public-policy/ and there's a useful graphic on page 12.

Heart Work
By Emma and Caroline

The beating heart of mental health services is the staff. Over and again, within failing organisations staff will be highlighted as 'caring'. The greater majority of people who go into health and social care work are commonly motivated by a desire to make a difference. They are led by their hearts. Heart work is:

> "Practice that is motivated from the heart, underpinned by love for fellow humans, and delivered through compassionate and kind interactions"[104].

The chapters written in this book expose the emotional impact of undertaking heart work. Being in touch with the values that motivate people to go into the helping professions is key to practitioners sustaining kind and compassionate practice. 'Burnt-out' practitioners can find compassion fatigue and exhaustion set in. You have read about practitioners who are kind, effective, and inspiring. Sadly, you have also read accounts of unkind or unsafe practice. We believe that, most of the time most staff will be doing their very best to provide care. Many are working in broken systems and emotionally barren organisations that have unhealthy cultures, it is all too easy for poor practice to creep in.

We are both heart-led practitioners. We give our all, and then some, because our work matters to us. Because people matter to us. Our authenticity is both a weakness and a strength. On the one hand, our empathy levels and genuine desire to help others can be exhausting and, at times, overwhelming. Recently, Emma gave a speech at a County Council meeting about the dire state of mental health services. Reflecting on many years of sitting alongside bereaved families, or listening to those in mental distress, has taken its toll. All that emotion spilled out into tears. Likewise, Caroline sometimes gets teary when hearing the harrowing stories of service-users, carers, and staff. Emotional spillage seems to be an occupational hazard of heart work.

On the other hand, there is a plethora of transdisciplinary evidence that argues people who are at the mercy of services, value authenticity, compassion, genuine relationships, and courageous practitioners. Values such as integrity, compassion, and empowerment are deep-seated in us.

---

104 This definition comes from *Heart Work: Love and Kindness in Social Work*, a book that Caroline has co-written with Siobhan Maclean (due for publication 2023).

We cannot just don them like a cloak. Professional codes of conduct require nurses, social workers, and others to practice from an ethical value-base. Our values come from our core being and they are powerful drivers of our attitudes and behaviours. Therefore, values-based practice is heart work. It requires practitioners to be reflexive and keep in touch with what motivates them.

Heart work can be rewarding but it can also be hard, even frightening. Our observations are that the impact on mental health practitioners of the crisis in services is often overlooked. The dissonance between the way practitioners want to work, versus the way they can within dysfunctional systems, can be stark. Many of the practitioners that we meet describe how their mental health has suffered due to work-related stress.

When Caroline 'met' chapter-writer, Sam, for the first time on Zoom, she was struck by how destructive having to work in a counter-intuitive way has been for them. These pressures were exacerbated by Covid. Sam described the impact that visiting care homes where 50% of the residents died because residents were discharged from hospital with Covid:

> *"It spread like wildfire. People who did not witness this cannot understand it. The toll it takes on care staff and partner services was immense."*

Sam's explanation of why they needed to protect their anonymity highlighted that the anxiety engendered by toxic organisations is real. The organisation they work for has created a culture of fear and cover-up instead of a culture of compassion and learning. So fearful were they about sharing their story, they hand-wrote their account because the only computer they have access to is a work one. Imagine working in a setting that leaves you feeling so silenced and afraid. Imagine being a kind, caring, competent, and hard-working nurse and feeling helpless to prevent your patients from meeting a premature death.

We expect there will be those who will be dismissive of Sam's fears. They might be tempted to problematise staff who say they are afraid to speak out and wonder what is wrong with them. Surely things cannot be that bad? In our experience, based on encounters with staff at all levels across mental health services and partner organisations, we are sure that Sam's experiences and feelings are not unusual. Things really are that bad in some places. Kate and Sam do not work for the same trust but they shared similar anxieties about speaking out. What struck us was they are both championing good practice. They might be citing examples of poor practice but it is with a view to encouraging fellow professionals to do right by the people they serve.

There is something so profoundly wrong about the way many organisations treat staff who want to challenge unsafe practice. The Francis Report[105] identified how the way NHS staff are responded to when they whistle-blow. It takes enormous courage to speak out. There are numerous examples of the way people's careers have been destroyed because they have whistle-blown[106].

Emma has first-hand experience of the might of the system closing in on her for daring to speak up. We think it is important to spell out the reality of what the 'system closing in on you' looks like. For Emma, it was harsh words in long corridors with no witnesses; short-notice invitations to meetings with chief executives or senior leaders, with no agenda or advance notice of what the meeting was about; rumours spread about her private life by politicians and trust executives; and using her volunteer trade union activity as a reason to withhold information from her that she legitimately needed access to in order to fulfil her nursing role. Much of this is evidenced within two box-files of emails and correspondence she received following a 'subject access request' under Data Protection legislation.

Despite no longer being a trade union representative or working in mental health, Emma continues to be contacted her many former colleagues. Her experience leads others to viewing her as a 'safe listening ear'. We remain full of admiration for staff working in services who continue to do their best and retain their compassion despite poor leadership and inadequate resources, and the lies spun by a government that tells the public that mental health is a priority. There has been no honest dialogue with the public and those who remain to work in services often bear the brunt of people's anger, dissatisfaction, and grief.

Staff speak regularly to us about working in a 'broken system', but what does that look like on the ground? There is no getting away from how difficult it is to try and provide care in some contexts. No amount of clinical supervision can make it feel okay for staff if they are working in under-staffed and under-resourced settings.

Staff report feeling gaslighted by the relentless, gushing 'positive news' emails, such as claims of being 'one of the fastest improving mental health trust in the country', that are meant to be motivating.

---

105 The Francis Report is online: https://researchbriefings.files.parliament.uk/documents/SN06690/SN06690.pdf

106 This report gives an account of some NHS whistleblowers experiences: https://www.theguardian.com/society/2015/feb/11/nhs-whistleblowers-the-staff-who-raised-the-alarm

Many find these demoralising because the content is so far removed from their day-to-day lived experience of trying to provide safe care. Their reality can mean managing an ever-growing waiting list with uncertainty about who is responsible for the safety of those languishing on it. It might mean having an unreliable patient record recording system where information disappears so you can't find a crisis plan you know you have uploaded. It could mean having to decide which patients to postpone seeing, so you can support someone heading for a crisis. Or, deciding who to telephone rather than see face-to-face, even though you know that the subtleties of body language and being able to check if people have food in the house and are opening post, is an important part of assessing their safety.

We often hear from staff about how let down they feel by the behaviours displayed by some senior managers and how at odds they are with the stated values of an organisation. They describe witnessing those that they have no respect for rising through the management ranks at speed. Or the treatment of managers, who display integrity and retain a focus on patient safety and staff wellbeing, being maligned and overworked to the point that they leave. This can make them never want to put themselves forward for leadership positions because they see how good leaders are treated. And so, the pool narrows, and a problematic culture is exacerbated. This is something we have observed in different settings.

We have noticed a significant impact on the mental health of staff who are working in environments that feel unsafe. Emma has supported former colleagues, who have been left without support for their own mental health or have needed to take carer's leave because the trust that they work for cannot keep their family member safe. This has led to severe financial hardship (such as not being able to pay rent or mortgages) and in some cases a bereavement or the loss of a career (and for some, both).

Emma's observations:

A nurse, who was very well-regarded by colleagues and services-users alike, received the most appalling treatment. They had voluntarily stayed on late to help a neighbouring service that was dangerously short-staffed. Some four hours after their shift should have ended, they were badly assaulted while trying to help deal with a violent incident. They received life-changing facial injuries. This incident triggered a relapse of Post-Traumatic Stress Disorder (PTSD) relating to a previous violent assault by a patient at another hospital. So, their mental health deteriorated significantly. They, quite rightly, expected access to evidence-based treatment for PTSD via occupational health. They were told that all they would be offered was six sessions of person-centred counselling via the staff welfare service. Their mental health further deteriorated and depression became so severe they were barely functioning. They stopped opening their post or taking phone calls. They were dismissed in their absence for misconduct, for failing to attend sickness absence reviews that they had been sent letters about. They missed the appeal date because they had not opened any post. They only knew they had lost their job when their pay stopped. No manager or trade union representative did the humane and pragmatic thing and went to their home to check if they were okay. No reasonable adjustment was made to allow a late appeal to be heard. That was it. A 20-year career. Over. All that experience and expertise lost because a trust put more effort into following a disciplinary process than providing care.

I am very mindful of the responsibilities that clinicians have under their codes of conduct. Now that I have temporarily re-joined the nursing register, I am bound by my professional code as a nurse. I always advise people to make sure that incidents are properly documented via the Datix[107] incident reporting system or the Freedom to Speak Up Guardian[108]. Sadly, some of the reasons people have contacted me about are the barriers they have faced to doing those things. Examples include: being pressurised not to Datix unsafe staffing levels or lack of beds and being told that only managers can Datix those issues; the pressure felt to admit patients to bedrooms that are not yet ligature-proof; or to discharge more quickly than feels safe in their clinical judgement.

The system that was set up to encourage whistleblowing and prevent deaths does not seem to be living up to the promises in some areas. Some people report that they perceive a direct negative consequence following contact with their Freedom to Speak Up Guardian. Others report waiting for contact more than six months after formally raising concerns via that route.

Staff are only too aware of the distress families experience during the inquest process. Another theme that has emerged over the past few years, has been pressure to change statements prepared for internal investigations or coroners court following 'feedback' from service managers or a trust's legal advisers. This has caused huge distress to staff who feel that, at the very least, families and the coroner should expect to receive everything that they (as the person involved) feels is relevant to a death.

107 Datix is a risk management system used in the NHS. Staff are expected to report all incident via Datix.

108 More information about the Freedom to Speak Up Guardians can be found on their national website: https://nationalguardian.org.uk/

When internal processes have been exhausted or are not possible to access, I advise staff to take those issues directly to the Care Quality Commission. But people express a palpable fear about doing this. Imagine feeling that you might be risking your whole career just to do you know what is your duty under your professional code of conduct.

Staff raise concerns in a professional and measured way. For example, staff were supported by their trades unions to write a formal letter detailing significant safety concerns about an inpatient area at my local trust. The letter was sent in autumn 2020, just over a year before the Care Quality Commission inspected that same area. The CQC report detailed a number of significant failings, many of which were the very same concerns that staff had raised over one year earlier. It seems to me that there are two possible explanations: either staff concerns were ignored and nothing was done, or action was taken but it had no impact on alleviating safety concerns. In my opinion, either option demonstrates evidence of a system impotent to change the things that need changing to protect patients. This is the kind of example that adds weight to the calls by campaigners[109] for a statutory public inquiry because harm has continued to be caused despite the alarm being raised so loudly and so clearly.

You will have noticed in our contributors' accounts that the unsafe culture in mental health services is a problem in a number of trusts across the UK. It is hard to deliver compassionate care when you are being treated with zero compassion yourself. Right now, working in mental health services has perhaps never been harder. The people who need services, their carers, and the organisations with duties to provide care, are all in crisis. Nevertheless, despite working in these difficult conditions, most staff manage to practice with care, compassion, and competence. They undertake heart work. We would encourage people with the right heart (values, strengths, and a love for their fellow humans) to consider working in mental health services.

We want to pay tribute to the bravery of staff who contributed to this book. Their courage and the way they don't give up when trying to get a service for the people they are responsible for are exemplars. And their courage to keep working in settings that continue to offer a sub-optimum service. Despite everything, they are still going to work every day and doing their best.

---

109 Discussed in *Dying Waiting: Waiting to Die* by John and Jane.

A Terrible Kindness
By Caroline

"If I could change one thing, it would be to increase kindness", this is the quote I use from *He Died Waiting* as my 'go-to' answer when I am asked about what needs to change and how that might happen. This is not me being trite. I genuinely believe that if everything we did came from a kind heart our decisions and actions would be better. Here are some basic practice principles of a kindness approach that I think should underpin best practice:

Values: Values are at the heart of kind practice. I often talk to students and practitioners in health and social care about what motivates them to go into social work or nursing. Values such as compassion, empathy, integrity, equality, inclusion, justice, honesty, and empowerment come up every time. These are all kind concepts. Reminding people of their core values and encouraging them to bring these to the fore can underpin kind practice. I urge people to be values-based practitioners and if possible to go further and be values-driven[110].

Intelligent kindness[111]: Interventions based on intelligent kindness are high quality because they involve understanding how the other person might experience our efforts. Ballatt and Campling say:

> "Intelligent kindness begins with deliberately directing our attention to connecting with the other person. It then involves allowing their need, experience, and personality to influence us, to prompt our imagination and knowledge to shape a response that will help reduce suffering".

Compassion: Compassionate practice[112] is critical it is the way that care is delivered via respectful relationships. Kindness and compassion are often used interchangeably.

Seeing the beauty in people: When people are in mental distress or they are grieving hard, they are unlikely to be their best selves. They might present in ways that others find difficult or unacceptable. When people are struggling so much they turn to services for help, they are seen at their

---

110 I explore this further in a webinar - *Values Driven Practice* hosted by Siobhan Maclean. https://www.youtube.com/watch?v=uTw-ddUy-Ys

111 I highly recommend the book *Intelligent Kindness: Rehabilitating the Welfare State* (2020 by John Ballat, Penelope Campling and Chris Maloney.

112 This is another excellent book: *Compassion in Nursing: Theory, Evidence and Practice* (2016) Alistair Hewison and Yvonne Sawbridge.

worst times. If we have a kind approach we are more likely to see past the presenting difficulties and be willing to see who the person really is. We need to look for the beauty.

Empathy for carers: Kind practice means valuing other peoples' perspectives and honouring what they do. Sometimes, this requires us to reframe what we see. For example, the angry or 'difficult' carer could be someone full of love who is fearful their loved one could die. Can we see them as loving rather than difficult?

Strengths: Kind practice and strength-based approaches go hand-in-hand because they both involve positivity. When we seek out what people's strengths are and we look for what works for them we are looking through a lens of attributes not deficits.

Relationships: Whoever we are, we all benefit from healthy relationships based on kindness, not criticism or control. 'Hit and run' practice, increasingly a feature of over-stretched services is counter-productive. It is when we feel connected to people that we can explore safely difficult or painful things and set the conditions for change.

Healthy teams: If we practise, as in reinforce by repetition, kindness, it has a habit of spilling over. We can start by developing kind teams that can help form a secure-base from which to practice. If professionals cannot be kind to each other it does not bode well for their interactions with those they serve.

Self-care: If we are not kind to ourselves our capacity to be kind will diminish because burnout or compassion fatigue can set in. I suggest we all need to build in more self-care into our lives. It is not being selfish - it enables us to be our best selves.

Leading by example: Social Learning Theory[113] tells us the power of learning with and from each other. We all tend to behave in ways we see modelled in others. It is critical therefore that leaders model the kind and compassionate practice they wish to see. If organisations want to have healthy (kind) cultures they need leaders who are values-based and kind.

Focussing the kindness: Working out where to focus your kindness when there is a conflict of interest can be tricky. I suggest that we should always focus our kindness on those with the least power. This might mean behaving in ways that could be construed as unkind, such as, making a complaint, calling out abuse, or challenging those in authority.

---

113 Social Learning Theory was introduced by Albert Bandura. For a straightforward explanation of this and other theories I recommend the *Social Work Theory Cards* by Siobhan Maclean.

Within this book, there are numerous examples of kindness and where this has made a big impact on people. Kindness is shown in the attitudes and actions of our contributors. Whether it is the love and kindness they demonstrated through care and advocacy for their loved ones, the actions of staff towards the people who use services and their families, the way bereaved people have reached out to others despite their own pain, or the activities of those supporting positive change, kindness is the underlying motivator.

Conversely, our contributors reveal numerous examples of unkindness. These acts wound and further traumatise people who are already diminished by the terrible grief associated with mental-health related deaths. These acts of unkindness are I suspect mostly rooted in thoughtlessness, ignorance, or the blunted emotional capacity of those working within emotionally barren systems. The narratives in *They Died Waiting* highlight institutional unkindness - systems, processes, organisational behaviours, and some practice, that is habitually unkind. At every level, there can be found examples of people (because organisations and systems are made up of people) who do not view those with mental illness and their families through a kind lens and do not treat those bereaved because of mental illness with the kindness they deserve. Frankly, when someone meets a premature or traumatic death because they did not get the support they needed with their mental health, their families are plunged into their worst nightmare. Too often this is compounded by the system, and by acts of omission or commission, that heaps on unkindness. Because the system is set up to self-perpetuate, distancing itself from the consequences of any failings.

Those who step into other people's distress to act with compassion and care are performing acts of kindness that can take an emotional toll on them. I am borrowing the phrase 'a terrible kindness'[114] from a novel about an embalmer's experience during the Aberfan disaster[115]. What the author conveyed was the importance of people performing their roles with calm, kind, competence at a time of disaster though this can be traumatising for everyone involved. What happened in Aberfan is a uniquely terrible disaster and it is not the same as the deaths due to mental illness discussed in this book. However, the bereaved people who have shared this story have experienced a disaster within their families and they deserve for that to be honoured and respected.

---

114 *A Terrible Kindness* by Jo Browning Wroe.

115 In 1966 a slag heap slipped down a mountain onto the school in Aberfan, Wales. 116 children and 28 adults were killed.

Within some areas of the country, the death rates associated with mental health are disproportionately high and therefore some communities are deeply affected by a collective grief. Anyone who involves themselves authentically in supporting those left behind is performing a terrible kindness in the sense they are doing something that others might shy away from.

Many terrible kindnesses are performed out of sight. They are found in everyday interactions within families, communities, and work settings. Many of them are performed by volunteers because statutory provision does not meet the need. One of the things that I have consistently asked for in my locality, is for the mental health trust to support those bereaved due to 'unexpected deaths' better. In my view, mental health trusts should take responsibility for the fallout from service failings. If they involved themselves in performing terrible kindnesses they might develop the emotional literacy required to motivate challenging systemic unkindness.

Several of the chapters offer examples of people willing to perform terrible kindnesses. People doing what they do because they turn towards the disaster and do what they can to help. They do this with kindness. They speak truth to power on behalf of those who cannot. Some have been accused of negativity but in my view, they are performing a public kindness.

Emma and I have both at times felt exhausted and overwhelmed by involving ourselves in terrible kindnesses. We have had to find ways of setting boundaries around what we can do for people because the need is much greater than our capacity. Nevertheless, we both find ourselves unable to stop because we live in communities experiencing pain and loss on a scale we have not seen before. We cannot turn away.

We Have to Stop
By Caroline and Emma

They Died Waiting: The Crisis in Mental Health – Stories of Love and Stories of Hope has brought together a collection of narratives that might not usually be placed alongside each other. What we have presented is, we believe, a unique collection of accounts of deaths resulting from the crisis in mental health services and how that is experienced by people with different viewpoints. We cannot think of another text on mental-health-related bereavement, let alone one with chapters from service-users, carers, health and social care professionals, campaigners, and journalists. We stand among our contributors, who are all trying to make a difference, and weave the threads of their narratives together.

Some of the chapters offer a fresh perspective that might have surprised, challenged, saddened, or frustrated you. Each of the stories are emotive, inspirational, and hopeful. We hope that these will provide rich learning opportunities for others because *They Died Waiting* is bursting with lived experience of people whose voices are seldom, or even never, heard. It has been so humbling and encouraging to be supporting people to tell their stories loudly and with purpose.

They Died Waiting really is a collection of love stories because love is threaded through the narratives. We have been moved by the accounts that have been shared with us. The memorial hearts have been emotive on another level. These carefully stitched visual vignettes somehow capture why it is important to remember those who have died and to learn.

A carer and campaigner sent us an encouraging message. She began by sharing a quote from Shakespeare's Hamlet (Act V scene ii).

I am dead:
Thou livest:
... draw thy breath in pain,
To tell my story.

She went on:

"This quote says it all and made me cry and think of all the terrible loss for everyone. I thought it was so true that I wrote it on a heart which I put on the hedge at the trust. I wonder if the leaders read the messages, I doubt it. I think it would take an earthquake to move them emotionally."

Everyone contributing to this book has drawn their breath in pain to tell their stories. We hope our readers have been moved emotionally.

As professionals, we feel utterly ashamed when reading about the failings in duty of care towards those who died and the thoughtless contempt heaped upon bereaved families. We are outspoken about the need for investigations following an unexpected death to be more open and honest and for the coronial process to be reformed. We urgently need these things to be trauma-sensitive, more inclusive, and kinder for bereaved families.

Nevertheless, there are threads of hope in the narratives. There are wonderful examples of professionals who show empathy and kindness, or members of the public who get involved and save lives. Despite their own loss and trauma, so many of the contributors to this book are doing outstanding work in trying to address the crisis in mental health services, or bring hope and healing to other bereaved people.

There is a never-ending supply of people who could have contributed to this book. We could have continued writing about the themes that emerged from the chapters and our observations of the crisis in mental health services. It was hard to know when enough was enough. We had to bring this book to a conclusion but we know there are other important stories that need telling. We are committed to hearing those stories and finding ways of bringing them to the public's attention.

We have been shouting into a void for years and supporting people that cannot access the help they need. It is relentless and exhausting. We continue to keep campaigning for improved services and compassionate practice because when we encounter someone bereaved or in distress there is often no one else that is going to step into their pain. There is limited support for people bereaved by suicide but even less for those bereaved due to other mental-illness related reasons. We keep shouting about the crisis in mental health services because we care about our communities and, if we are honest, we are too bloody-minded to stand down when nothing has changed. We would like to stop but until it's safe to do so, we will continue.

We would like to end by issuing a plea to our readers to consider what you might do. You might want to do something as an individual, such as extend your kindness to those struggling with mental illness or grief, lobby your MP, join with campaigners, or simply tell people about *They Died Waiting*. You might be an educator or leader who could use this book as a platform for learning or to support best practice (we would be happy to talk to you about that). If you are a student or professional, you might want to use the chapters from this book to support meaningful reflective discussions and develop your skills. If you are in a position of power, we urge (beg) you to use that power to support improvement. Whoever you are, whatever your position, please do something. If every reader did a tiny thing, together you could make a difference. If you can do nothing else, be kind.

Postscript

The brutality of the system is relentless. Since writing this book, events keep overtaking us and our contributors. Heidi and Lydia both endured inquests for their loved ones that further traumatised them and left them feeling betrayed and let down by a system that is supposed to protect people and have integrity. Some of our contributors are facing with fortitude the loss of another beloved family member. The campaigners continue to uncover things the system would rather did not come into the light and they carry on calling for accountability and change. We face continual reminders that mental health services remain in crisis. We can no longer keep up with the deaths in our locality. Something needs to change, until it does, we cannot, we will not, stop.

Sources of Help

Al Anon

For anyone affected by someone else's drinking. Free helpline 0800 0086 811 from 10 am - 10 pm, 365 days a year or email helpline@al-anonuk.org.uk

Alcoholics Anonymous

For help with a drinking problem. Fee helpline 08009177650 or email help@aamail.org

At A Loss

Bereavement support signposting service www.ataloss.org

Compassionate Friends

Supporting bereaved parents and their families. 0345 123 2304 helpline or helpline@tcf.org.uk

Cruse

Bereavement support 0808 808 1677 or www.cruse.org.uk

Emergency services

If someone is at risk of immediate harm the police or ambulance service should be called on 999

Help is at hand

The booklet, *Help is at Hand: Support After Someone May Have Died by Suicide* is available here: https://www.nhs.uk/Livewell/Suicide/Documents/Help%20is%20at%20Hand.pdf

INQUEST

A charity providing representation and support on state related deaths: www.inquest.org

Mental Health Trusts

All mental health trusts should display on their websites details of how to make a referral to their services or how to access help if you are worried about your own or someone else's mental health.

Papyrus (prevention of young suicide)

For confidential suicide prevention advice contact HOPELINEUK. Open 9am–midnight every day. 0800 068 4141 or pat@papyrus-uk.org

Samaritans

For confidential support 24/7 support via 116 113 (this number does not appear on phone bills).

Acknowledgements

First and foremost, we would like to thank our contributors. Without them there would be no book. Their courage and creativity have blown us away and it has been an honour to help them bring their stories into the public domain.

We would also like to thank everyone who has encouraged us to write *They Died Waiting* and supported us with the many practicalities. You are all appreciated.

We wouldn't be who we are today without the love and support of our families who enable us to be who we want to be. They are our solid ground. We are driven forward by our love for our friends and communities.

We want to acknowledge Tim, whose life and death inspires us. We hold in our minds everyone we have known who struggles with their mental health, those who have lost their lives, and those who have been bereaved. We stand with them.

Meet the Editors

Caroline Aldridge

Caroline is a freelance speaker, trainer, and author. *They Died Waiting* is Caroline's second book. More information can be found about Caroline and her work can be found on her website: www.learningsocialworker.com. Caroline enjoys spending time with her family and friends. When not working, studying, or writing, Caroline can usually be found in her sewing room at the bottom of the garden.

Caroline is happy to be contacted via e-mail: caroline.aldridgesw@yahoo.com or Twitter: @waiting_he, Instagram: @hediedwaiting, LinkedIn: Caroline Aldridge, Facebook: Caroline Aldridge

Emma Corlett

Emma is a County Councillor. She has temporarily returned to nursing to work in the Covid vaccination team. She spends much of her time working in her local community on projects that tackle inequality and poverty, and reduce isolation and loneliness. She is a fierce advocate for those shut out of mental health and other helping services. When not raging about the state of our society, she can be found enjoying comedy with her daughter; gigs and festivals with her partner and friends; or a pre-match glass of wine with friends before heading off to watch her beloved Ipswich Town Football Club.

Future plans

He Died Waiting is an in-depth case study (Tim and Caroline's story) and *They Died Waiting* is a collection of other people's stories. Plans are in place for a final book in the trilogy which will focus on the different ways people are trying to prevent future deaths.

Caroline and Emma are also working on creative ways (for example, arts projects) of supporting bereaved people and using *They Died Waiting* as a springboard for positive change. We are happy to talk to anyone who might want to be involved in supporting healing and change.

Caroline is working on a co-authored book with Siobhan Maclean – *Heart Work: Love and Kindness in Social Work*. She plans to continue following her heart, rather than a career plan, and be guided by what might make the biggest difference.

Emma is contemplating a return to the permanent nursing register. She has no idea what the future holds for her, but will continue to work with kindness and compassion in her community, and throw her energy in to campaigning for a change of government.

APPENDIX 1

The Pit of Inaction Model: Caroline Aldridge 2022

Senior management
In meetings, panels, Boards, consultations so no time to action or check

Chosen few only

Boards, subgroups, workstreams, committees, meetings: To decide actions, oversee and report back but often cannot make decisions or act without senior management (writing reports no one reads)

Audits and reviews

Endless meetings going nowhere (creating minutes no-one has time to read)

Pit of inaction

Service-users and carers

Feedback

Upper middle management
To action and/or report back but only have time to attend back-to-back meetings

Conflict

Middle management
Cannot progress without input from decision makers. Write reports that no-one reads

Feedback

Front line staff
Carry on without clear direction or change